*PROCEEDINGS OF THE CONFERENCE
ON GENETIC POLYMORPHISMS
AND GEOGRAPHIC
VARIATIONS IN DISEASE*

Proceedings of the Conference

on

GENETIC POLYMORPHISMS

and GEOGRAPHIC

VARIATIONS *in* DISEASE

sponsored by
The National Institute of Arthritis and Metabolic Diseases
and The National Heart Institute
and held at
The National Institutes of Health, Bethesda, Maryland
February 23-25, 1960

Edited by

Baruch S. Blumberg

G R U N E & S T R A T T O N

NEW YORK • LONDON • 1961

Library of Congress Catalog Card No. 61-17273

Printed and bound in U.S.A. (*H*)

CONTENTS

PREFACE

THIS Conference on Genetic Polymorphisms and Geographic Variations in Disease marks the initiation of a new program of research within the National Institute of Arthritis and Metabolic Diseases. A Section on Geographic Medicine and Genetics, headed by Dr. Blumberg, has been established within the Institute to explore ways in which the rapidly expanding discipline of biochemical genetics can be linked effectively with other laboratory, clinical and epidemiologic approaches to the study of the unequal distribution of disease, and particularly metabolic disorders, in different parts of the world and in different population groups.

The planning of this program began in the closing months of 1958 when Dr. James M. Hundley returned to the staff of the NIAMD after a leave of absence as Food and Agriculture Organization Nutrition Advisor to the United Nations International Children's Emergency Fund. He suggested that the National Institutes of Health intensify their efforts to elucidate, through field investigations, the natural history of certain diseases with which the Institutes are concerned. He proposed that through a new research unit formed for this purpose a combination of different disciplines including epidemiology, medical genetics, nutrition, the behavioral sciences and various others be brought to bear on the study of the many conditions whose etiology and pathogenesis remain obscure. These studies would be designed to complement and extend the well established programs of laboratory and clinical research within the Institutes.

This idea was not new. Several of the Institutes had long been active in this area. In fact, one of the original purposes of the Hygienic Laboratory of the Public Health Service, organized in 1887, was to investigate disease from an ecologic point of view. With the establishment of the National Cancer Institute in the 1930's and the present organizational pattern of the National Institutes of Health, an ecologic approach to disease study continues to play an important part both in direct research activities as well as in the research grant programs. Today, we find that each of the seven categorical Institutes as well as the Division of General Medical Science and the Division of Research Grants are actively pursuing epidemiologic approaches to various disease problems. Perhaps the unique attribute of Dr. Hundley's proposal was that the time had come for a consciously planned and organized inter-Institute program of epidemiologic studies combining the resources and interests of two or more Institutes.

At Dr. Hundley's instigation, the National Heart Institute and the National Institute of Arthritis and Metabolic Diseases agreed to sponsor a joint program in this area and this Conference has been convened under their joint auspices. Shortly after the organization of the Geographic Disease Studies program, Dr. Hundley was requested by the Surgeon General to help in planning the future organization and programs of the Public Health Service. With Dr. Hundley's assignment to new duties, the Section on Geographic Medicine and Genetics has been incorporated within the Epidemiology and Biometry Branch of the NIAMD, so that even greater emphasis can be given to the investigation of ecologic problems of concern to that Institute.

We are deeply indebted to each of the participants of this Conference who, in a real sense, has aided us in visualizing the broad avenues of productive investigation that this new research unit may be expected to undertake or to sponsor as its program develops.

Thomas D. Dublin

July 1, 1961

INTRODUCTORY NOTE

This conference has brought together workers from two major disciplines. The first group, comprising epidemiologists and their co-workers, has been concerned with differences in the distribution of disease in different populations, and the relationship of these diseases to environmental and "host" factors. The second group, the human geneticists, has been concerned with inherited biochemical differences among individuals and among populations, and the relationship of these differences to disease susceptibility and to differential fertility and survival. These two groups have much to contribute to each other. The study of inherited biochemical differences in different populations may provide answers to some of the questions posed by the epidemiologists; and in turn epidemiologic investigations of disease may offer clues to help explain some of the individual and population differences discovered by the biochemical geneticists.

The particular biochemical variations discussed in the conference were genetic polymorphisms. According to Ford's (1940, 1942) widely accepted definition, a genetic polymorphism is the occurrence in the same habitat of two or more discontinuous forms of a species in such numbers that the rarest form could not be maintained by recurrent mutation alone. In the classic examples these traits are determined by two or more alleles at a single locus. Each of the phenotypes may have different selective value and, in many polymorphisms the heterozygote may have an advantage to either homozygote. The selective forces operating on these systems are frequently diseases, and in some cases, the differences in geographic distribution of diseases uncovered by epidemiologists may be related to the genetic constitution of the susceptible population.

The proceedings of the conference were recorded stenographically and copies sent to the participants for corrections. These were further edited and, in some cases, altered and annotated to include material published after the conference. An attempt has been made to maintain the conversational tone of the conference, but the proceedings do not represent a verbatim report. A general discussion follows the formal presentations.

A limited edition of the Proceedings was published by the Government Printing Office, approximately six months after the conference. The present edition has been further corrected and up-dated.

Baruch S. Blumberg

ACKNOWLEDGMENTS

We are indebted to the following for permission to publish the figures and tables:

Boyd, table 1—Reprinted with the permission of Dr. J. M. Lerner and John Wiley and Sons, from "Genetic Homeostasis," John Wiley and Sons, Inc., 1954.

Boyd, table 3—Reprinted with the permission of Dr. W. E. Herrell and the Annals of the New York Academy of Sciences from "Some Bacteriologic, Pharmacologic, and Clinical Observations on Terramycin." Annals of the New York Academy of Sciences 53: 449, 1950.

Boyd, table 5—Reprinted with the permission of Dr. W. C. Boyd and Little, Brown & Co., from "Genetics and the Races of Man," Little, Brown & Co., Boston. 1950.

Boyd, figure 1—Reprinted with permission of Dr. Th. Dobzhansky and the Columbia University Press, from "Genetics and the Origin of Species," Columbia Univ. Press, New York, 1951.

Boyd, table 6—Reprinted with permission of Sir McFarlane Burnet, O.M., F.R.S., and the Cambridge University Press, from "Natural History of Infectious Diseases," Cambridge, 1952.

Boyd, table 7—Reprinted with permission of Dr. A. B. Sabin and the Annals of the New York Academy of Sciences, from "Genetic, hormonal, and age factors in natural resistance to certain viruses," Annals of the New York Academy of Sciences 54: 936, 1952.

Boyd, table 8—Reprinted with the permission of Dr. I. Aird and the British Medical Journal, from "The blood groups in relation to peptic ulceration and carcinoma of the colon, rectum, breast and bronchus," Brit. Med. J. 2: 315, 1954.

Boyd, table 9—Reprinted with the permission of Dr. A. C. Allison and the Transactions of the Royal Society of Tropical Medicine, from "The distribution of the sickle-cell trait in East Africa and elsewhere and its apparent relationship to the incidence of sub-tertian malaria," Trans. Roy. Soc. Trop. Med. & Hyg. 48: 312, 1954.

Boyd table 10—Reprinted with the permission of Dr. A. C. Allison and the British Medical Journal from "Protection offered by the sickle-cell trait against subtertian malarial infection," Brit. Med. J., 1: 290, 1954.

Boyd figure 2—Reprinted with the permission of Dr. I. M. Lerner and J. Wiley and Sons, Inc., from "The Genetic Basis of Selection," J. Wiley and Sons, Inc., 1958.

Lillienfeld figure 1—Reprinted with the permission of Dr. Alice Stewart and the British Medical Journal, from "A survey of childhood malignancies," Brit. Med. J., 1: 1495, 1958.

Lillienfeld, table 2—Reprinted with the permission of Dr. A. M. Lillienfeld and the A. M. A. Archives of Internal Medicine, from the "Association of smoking with cancer of the urinary bladder in humans," A. M. A. Arch. Int. Med. 98: 129, 1956.

Lillienfeld, table 3—Reprinted with the permission of Dr. A. M. Lillienfeld and Public Health Reports from "Diagnostic and therapeutic x-radiation in an urban population," Pub. Health Rep. 74: 29, 1959.

Lillienfeld, figure 2—Reprinted with the permission of Dr. H. T. Dean and Public Health Reports, from "Domestic Water and Dental Caries," Pub. Health Rep. 57: 1155, 1942.

xi

Reed, table 1—Reprinted with the permission of Dr. J. A. Fraser Roberts and the British J. of Preventive and Social Medicine, from "Blood groups and susceptibility to disease: A review," Brit. J. Prev. Soc. Med. *11:* 107, 1957.

Giblett, figure 5—Reprinted from Science by permission of Dr. A. G. Bearn and the American Association for Advancement of Science, from "Some genetical implications of physical studies of human haptoglobins," Science *128:* 596, 1958.

Motulsky, table 6—Reprinted with the permission of Dr. A. Szeinberg, from "Selective occurrence of glutathione instability in red blood corpuscles of the various Jewish tribes," Blood *13:* 1043, 1958.

PARTICIPANTS

Fred H. Allen, Jr., M.D.
Associate Director
The Blood Grouping Laboratory
Boston, Massachusetts

Gordon Allen, M.D.
Laboratory of Socio-Environmental
  Studies
National Institute of Mental Health
Bethesda, Maryland

Raymond K. Appleyard, Ph.D.
Secretary, The Radiation Committee
United Nations
New York, New York

Alexander G. Bearn, M.D.
Associate Professor and Physician
The Rockefeller Institute
New York, New York

Baruch S. Blumberg, M.D., Ph.D.
Chief, Geographic Medicine and
  Genetics Section
Epidemiology and Biometry Branch
National Institute of Arthritis and Met-
  abolic Diseases
Bethesda, Maryland

William C. Boyd, Ph.D.
Professor of Immunochemistry
Department of Biochemistry
Boston University School of Medicine
Boston, Massachusetts

Samuel H. Boyer, IV, M.D.
Assistant Professor of Medicine
Johns Hopkins University
Baltimore, Maryland

Floyd S. Daft, Ph.D., D.Sc.
Director
National Institute of Arthritis and
  Metabolic Diseases
Bethesda, Maryland

Thomas D. Dublin, M.D., Dr. P. H.
Chief, Epidemiology and Biometry
  Branch
National Institute of Arthritis and Met-
  abolic Diseases
Bethesda, Maryland

Stanley M. Gartler, Ph.D.
Division of Medical Genetics
Department of Medicine
University of Washington
Seattle, Washington

Eloise Giblett, M.D.
Associate Director
King County Central Blood Bank, Inc.
Seattle, Washington

Gordon Gibson, Ph.D.
Associate Curator
Division of Ethnology
U. S. National Museum
The Smithsonian Institution
Washington, D. C.

Alexander G. Gilliam, M.D., Dr. P.H.
Assistant Chief, Field Investigations and
  Demonstrations Branch
National Cancer Institute
Bethesda, Maryland
  Dr. Gilliam's present address:
  Associate Professor of Epidemiology
  Johns Hopkins University
  School of Hygiene and Public Health
  Baltimore 5, Maryland

Hymie Gordon, M.D.
Department of Medicine
Johns Hopkins University
Baltimore, Maryland
  Dr. Gordon's present address:
  Clinical Investigator
  Department of Medicine
  University of Capetown
  Rondebosch, Capetown, South Africa

xiii

John E. Gordon, M.D.
Professor of Preventive Medicine and
   Epidemiology Emeritus
Harvard University School of Public
   Health
Boston, Massachusetts

Ralph E. Knutti, M.D.
Associate Director in Charge of Extra-
   mural Programs
National Institute of Arthritis and Met-
   abolic Diseases
Bethesda, Maryland

Robert S. Krooth, M.D., Ph.D.
Medical Geneticist
Epidemiology Branch
National Institute of Neurological
   Diseases and Blindness
Bethesda, Maryland

Philip Levine, M.D.
Director, Division of Immunohematology
Ortho Research Foundation
Raritan, New Jersey

A. M. Lilienfeld, M.D., M.P.H.
Professor of Public Health Administra-
   tion
Division of Chronic Diseases
Johns Hopkins University
School of Hygiene and Public Health
Baltimore, Maryland

Robert H. McCauley, Jr., Ph.D.
Executive Secretary
Genetics Training Committee
Division of General Medical Sciences
Bethesda, Maryland

Victor A. McKusick, M.D.
Professor of Medicine
Johns Hopkins University
Baltimore, Maryland

Arno G. Motulsky, M.D.
Professor of Medicine
University of Washington School of
   Medicine
Seattle, Washington

Ntinos C. Myrianthopoulos, Ph.D.
Geneticist
Epidemiology Branch
National Institute of Neurological
   Diseases and Blindness
Bethesda, Maryland

James V. Neel, M.D., Ph.D.
Chairman, Department of Human
   Genetics
University of Michigan Medical School
Ann Arbor, Michigan

Marshall T. Newman, Ph.D.
Associate Curator
Division of Anthropology
U. S. National Museum
The Smithsonian Institution
Washington, D. C.

John R. Paul, M.D.
Professor of Preventive Medicine
Yale University School of Medicine
New Haven, Connecticut

George St. J. Perrott
Executive Director
Conference on Community Population
   Laboratories
Public Health Research Study Section
Division of Research Grants
Bethesda, Maryland

T. Edward Reed, Ph.D.
Department of Human Genetics
University of Michigan Medical School
Ann Arbor, Michigan
      Dr. Reed's present address:
   Associate Professor of Zoology and
      Pediatrics
   Department of Zoology
   University of Toronto
   Toronto 5, Canada

J. Francesco Sella, Ph.D.
Radiation Committee
United Nations
New York, New York

H. Eldon Sutton, Ph.D.
Department of Human Genetics
University of Michigan Medical School
Ann Arbor, Michigan
  Dr. Sutton's present address:
  Department of Zoology
  University of Texas
  Austin, Texas

Jerome A. Uram, Sc.D.
Executive Secretary
Nutrition Study Section
Division of Research Grants
National Institutes of Health
Bethesda, Maryland

Katherine Wilson, Ph.D.
Executive Secretary
Human Genetics Study Section
Division of Research Grants
National Institutes of Health
Bethesda, Maryland

Marjorie Whiting, Sc.D.
Geographic Pathology Section
National Heart Institute
Bethesda, Maryland

Carl J. Witkop, Jr., D.D.S.
Chief, Human Genetics Section
National Institute of Dental Research
Bethesda, Maryland

J. Franklin Yeager, Ph.D.
Chief, Grants and Training Branch
National Heart Institute
Bethesda, Maryland

1

NATURAL SELECTION AND DISEASE

WILLIAM C. BOYD

SINCE THE MATERIAL in the present paper was presented to a group representing more than one scientific discipline, it was sometimes necessary to make statements which may have sounded quite elementary to some of the audience, for the sake of not sounding incomprehensible to others. Since it may be suspected that the readers of the paper in its published form may likewise come from different backgrounds, some of these statements have been retained.

Because we are going to be concerned here with selection, it may be well to begin with the simple statement that selection works. The achievements of plant and animal breeders are familiar to all, and they have depended mainly on the skillful and persistent application of selection to the populations the breeder wanted to alter, or in his language, "improve." To choose a single example, we may consider the results of selecting for greater poultry shank length (Lerner 1954), shown in table 1.

TABLE 1—*Results of Selection for Increased Shank Length in Poultry* (Lerner 1954)

| | SHANK LENGTH IN CM. | | | INDEX OF FITNESS | |
Year of Hatch	Control Line	Selected Line	Selection Suspended	Selected Line	Selection Suspended
1938	9.69				
1939	9.62	9.92			
1940	9.55	9.92		4.67	
1941	9.37	10.20		4.47	
1942	9.46	10.29		3.56	
1943	9.42	10.46		4.63	
1944	9.41	10.73		2.48	
1945	9.48	10.84		2.62	
1946	9.44	10.71		3.09	
1947	9.77	10.73		1.57	
1948	9.89	10.96		2.22	
1949	9.53	10.78		3.12	
1950	9.58	11.10		2.54	
1951	9.59	11.08	10.86	1.63	1.33
1952	9.66	10.99	10.60	0.96	2.27

It can be seen that continued selection resulted in longer and longer shanks in the selected line, as opposed to essentially constant shank length in the controls. At the same time, however, the index of fitness of the selected line steadily decreased. We shall return to this phenomenon later.

Another example is provided by the results of selecting for an increased number of abdominal chaetae in the fruit fly *Drosophila melanogaster*, as reported by Mather and Harrison (1949). This is shown in table 2.

TABLE 2—*Effects of Artificial Selection on Number of Abdominal Chaetae in* Drosophila (Modified from Mather and Harrison 1949)

Generations of Selection	Number of Chaetae	
	Low Line	High Line
0	36	36
5	33	42
10	35	45
20	32	56
35	26	54
40	died out*	56
60	—	54
100	—	55
120	—	57

* *Due to sterility*

It will be seen that it was possible, by artificial selection, to decrease the number of abdominal chaetae or to increase it. It will also be noted there is a suggestion that the rate of increase has slowed down towards the end. It is again evident that the fitness of the organism has been decreased by selection for this character, as the line selected for fewer

TABLE 3—*Induced Resistance to Antibiotics* (Herrell et al. 1950)

Organism	Made Resistant to	Sensitivity in milligrams/liter			
		Terra-mycin	Aureo-mycin	Chloram-phenicol	Strepto-mycin
E. coli	——	3.12	6.25	6.25	12.5
"	Terramycin	100.00	50.00	100.00	6.25
A. aerogenes	——	1.56	3.12	6.25	3.12
"	Aureomycin	100.00	50.00	200.00	0.78
E. coli	——	3.12	3.12	12.5	12.5
"	Streptomycin	1.56	1.56	6.25	200.00

abdominal chaetae died out because of sterility. Again we shall return to this point.

It was also observed, although this is not shown in table 2, that if selection is stopped, the number of chaetae may stay about the same, or tend to return to the normal number.

Another example of the effects of selection is the increased resistance of microorganisms to antibiotocs (Herrell et al. 1950) as shown in table 3.

The numbers indicate the micrograms of the antibiotic required to inhibit the growth of the microorganisms. It will be seen that when an organism has been made resistant to terramycin, for example, a good deal of terramycin is needed to inhibit the growth, whereas not so much streptomycin is required. Similar results were found by other workers, for example Monnier and Schoenbach (1951). (See table 4.)

TABLE 4—*Induced Resistance to Antibiotics* (Monnier and Schoenbach 1951)

| Organism | Ratio of Final to Initial Minimal Inhibiting Concentration of Penicillin after Growth in | | | | |
	Peni-cillin	Aureo-mycin	Chloram-phenicol	Terra-mycin	Strepto-mycin
Staph. aureus	8	1/2	1/2	1/8	1/16
Str. fecalis	16	1	1	1	1/2
A. aerogenes	—	1/32	1/16	1/64	1/8
K. pneumoniae B	—	1/4	1/16	1/8	1/8

The production of resistance in microorganisms is natural selection in a sense, for in an environment containing the antibiotic the more restistant organisms have a better chance of growing. The experiment shown in table 4 was carried out in the laboratory, but drug resistance also develops under clinical conditions. If an inadequate dose of an antibiotic is given, so that not all the infecting microorganisms are killed, the more hardy ones, that is, those more resistant to this particular antibiotic, survive and their descendants may constitute a resistant strain.

The fact that strains of microorganisms resistant to almost every antibiotic have been produced and now are a grave problem in hospitals shows how effective selection is in changing characteristics of organisms.

Selection of course only produces permanent changes if the character we select is inherited. If it is controlled by the genes at a single locus, a fairly simple mathematical treatment, such as that proposed by Haldane (1924 and later papers), enables us to predict the effect on gene frequencies of selection at a given rate for a given number of generations. For the case of slow selection, Haldane found

$$kn = v_n - v_o + log_e(v_n/v_o).$$

In this equation, k represents the selective coefficient. If out of each 1000 individuals of the type being selected against, only 999 are allowed to survive and reproduce, but if for the favored type 1000 out of 1000 survive and reproduce, k has the value 0.001. When k is of this order of magnitude, selection is said to be slow. Of the other symbols in the above equation, n stands for the number of generations, v_o the ratio of the frequency of the dominant to that of the recessive gene at the beginning of selection and v_n the corresponding ratio after the lapse of n generations of selection at rate k.

The above equation applies only to slow selection because, in its derivation, k was assumed small. For rapid selection, Haldane gives the more exact equation

$$n = \frac{v_n - v_o}{k} + \frac{\log_e \dfrac{1 + 1/v_n}{1 + 1/v_o}}{\log_e(1-k)} + \frac{1-k}{k} \log_e \frac{1+v_n}{1-v_o}.$$

From Haldane's equation for slow selection, I have calculated the changes in gene frequency which would be produced by various numbers of generations of selection. This is shown in table 5, which was suggested by a similar table calculated by Pätau.

TABLE 5—*Time Theoretically Required for a Given Change in Gene Frequency of a Gene Having a Selective Advantage of 0.01 (1 Per Cent), Calculated from Haldane's Equation (Boyd 1950)*

Dominant Gene		Recessive Gene	
Change in Frequency	Number of Generations	Change in Frequency	Number of Generations
0.01 → 0.1	230	0.01 → 0.1	900,230
0.1 → 1.0	231	0.1 → 1.0	90,231
1.0 → 50.0	559	1.0 → 3.0	6,779
50.0 → 97.0	3,481	3.0 → 50.0	3,481
97.0 → 99.0	6,779	50.0 → 99.0	559
99.0 → 99.9	90,231	99.0 → 99.9	231
99.9 → 99.99	900,230	99.9 → 99.99	230

It will be seen that selection at even the relatively slow rate of k = 0.01 is ultimately effective in changing gene frequencies from only slightly more than zero to nearly one, or, if selection is negative, the reverse.

The frequencies of recessive genes change much more slowly at first because in this case selection acts only against the homozygotes. Nevertheless, in the long run selection produces its effects in this case also.

Selection leads to the formation of races. Some examples of races in the insect *Harmonia axyridis* are shown in figure 1. These races are conspicuously different because of the color patterns on the wing covers. Other races might look about the same but differ in some important or unimportant biochemical mechanism which is not obvious to the eye. The races shown presumably are the result of the fact that in the different geographical areas where they were collected there was some selective advantage for the gene or genes which produce the wing cover pattern shown, thus leading to the formation of local races. We do not know what sort of advantage it was that made insect "g" better adapted to en-

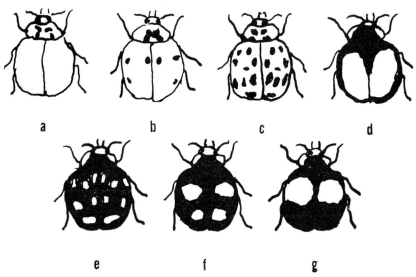

a   b   c   d

e   f   g

Fig. 1—Geographic Races in *Harmonia axyridis* (Dobzhansky, 1941).

vironment "G" and insect "b" to environment "B." In some species, the advantage which is probably operating can be seen, as when a desert insect's coloration matches that of the sand. Such cases are, on the whole, exceptions rather than the rule.

Racial differences in a species include of course differences in susceptibility to disease, because disease is also an agent of natural selection, tending to eliminate those who are least resistant. Such an agency acts differently in different environments, for what is an advantage in one environment may be a disadvantage in another. It is this variation in selection from one geographical area to another that explains the formation of local races, including the present human races.

Any disease which produces an appreciable mortality in a population would provide a good example of a natural selective agency, if it could be shown that the more susceptible individuals are generally more likely to die from the disease, or not reproduce so effectively, and if it could be shown that natural resistance to the disease on the part of the individual members of the population tends to be inherited. For this argument it does not matter what form the natural resistance takes; it might be that the more resistant individuals synthesize antibodies to an infectious microorganism more rapidly, or to a greater extent, than do susceptible individuals, or it might be merely that their blood and tissues offer an unsuitable soil for the growth of the microorganism. We do not even need to limit ourselves to a consideration of infectious diseases; in fact, the differential mortality due to hereditary metabolic or physical abnormalities furnishes an even clearer illustration. In disease resistance, too, it may be possible to have too much of a good thing; it is possible that innate tendencies to produce antibodies too freely may, insofar as they lead to the production of antibodies to the individual's own tissues, tend to eliminate such victims of "autoimmune" diseases from the population.

Here is a paragraph from my *Fundamentals of Immunology* (Boyd 1956) which summarized what I knew in 1956 of racial differences in susceptibility to disease.

"Racial differences in susceptibility in man probably exist also but are harder to verify because of the complexity of the problem. In some cases apparent innate differences in susceptibility are really due to differences in habits or living conditions or to immunity acquired from mild, inapparent infections during childhood. It seems likely, however, that some aboriginal peoples were much more susceptible than we are, on first contact, to diseases introduced by the Europeans, such as measles and tuberculosis. Russell and Salmon (1934) have presented evidence that the Welsh are racially more susceptible to tuberculosis than are the English. Negroes are more susceptible to tuberculosis than white persons (Roth 1938). The data of Hopkins (1938) suggest a hereditary factor in susceptibility to leprosy. Very little is known of the genetic mechanism of such differences in man."

In regard to racial differences in susceptibility to measles, mentioned above, it seems that measles was a much more serious disease to the inhabitants of the Pacific islands, when first introduced, than for the European peoples who brought it. According to Burnet (1953), when measles was introduced into the Sandwich Islands, "Practically all the population went down with the disease, and many thousands died."

One of the fallacies which has vitiated many past attempts to demonstrate racial differences in susceptibility has been the assumption that differences which were actually due to environmental differences were due to genetic differences. In the studies of Russell and Salmon (1934) and Roth (1938), referred to above, attempts, successful in my opinion, were made to avoid this error.

One technic which largely avoids the objection that the observed differences might be merely environmental effects is the study of twins, which has proved itself a powerful method of investigating the relative roles of nature and nurture. An application of this technic to tuberculosis is shown in table 6, which gives results of a study by Kallmann and

TABLE 6—*Tuberculosis in Relatives of Tuberculous Patients*
(Burnet 1953)

Relation to "Index Case"	Percentage with Tuberculosis
One-egg twin	87
Two-egg twin	25.6
Other brother or sister	25.5
Marriage partner	7

Reisner, quoted by Burnet (1953). It will seem that there was a close agreement in identical twins with respect to a history of clinical tuberculosis, whereas nonidentical twins showed only the same degree of agreement as that found in nontwin brothers or sisters. There can be hardly any doubt that this observation is to be explained by the fact that identical twins, originating from the same fertilized ovum, have identical heredities, whereas nonidentical twins are no more similar genetically, on the average, than brothers and sisters in general. In addition to the 87 per cent correspondence between identical twins in incidence of clinical tuberculosis, there was also a close resemblance in the type and progress of the disease.

Fraternal (nonidentical) twins, although less likely to be genetically alike than identical twins, are of course nevertheless more likely to be similar genetically than are persons selected from the population at random, since they do after all have the same mother and father. It is therefore not surprising, if we grant the assumption that heredity plays a large role in tuberculosis, that the marriage partner is less likely to have tuberculosis than is a brother or sister of a patient. If the main factor were exposure, one would expect the reverse to be true.

In view of the fact that everyone is exposed to infection with tuberculosis, and in fact virtually all of us eventually develop inapparent infection, these figures leave little doubt that genetic factors play a considerable, perhaps a predominant role, in determining that degree of resistance preventing the development of clinically recognizable disease.

Similar evidence exists to show the role of heredity in other infections.

A particular simple example of genetically determined resistance in animals was studied by Sabin (1952), who found that the striking difference between Swiss and PRI mice to the 17D strain of yellow fever virus was apparently determined by a Mendelian pair of genes. (See table 7.)

TABLE 7—*Inheritance of Resistance of Mice to 17D Strain of Yellow Fever Virus* (Sabin 1952)

	OBSERVED		THEORETICAL		
Mice Used	Number of mice inocu- lated	Mortality (per cent)	Genetic for- mula of mice used for breeding	Genetic for- mula for prog- eny	Expected mortality (per cent)
Swiss (S)	300	100	aa×aa	aa	100
PRI (R)	100	0	AA×AA	AA	0
F_1 (S×R)	51	0	aa×AA	Aa	0
F_2 (F_1×F_1)	213	28.2	Aa×Aa	AA+2Aa+aa	25
Backcross:					
F_1×R	79	0	Aa×AA	Aa+AA	0
F_1×S	90	50	Aa×aa	Aa+aa	50
F_2 (suscep- tible)×S	21	100	aa×aa	aa	100

The mice were tested by intracerebral injection of approximately 10000 LD_{50} of the virus. The theoretical genetic formulas and expected percents mortality are calculated on the assumption that the PRI mice are homozygous for a dominant gene for resistance (A) and the Swiss mice homozygous for a recessive gene for susceptibility (a).

Since people do die from infectious disease, and since resistance to such infections is partly determined by hereditary factors, there can be hardly any doubt that natural selection tends by this means to change the frequencies of genes concerned with disease resistance. In addition to infections, there also exist a number of noninfectious hereditary diseases in which environment seems to play virtually no role—and here it is even easier to see how selection must be operating to lower the frequency of the genes responsible for the disease. The hemophilias, sex-linked hereditary defects of blood coagulation, are good examples. Here the disadvantage to the individual of having the disease is so great that those afflicted with it seldom live to any great age, and usually die before producing offspring. The gene for hemophilia is thus practically a lethal, and selection must be acting on it about as strongly as it ever does on any gene.

Sickle cell anemia is another example of such a hereditary disease. The cells of individuals with this trait, when they are deprived of oxygen, take on abnormal shapes, sometimes reminiscent of sickles. In the heterozygous individual, this does not seem to result in any particular damage, but the individual homozygous for the gene develops a profound anemia that is generally fatal before puberty. There is thus a strong selection against the homozygote for the trait.

Selection can also act against genes, which, so far as we know, are not directly disadvantageous to their possessors. An example of this in our population is provided by the Rh negative gene (cde). When a Rh negative woman (cde/cde) becomes pregnant with a fetus which inherits from the father one of the Rh positive antigens C, D, or E (especially D) there occurs, in about one case in twenty, the following sequence of events. Rh positive blood cells, or at all events Rh antigen, gets into the mother's circulation from the blood of the fetus and stimulates the mother's immunological apparatus to produce anti-Rh antibodies. Of the three antigens mentioned, D is the most antigenic, so anti-D is the antibody most frequently observed. The mother's antibody diffuses back through the placenta into the fetal circulation, and causes red cell destruction, jaundice, edema, and the other symptoms of the disease erythroblastosis fetalis. The fetus may be aborted, stillborn, or may die soon after birth, especially in the absence of treatment.

It can be shown by simple mathematics that this process, in a population such as ours which contains more Rh positive than Rh negative genes, leads to a selective force tending to reduce the frequency of the Rh negative genes.

More recently, evidence has been accumulating that disease may be affecting the frequencies of genes which have no obvious influence on the production of hereditary disease or resistance to infection. The pioneers in this field were Aird and co-workers (1954), who observed in patients with peptic ulcer and cancer of the stomach significant departures from the ABO blood group frequencies of the general population (table 8). At the same time, the blood group distribution of patients with other malignancies were found to be normal (see results for cancer of the colon and rectum in table 8). The results of Aird, et al., suggested that, if their series were typical, persons of blood group O are about 35 per cent more likely to develop peptic ulceration requiring hospital treatment than are persons of other blood groups. It was subsequently found that the O ulcer association is more marked for duodenal than for gastric ulcer. Later workers found similar associations between the ABO blood groups and certain other diseases, but most diseases showed no such association. The subject has been reviewed by Roberts (1957, 1959). Until recently, no disease was found to be associated with any blood group system other than the ABO blood group system, but in my

TABLE 8—*Association between Blood Groups and Disease* (Aird, et al. 1954)
(*Blood Group Frequencies Shown in Per Cent*)

Blood Group	Peptic Ulcer (3,011 cases)		Cancer of Stomach (2,745 cases)		Cancer of Colon and Rectum (2,599 cases)	
	Control	*Disease*	*Control*	*Disease*	*Control*	*Disease*
O	47.00	55.40	46.78	42.95	46.07	44.79
A	40.99	34.67	41.38	46.19	41.78	43.63
B	8.98	7.44	8.79	7.76	8.94	8.66
AB	3.03	2.49	3.05	3.10	3.21	2.92

laboratory we have recently observed an apparent correlation between the Rh blood group system and ulcerative colitis.

The correlation between blood groups and disease has been doubted by certain workers, but in certain cases one can discern an emotional bias back of their arguments. The correlation between duodenal ulcer and group O has been confirmed by workers in other countries and other types of populations, which seems to dispose of one of the arguments of the opponents of such correlations. This argument was that the correlation might be fictitious because there was a racial stratification within the population tested. If in England, for example, there were a stratum of the population which is more susceptible to duodenal ulcer and has more blood group O than the English population in general, this could give rise to the observed correlation in the absence of any genetic connection between blood group O and susceptibility to duodenal ulcer. But it is asking too much to suppose that the same stratification should be present in the ethnically quite different populations of Japan, Switzerland, Norway, and other countries where the same correlation has been found. Therefore there is little reason to question the significance of the correlation, although we do not as yet know the reason for it.

To account for the correlation of blood group A and cancer of the stomach it has been suggested that the blood group A substance, which occurs in large amounts in the gastric juice of group A individuals (of the secreting type), might be mildly carcinogenic. I personally do not consider this a very likely explanation. It seems more likely that we have here either genetic linkage or a pleomorphic effect of the blood group genes. We know that most genes in *Drosophila* are pleomorphic (have multiple effects), and this is probably true of human genes, including the blood group genes. We happen to detect the blood group genes by what they do to the red cell, but we know that these substances are not confined to the red cell, but are present in the whole body. It may well be that these genes have other effects, possibly quite unrelated to blood groups, of which we as yet know nothing.

One of the objections to these correlations has been based on the fact that the "normal" controls with which the diseased groups were compared were either hospital or Red Cross voluntary blood donors, or hospital patients suffering from some other disease. Such individuals are of course to some degree selected, as compared with the general population. Careful study of the whole problem of control populations, however, does not suggest that the use of the above groups as controls has led to any spurious correlation. However, to make sure that we are detecting an actual effect of the blood group genes, it would be desirable to make use of controls closely related to the affected group and thus similar with regard to the other genes they possess and to their environment. Such controls are provided by brothers and sisters of the diseased patients, and Clarke (1959) has studied a number of these. In these studies, Clarke did not find a significant correlation between blood groups and duodenal ulceration, but Levene (1959) points out that this may be because there are as yet insufficient data. To obtain a significant result, relatively large numbers of relatives would have to be examined—something of the order of 1,500. Levene points out that the sib study of Clarke is *compatible* with an even greater association than that suggested by the population studies.

Hardin (1960) has pointed out in a brilliant paper that the adaptive nature of the blood group genes could have been deduced from a general biological principle which has been called Gause's principle. This author has also pointed out the strong emotional bias in those who deny the consequences of this principle.

The question now arises: If selection is acting on man, and if disease is an agent of natural selection, and is acting to increase the resistance to disease, why haven't we all become so resistant that we don't get disease any more?

There are probably a number of very good reasons. First, however, let us pause to consider that none of the correlations thus far observed is likely to be an indication of strong natural selective action. The number of persons who die from such diseases before performing their reproductive function is too small (Reed 1961). I regard the associations between blood groups and diseases, in so far as we know them now, as valuable mainly in their suggestion that blood group genes are probably no more exempt from the action of natural selection than are other genes. There is indeed no reason why they should be.

That natural selection may actually be acting on the human blood groups is made more probable by findings that selection in domestic animals sometimes affects their blood group gene frequencies. For example, Shultz and Briles (1953) found good evidence that selection of chickens for certain desirable (from our point of view) characteristics, such as egg production, favored heterozygotes at one, and possibly two, blood group gene loci. Shultz and Briles thought this to show the adaptive value of blood group alleles (or gene blocks having them) in this species.

Even in the case of diseases where there is reason to think the observed mortality does suggest a significant selective action, we must remember that deleterious genes can be continually recruited by mutation. For example, although there is no reason to doubt that the gene for hemophilia is being eliminated from human populations by the great disadvantage it confers on males who carry it, there is reason to think that the gene is continually being produced again. The evidence from the study of the European royal families seems to indicate that such a mutation occurred in the person of Queen Victoria and was transmitted by her descendants to the male members of various families, notably the Spanish and Russian royal houses.

If a gene is continually being eliminated by selection and continually being produced by mutation, an equilibrium between these two opposing forces will result. Sewall Wright (1940) derived a simple formula for this:

$$q = \sqrt{(\mu/k)}$$

where μ is the mutation frequency, q the frequency of the mutated gene, and k the selection coefficient. The frequency of the gene which can be maintained by mutation is higher than might be supposed. For example, if the mutation frequency is 3×10^{-5}, which is not at all unusual, and the selection coefficient is 0.001 which used to be taken, at any rate, as a very reasonable selective coefficient, you have q, the frequency of the deleterious gene, equal to 0.17, or nearly 20 per cent.

Another reason why selection has not made us completely resistant to all diseases is connected with the fact that probably most of the genes causing hereditary diseases are recessives, and selection acts very slowly to eliminate recessive genes, particularly when their frequency is already low (see table 3). Nearly thirty years ago Hogben (1931) pointed out that even if we could exercise the most drastic imaginable selection, such as sterilization of all homozygotes, against a rare recessive gene, such as the one causing diabetes or the one causing Friedrich's ataxia, the reduction in the incidence of the disease would be small even if our "eugenics" program went on for a period of time equal to the length of the whole Christian era.

One reason selection has not made us all completely resistant to all diseases is because this is just one of the things nature won't permit. Natural selection is wonderful and has produced the organisms, species, and races we see today, but there are limits to what it can do, and we should no more expect it to make us completely resistant to disease than to expect is to make us so resistant to high temperatures that we can stick our fingers into a lit Bunsen burner without having them burned.

I am reminded of another attempt to beat nature's game, when plant breeders had the bright idea of crossing the cabbage and the radish to get a hybrid with the foliage of the cabbage and the root of the radish. This would be a great economic step forward. The cross worked beautifully, and they obtained a luxuriant, hardy and prolific plant, but it had the foliage of the radish and the root of the cabbage.

There are reasons for this. If you try to beat the game and make an animal completely resistant to every disease, or even *completely* resistant to any one disease, you will generally find you have done something else that is not so good. An example of something similar is provided by the experiments shown in tables 3 and 4, where you find that if you make a microorganism resistant to a certain antibiotic, you will find that, although it may have become resistant to certain other antibiotics (generally the ones with a similar mode of action), it has also become less resistant to other antibiotics. From the point of view of the microorganism, becoming more resistant is good and becoming less resistant is bad.

There are other examples. In the domestic goat, for instance, breeders have been selecting for a number of years for hornlessness. Horns were not considered a desirable attribute of goats, and the breeders selected quite successfully for goats without horns. But it was noticed a number of years ago that at the same time they got herds with a high percentage of animals that were intersexes and consequently sterile. This was a disadvantage both from the point of view of the goat breeder and the goat (Asdell 1944).

Another example of the fact that selection in one direction may produce unexpected undesirable effects in another is the case of abdominal chaetae mentioned earlier (table 2). These experiments had to be terminated in all cases because the experimental strains of *Drosophila*, whether they had been selected for more chaetae or for fewer, became sterile in the long run and died out.

It becomes understandable, therefore, that while selection can indeed improve the resistance of an organism to a certain disease, it may do this, beyond a certain point at least, at the price of producing undesirable effects in other ways.

There are several reasons why this happens. One reason, already men-

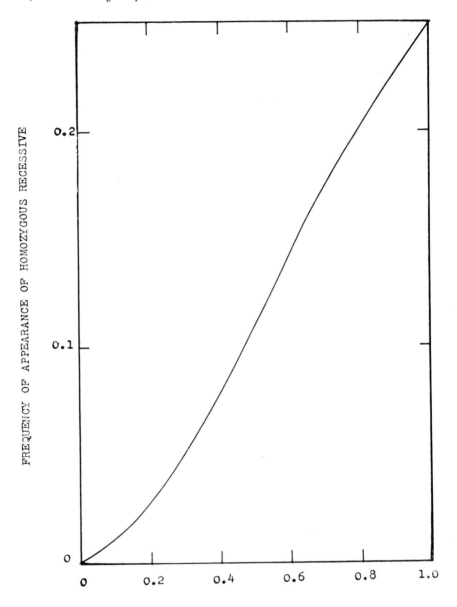

ADVANTAGE OF HETEROZYGOTE OVER NORMAL

Fig. 2—Incidence of recessive lethals maintained in a population by heterozygote superiority, (redrawn from Lerner, 1958).

tioned, is that genes are pleomorphic, that is, they may affect more than one characteristic of an organism. So if you increase the frequency of a gene which has the effect of producing resistance to a disease, or increase it too much, the gene may begin to produce some effect you never noticed before, and there may be undesirable consequences such as sterility, lowered resistance to some other disease, or something of the sort.

Another reason for this is that all organisms, including man, are made what they are by a delicately balanced system of genes that interact in a complex way. If you change the frequency of one of these genes, the effects of some of the others becomes different. The effects of most genes depend partly upon the environment, and one of the most important parts of this environment is the background provided by the other genes that the organism possesses. Waddington (1957) has attempted to visualize this situation by his ingenious picture of the "epigenetic landscape."

Therefore, the extent to which natural selection can increase the frequency in a given population of a gene for resistance to some disease, which of course depends, among other things, on the severity of the disease and the extent to which it is endemic, depends also on the genetic composition of the local population.

Another factor which often, perhaps usually, limits the extent to which we can increase the frequency of a given gene in a population is the phenomenon of balanced polymorphism. Fisher (1930) showed in his classical book, "The Genetical Theory of Natural Selection," that if two alleles are acting in a population (whence it is termed "polymorphic"), and the heterozygote happens to have a selective advantage over both of the homozygotes, such that the three genetypes which occur with frequencies p^2, $2pq$, and q^2 have relative selective advantages in the ratio a:b:c, then there will be an equilibrium such that the ratio of the two gene frequencies

$$p/q=(b-c)/(b-a).$$

In such a situation appreciable frequencies of a gene which is deleterious or even lethal in homozygous dose may be maintained in the population. This is illustrated by figure 2, taken from the book by Lerner (1958), which shows how the frequency of appearance of the homozygote of a lethal recessive depends on the degree of advantage the heterozygote enjoys over the homozygote for the normal dominant gene.

An example of balanced polymorphism in man is evidently provided by the sickle cell trait in man, already mentioned. Anthony C. Allison (1954c) noticed that in Africa the incidence of this trait was highest in those regions where falciparum malaria is most endemic (table 9).

In this table the plus signs indicate the regions of highest malaria

TABLE 9—*Apparent Relationship of the Sickle-Cell Trait (S.C.T.) to Subtertian Malaria* (Allison, 1954c)

Tribe	Linguistic or ethnic affinity	District or location where tested	Total number tested	Total S.C.T.	% S.C.T.	Malarial severity
1. Ganda	Bantu	Kampala	334	65	19.5	+
2. Amba	”	Bundibugyo	220	86	39.1	+
3. Konjo	”	Kichwamba, Kisomoro	124	12	9.7	– (+)
4. Chiga	”	Kabale	206	2	1.0	–
5. Hutu	”	Kisoro	135	4	3.0	–
6. Twa	Bantu pigmoid	Kisoro	33	0	0	–
7. Iru	Bantu	Mbarara	127	7	5.5	–
8. Hima	Hamitic	W. Ankole	134	3	2.2	–
9. Teso	”	Kampala	81	12	14.8	+
10. Lugbara	Nilotic	Kampala	76	18	23.7	+
11. Madi	”	”	62	14	22.6	+
12. Luo	”	Kisumu	288	74	25.7	+
13. Suba	Bantu	Rusinga Island	173	48	27.7	+
14. Kuria	”	Musoma, Busigire	102	28	27.5	+
15. Kwaya	”	Musoma	107	33	30.8	+

No.	Name		Location				Sign
16.	Simbiti	"	Musoma, Kanesi	126	51	40.5	+
17.	Jita	"	Musoma, Ukerewe	124	36	29.0	+
18.	Zamaki	"	Musoma, Busegwe	104	37	35.6	+
19.	Kizu	"	Musoma, Ikizu	52	15	28.9	+
20.	Sukuma	"	Mwanza	175	47	26.9	+
21.	Kerewe	"	Ukerewe Island	92	29	31.5	+
22.	Kara	"	"	52	15	28.8	+
23.	Kisii	"	Chemagal	160	7	4.8	—
24.	Kikuyu	"	Nairobi	227	1	0.4	—
25.	Kamba	"	Machakos	213	0	0	—
26.	Chagga	"	Old Moshi	130	0	0	—
27.	Rusha	"	Arusha	126	1	0.8	— (+)
28.	Pare	"	Same	54	4	7.4	— (+)
29.	Sambaa	"	Amani, Tanga	103	9	8.7	— (—)
30.	Zigua	"	Tanga	57	8	14.0	+
31.	Digo	"	"	66	18	27.3	+
32.	Bondei	"	"	81	23	28.4	+
33.	Kipsigis	Hamitic	Letain	75	0	0	—
34.	Masai	"	Magadi	104	0	0	—
35.	Iraqw	Unique,? semitic	Mbulu	102	2	2.0	—
			Total:	4,605			

TABLE 10—*Results of Experimental Infection of Normal and Sickle Cell Trait Individuals with Subtertian Malaria*
(Allison 1954a)

Luo With No Sickle-cells

No.	Mode of Infection and Strain	8	10	12	14	16	18	20	22	24	26	28	30	32	34	36	38	40
1	M_2B_1	0.03		0.07	2.5	5.0	2.5	5.0	1.2	0.4	0.02	0.01			0.1	0.01	0.01	ST
2	M_2B_1								0.03	0.13	0.41	5.0	2.5	1.25	1.67	0.03	5.0	ST
3	M_2B_1								0.1	0.02	0.20	1.0	1.0	0.83	0.25	0.2		2.0 S
4	M_2B_1					0.02	0.02	0.5	0.83	0.12	0.2	0.25	1.2	1.0	0.03	0.17		ST
5	M_2B_2	0.02	5.0	10.0	10.0	0.05	1.0	1.67	0.25	0.05	0.07							ST
6	B_2					1.0	0.1	0.01	ST									
7	B_2					15.0	50.0	ST										
8	B_1			0.13		1.67	0.33			ST		1.0		2.5	10.0	5.0	0.5	ST
9	B_2				5.0	5.0		0.1	0.5	2.5		0.67	0.1	0.1	0.05	5.0	5.0	ST
10	**B_2**		0.05					0.05	0.05									
11	B_2			0.3				0.2	ST									
12	B_1			0.3	0.3	0.3	0.1	0.3	ST		—						ST	
13	B_2			2.0				ST										
14	B_2	2.0	1.7		60.0	5.0	0.6	ST										ST
15	B_2	0.05	0.3		0.4	0.1	0.3	ST										ST

Luo With Sickle-cell Trait

No.	Mode of Infection and Strain	8	10	12	14	16	18	20	22	24	26	28	30	32	34	36	38	40
1	M_1B_2																	ST,
2	M_1B_2																	"
3	M_1B_1																	"
4	M_1B_1																	"
5	M_1B_1																	"
6	M_1B_1															5.0	0.5	"
7	M_1B_1	0.7																"
8	M_1B_1																	"
9	M_1B_1														0.03			"
10	M_1B_1																	"
11	B_2M_2											0.03	0.1	0.03				"
12	B_2M_2																	"
13	B_2M_2																	"
14	B_2M_2																	"
15	B_2M_2																	"

Figures represent parasite counts in hundreds per mm.³ of blood. ST=Stopped by chemotherapy. M=Infected by mosquito bite. B=Infected by injection of infected blood. Subscripts indicate strain of P. falciparum.

endemicity, and it is evident that they correlate well with the highest percentages of the sickle cell trait.

Allison calculated the equilibrium frequencies for this situation, assuming that the homozygous recessive had (a) a fitness one-fourth of that of the normal, and (b) zero fitness (i.e., assuming the homozygous recessive does not reproduce at all). In either case, he found that the Fisher equilibrium was arrived at in relatively few generations (about 30 to 40). It did not matter whether the equilibrium was approached from the side of an excess of the dominant (normal) gene, or an excess of the recessive (sickle cell) gene.

It occurred to Allison that it ought to be possible to demonstrate this hypothetical advantage of the heterozygote experimentally, so he took 15 heterozygotes (individuals with the sickle cell trait but not the anemia) and 15 normals and infected them experimentally with falciparum malaria (table 10). The numbers in this table represent parasite counts. It will be seen that only two of the individuals with sickle cell trait developed malaria, and the parasite numbers were small, whereas all of the controls got malaria, which in some cases was so severe that it had to be stopped by chemotherapy (ST in the table). There has been much discussion of Allison's results, but the prevailing opinion seems to be that the phenomenon reported by him is real, Edington and Lehmann 1956a).

It is not necessary for the heterozygote to have such a large advantage over the homozygote for the phenomenon of balanced polymorphism to operate, for it will be seen from Fisher's formula, above, that the ratio of the two gene frequencies at equilibrium depends upon the ratio of two differences in relative selective advantage. However, when the advantage of the heterozygote is large, the approach to equilibrium is faster. Allison (1954b) and Lerner (1958) have given examples of the rate of approach to equilibrium under different conditions.

We have already seen in figure 2 how appreciable frequencies of even a lethal gene may be maintained by this mechanism. Even if the advantage of the heterozygote is only 10 per cent (110 heterozygotes survive to breed as opposed to 100 normal homozygotes), the frequency of the lethal recessive gene at equilibrium will be 1/11 of that of the normal gene. For the sickle cell gene Lehmann and Raper (1956) estimated that the relative selective advantages of the genotypes AA, Aa and aa (homozygous normal, heterozygote, and homozygous sickle cell individual) are in the ratio 1:1.32:0, whence the equilibrium frequency of individuals with the sickle cell trait in the adult population would be 39 per cent.

In the case of the sickle cell trait, it has been possible, though not exactly easy, to detect the fact that the heterozygote enjoys a selective advantage over the normal homozygote, and to estimate the amount of this advantage. In the case of alleles where the disadvantageous gene is not a lethal and the selective advantage of the heterozygote is not so large, it is not at all easy to detect the fact that balanced polymorphism is operating. I have previously pointed out (Boyd 1955) that in order to have a good chance of detecting a heterozygote advantage of the order of 2 per cent, one would have to examine about 108,530 individuals, a rather formidable task.

Yet a selective advantage of this order of magnitude could still stabilize the gene frequencies at values which include considerable amounts of the slightly disadvantageous gene. It seems not at all unlikely that this is in fact often happening, and the phenomenon of balanced polymorphism is operating to maintain in various human populations appreciable frequencies of genes which in homozygous dose confer an appreciable disadvantage on their possessors. Among these genes there are doubtless some that lower the resistance of the individual to some disease. It is clear that we cannot expect in such cases that natural selection will ever reduce the frequencies of these disadvantageous genes to zero, so that some individuals susceptible to the disease will continue to be produced. The facts that we usually do not know wherein consists the advantage of the heterozygote and that the genetics of disease resistance are undoubtedly more complicated than the simple models considered here, have no bearing on the main argument.

DISCUSSION

DR. MOTULSKY: Dr. Boyd has done an admirable job of summarizing a large amount of material on selection in a variety of species, and especially in man. I would like to comment more specifically on the selective effects of disease in man (Motulsky 1960). It is worthwhile to think about selection in man from two general approaches: differential mortality and differential fertility.

Differential fertility may be thought of as acting anywhere along the line from gametogenesis to birth, starting with differential viability of sperm and egg—differential viability of zygotes—and ending with genetically conditioned fetal losses. There are many genetic mechanisms that could act on processes of differential fertility, and certainly much work needs to be done in this area. Some years ago, Dr. Neel published a paper on this problem (Neel 1958). One statement he made is quite interesting. He pointed out that one-fifth of the present generation gives rise to one-half of the next generation. There must be very significant genetically determined fertility factors. In modern societies such as ours there are many social factors affecting fertility, and it is very difficult to untangle social from genetic fertility factors. Studies in primitive societies, where the social factors do not play such an important role, might help us to understand a little more the selective effect of genetically determined fertility differences in man.

What about differential mortality? Selective mortality probably has acted by two principal mechanisms: starvation and disease.

Certainly, in the past, human populations must have gone through many episodes of famine. If there are genotypes that were resistant to death from starvation, these genotypes would be represented in larger numbers at the present time.

There are very few definite data on this particular point. It is quite clear from animal studies that there are genetically determined differences in nutritional requirements, for example, for vitamins and amino acids. Some recent work suggests that obesity also might be under genetic control (Tepperman 1958), i.e., some persons with identical energy expenditure and food intake get obese while others do not.

The most important diseases that have had the most decisive selective effect on the human species were probably infectious diseases, which in the past have caused a tremendous mortality. A priori, any disease with a high mortality, especially during childhood, will be a disease that can act as an important selective agent. A disease of middle age, such as cancer, arteriosclerosis, or peptic ulcer, cannot on general principles, be as good a selective agent as diseases that kill during childhood, since most people will have had their children by the time they develop such a disease of middle age. Some of the differences in ABO blood group distribution, for example in cancer of the stomach and peptic ulcers, must be based on very slight selective disadvantages. I would think that they represent pleomorphic effects of the ABO genes such as fertility differentials, which no doubt are considerably removed from the primary action of blood group substances. The truly killing infectious diseases, therefore, would be more likely candidates for examination as selecting agents.

Haldane, some years ago, pointed out that infectious diseases possibly have been the most important selective agents in man during the past 5,000 to 7,000 years (Haldane 1957). Before that time, human groups roamed in small bands and large populations did not live very close together. When agriculture and urbanization came about, diseases whose spread was facilitated by crowding could take their toll.

It is interesting that genetically acquired natural resistance to infectious diseases in animals, whenever this has been found (and there are a number of examples) (Gowen 1951; Gowen 1948), is specific for a given infectious disease and does not make the animal resistant to other diseases. A given infectious disease in these instances has acted as a sieve to select those genotypes conferring resistance for that disease alone.

A very good field study, rather than laboratory investigation, which can serve as a model for the interaction of natural selection and disease, has been done in Australia by Fenner on the myxomatosis virus in rabbits (Fenner 1959). When the virus was first introduced into a rabbit population, there was a tremendous mortality. However, from year to year and epidemic to epidemic, fewer rabbits died. These findings were resolved into two general explanations. With each succeeding epidemic susceptible animals died, and a genetically resistant strain of rabbits emerged. This was demonstrated by infecting rabbits caught in successive epidemics with the standard virus obtained in the first epidemic. It could be demonstrated that fewer and fewer rabbits died from year to year. Breeding experiments showed that this resistance was heritable.

At the same time, the virus also mutated. If viruses isolated in succeeding epidemics were used to infect standard laboratory rabbits, the mortality also became less, showing that the virus also became less and less virulent. Reduced mortality in the field thus resulted from the interplay of two factors: increased genetic resistance of the host and diminished virulence of the virus.

We have heard about human tuberculosis and possible selective factors. Most studies suggest that there are populations and people that are genetically susceptible to tuberculosis (Ferguson 1955). A comment might be made in relation to the problem of resistance of Jewish people to tuberculosis. This has been tentatively explained by the suggestion that the Jews in the Ghettos of the Middle Ages were severely crowded for many generations. They contracted more tuberculosis, with death of the susceptible genotypes, so that today we are dealing with a population that is more resistant to tuberculosis mortality. It is interesting that the Yemenite Jews, who lived in an agricultural milieu before coming to Israel, develop a much more acute type of tuberculosis with acute miliary tuberculosis and tubercular meningitis, such as seen in populations which never had tuberculosis previously. This is in striking contrast to the more chronic fibrous tuberculosis in the Jewish populations of European extraction living in Israel (Dubos and Dubos 1952). On the other hand, genetically acquired resistance can be overcome by poor environment. Statistics from the Warsaw Ghetto in World War II, where conditions were abominable, showed that tuberculosis mortality among the Jews there was much higher than that of the surrounding population.

Although heritability of factors conferring resistance to tuberculosis has never been clearly demonstrated in man, there is very excellent evidence for the existence of strains of rabbits rendered either susceptible or resistant to tuberculosis by artificial selection (Lurie, et al, 1951) (Diehl 1958).

Plague is a disease with high mortality. Millions of people were killed by plague in the past. This disease therefore could have acted as an important selective agent. There is some suggestive animal evidence in this direction. When rats, which are the carriers of the human plague bacillus, were caught in various cities in India, it turned out that those rats living in cities with a lot of recent plague had a 10 per cent mortality when infected in the laboratory. Rats taken from other cities where plague had not occurred for many years, had a 90 per cent mortality (Sokhey and Chitre 1937). These data suggest that, as a result of natural selection of resistant strains, rat populations with much plague in the recent past contained more individuals with genetic resistance than other populations.

In all these studies, one has to be careful to distinguish between acquired immunity and the genetically determined native resistance we have been talking about. The acquisition of immunity also may have genetic determinants, but this is a completely different story. Genetically determined natural resistance in an individual is operative in the absence of prior contact with the microorganisms. The studies on myxomatosis definitely and those on plague probably rule out the operation of acquired immunity.

The problem with diseases like plague, tuberculosis, and smallpox is that, although we may suspect genetic resistance in modern populations, we don't know exactly the primary nature and action of the genes that protect individuals. Usually, more than one gene is involved. In none of these cases, however, has there been much success in isolating the biochemical or immunologic pathways determined by the genes that protect these individuals.

In contrast to the diseases cited, advances have been made in isolating fairly primary gene effects in natural resistance to malaria. At this time, there is little question that children who have the sickle cell trait are less likely to die from falciparum malaria at an age when this disease takes its greatest toll, i.e., between six months and four years. This age factor is quite important. Acquired immunity to malaria occurs when children get older. In an older child, one may have very high malarial parasite counts in the red cells and the child may be clinically quite well. At that point, the possession of genetically acquired resistance factors such as the sickle cell trait is of little importance in determining survival, while it may be highly important at an earlier age. Two other red cell polymorphisms—thalassemia trait and glucose-6-phosphate dehydrogenase deficiency—probably also protect against malarial death, as will be discussed in more detail later in this conference.

One might ask: Why protection by three different red cell traits against malaria? The malarial organism requires the red cell for proliferation. One might expect any abnormality of the red cell to lead to failure of growth of the plasmodial organism, since this organism depends upon the red cell for its nutrition. It is therefore not too surprising that several red cell abnormalities have been correlated with malarial resistance. Malaria, furthermore, is a disease which on general grounds could act as a very good selective agent because it is endemic and has had a fairly high childhood mortality for many generations.

My hope is that as we make progress in detecting polymorphism in other body tissues, other correlations with disease resistance such as those found for malaria will be disclosed. The relation of PTC tasting to various thyroid disorders is an example. One difficulty is that in most cases we have been unable to take internal tissues such as liver, lung, kidney, and brain and study them for polymorphisms in many members of a population. We are lucky that blood can be removed easily. The consequence is that most of the polymorphisms that have been discovered affect the blood.

If a given infectious disease does not need the blood for proliferation, one would not expect that a polymorphism affecting the blood would have anything to do with that particular disease.

There is one potential bypass to this situation. In many cases, it has been found that enzyme systems that are present primarily in other tissues, such as the liver, brain, or kidney, may exist as vestigial enzyme systems in the blood cells. Possibly, the blood could be used as a model in a number of situations to look for polymorphisms in other tissues.

This field will be difficult to pursue because many of the very important selective diseases with high mortality do not exist in our environment any more and are disappearing rapidly all over the world. It will therefore be quite difficult to do active studies on selective processes underlying the killing disease such as plague or cholera.

I should say one other thing in relation to blood groups. Dr. Livingstone (1960) at a recent symposium pointed out that natural selection, rather than drift or migration, was highly important in explaining present ABO blood group distributions. He feels that the ABO blood group polymorphism has been shaped by the type of infectious disease mortality I have talked about. He indicated, for instance, the chemical similarity between pneumococci and blood group A substances as a possible mechanism.

DR. McKusick: It is not necessary to remind this group that interpretation of racial differences in the frequency of diseases, at least the interpretation of same in genetic terms, must be approached with great caution and can be exceedingly treacherous.

Early in this century, as many of you probably know, heredity was assigned a more prominent place in the etiology and pathogensis of pellagra than we would now be willing to assign it. And the racial difference was an important part of the argument for heritability of pellagra—specifically the difference in whites and Negroes, with a lower frequency in Negroes in the South.

Incidentally, I recently looked again at the data of Davenport and Munsey (1916) supporting the heritability of pellagra. The data contain one important bit of information against the genetic basis; namely, the proportion of affected offspring, according to whether one, neither, or both parents were affected by pellagra. The proportions among the offspring did not make any sense in terms of a genetic hypothesis.

In connection with tuberculosis, I think the differences in frequency of disease and in behavior of the disease between whites and Negroes is a genuine one which is not explicable entirely on environmental bases, and is probably partly genetic in nature.

I have been rather interested in racial differences in cardiovascular disease. As. Dr. Motulsky has pointed out, when dealing with condi-

tions like hypertension and coronary artery disease, one would anticipate that the selective force would be less potent than in the case of
other examples that have been cited here.

In the case of hypertension, it has seemed to me that some of the
best data indicating a racial difference which probably has a genetic
basis is represented by the data of Comstock (1957) collected in
Muskogee County, Georgia, where in careful observations on whites
and Negroes, he found that Negroes had higher blood pressures for
both sexes, and at essentially all ages. I can leave it to you as to how
comparable you think the environmental circumstances of the two
races are in Muskogee County, but I am inclined to think the explanation must be largely genetic.

In the case of coronary artery disease, information is more fuzzy.
Information which would permit one to exclude environmental bases
for racial differences in frequency is usually scanty. I think it interesting to examine the data of Epstein (1957) on New York garment
workers, from this point of view. Epstein compared Italian and Jewish
garment workers and found a frequency, as I recall, of coronary artery
disease among Jewish males two and a half times—or something of
this order—the frequency among the Italian males. He also did a
dietary investigation in the two groups, and came to the conclusion at
that time that there was inadequate difference in diet to account for
the difference in frequency.

However, the unsaturated-saturated fat story had not, at that time,
unfolded in its full bloom, and this may illustrate how difficult it is
to be certain about environmental comparability in these matters—
not only in diet, but in other factors such as alcohol consumption,
which one might suspect from other evidence is different in the two
groups—and so on.

I regret to say, and I apologize, that I will not be able to be here
tomorrow and the next day, and for that reason will take the license to
mention some things which might more appropriately be discussed
tomorrow.

For one thing, together with the other polymorphisms that have
already been mentioned, I might mention isoniazid metabolism which
my colleague, David Price Evans, and I have been studying for the
last two years. This appears to be a clean genetic polymorphism—rapid
inactivation, versus slow inactivation, of this antituberculous drug—
and it appears to be a 50-50 proposition as to which phenotype one
falls into, this being the same whether one is Caucasian or Negro. It
will be a nice puzzle to determine what maintains this polymorphism.

I think the possibility that natural foods, the point raised by Dr.

Motulsky, operating in conjunction with biochemical systems such as this, will provide the explanation when the truth is known.

Dr. G. Allen: I find very little that I can add to this, but I would like to re-emphasize, briefly, two really obvious generalizations. One is the fact, always annoying to geneticists, that the more common and more important the disease, the more difficult is the genetic analysis of it. For this reason, resistance to common diseases, at least diseases which have been prevalent in the population for any length of time, is found to be multifactorial. We can't expect to find some single factor as we have in a few rare diseases which will explain a large proportion of the resistance-susceptibility polymorphism, if you want to call it that.

Yet in these common diseases we can expect to find components which can be isolated, like the blood groups. And as time goes on and we study more polymorphisms, we may expect to find a good many single factors which are components in these multifactorial systems of resistance. So that even the common diseases do lend themselves to genetic study from this point of view.

The second generalization is that disease is not the only selective force concerned in these variations, and it is quite likely that the frequency of disease is sometimes due to positive selection for quite different traits. I think it very likely that the adrenal cortex and Selye's stress phenomenon is an example of how positive selection over a long period of time has developed adaptive responses which under less common circumstances precipitate disease. And perhaps another example, if I may speculate more, is mental disease. I think there can be little question that many of the phenomena of psychopathology represent misfirings of adaptive behavior, adaptive behavior which has been selected in man and which in certain rather uncommon genetic or environmental situations becomes pathological.

Genetic selection here is almost beside the point. We can't expect to eliminate this adaptive behavior and the only way selection may operate on such things is by what is called stabilizing selection. Multifactorial systems will gradually be built up by prolonged selection to control or compensate these adaptive phenomena so that they won't so often lead to pathology.

Dr. Reed: From the possibly biased point of view of a geneticist, I think there is one thing that might be helpful in considering how selection may determine these genetic polymorphisms, and that is to consider that the gene in a sense goes through a cycle, a closed cycle. In any population the gene goes, in the persons of various individuals, from zygote to adult and back to zygote, making a closed biologic cycle.

A person who has a child then closes the gap from adult to zygote. What this person does after reproduction obviously does not affect the future gene frequency and is irrelevant for purposes of determining genetic polymorphism.

So, you need consider only those different stages in the life cycle which may vary the gene frequency. And it is convenient to class them as either mortality effects or fertility effects, although, as you see in any given case, these may overlap.

This calls attention to one area in which there is still much selection going on now, which has not been specifically pointed out, but which is obvious, and that is in the gap between conception and birth. As you all know, approximately 20 per cent of recognized pregnancies do not result in a viable infant. That is 20 per cent of recognized pregnancies, and there are certainly many unrecognized pregnancies as well. This is a large area in which we have essentially no information. There is clearly mortality here. The question is: Is there differential mortality? I leave this open for consideration.

DR. DUBLIN: Dr. Motulsky, you made the assertion that one-fifth of the population produced one-half of the progeny. I am not quite sure of the connotation of that observation. Would you elaborate on it?

DR. MOTULSKY: I got this from a paper by Dr. Neel (1958). I think this may come originally from Pearson, doesn't it?

DR. REED: This comes from Pearson. Dr. Neel was able to find additional examples of this phenomenon in India and West Africa.[1]

DR. REED: They found this phenomenon occurred there. And then Dr. Neel went to American vital statistics for fertility data and found the same phenomenon operating in our own population.

DR. BLUMBERG: We recently have made some observations on the population (approximately 225) of Rongelap Atoll, Marshall Islands, in the Central Pacific. On the basis of rather incomplete pedigree data, it appeared that 25 per cent of the women produced approximately 75 per cent of the next generation. Not all of the women had reached the end of the childbearing age.

DR. F. H. ALLEN: Dr. Reed's comments bring up the question of what one means by "gene frequency." If one considers the entire population and the genes they have as representing gene frequency, then something which affects mortality in the older people does automatically affect gene frequency. And perhaps we should concentrate not on the population as a whole, but on segments of the population. "Gene fre-

---

[1] DR. BOYER: This phenomenon was also described by Stern (1949) as the "loss of ancestors concept."

quencies" so calculated may have more significance for some purposes than what you might call the true gene frequency.

I wanted also to make a comment on what Dr. Boyd was saying with respect to the unlikelihood that one could increase resistance to many different things at the same time. He undoubtedly had good reason for emphasizing this.

In the Rh system there is a simple example that will illustrate a point I want to make. Here are the four major genes that produce blood factor C, which we can suppose for purposes of this illustration is an advantageous factor:

Genes	*Frequency*	*Factors Produced*		
		C	D	E
R^1	.42	+	+	0
r'	.01	+	0	0
R^z	.002	+	+	+
r^y	Very rare	+	0	+

Let us suppose further that E is also advantageous, but D is disadvantageous. The only common gene producing the desirable C has disadvantages with respect to both D and E, while only the very rare gene r^y has the most desirable combination. In real life, the gene you wanted to promote might well be impossible to identify in the individual in addition to being very rare.

My question, Dr. Boyd, is this: Would you suppose your goal to be unattainable, even though you could recognize and select for the gene you thought you wanted? In other words, is the rarity of the gene the result of still other advantages that you don't know about?

DR. BOYD: Yes. Shall I try to answer that?

We may consider these genes, for the moment as pleomorphic. In addition to the antigens they produce which can be detected, they have other effects which we do not know of. The reason r^y is so rare may be that there is indeed some disadvantage connected with it. I do not know what that disadvantage is. I doubt if it is connected with the Rh system as we know it. But that is only a guess.

DR. BOYER: I think a note of caution should be introduced concerning the role of infection in relation to the production of a substantial number of the existing polymorphisms. Although it may be true that infection as a selecting force has played a recent role (that is recent over two or three hundred generations), it does not necessarily follow that many of the present polymorphisms are largely the result of resistance to infection.

Prior to the urban stage of society, groups of men were small and were isolated from one another. In such a period of isolation, small and essentially homozygous groups could develop. With expanding population these groups would mingle and create the situation of multiplicity of alleles at various loci. Thus, most of our polymorphisms which have little selective advantage came into existence at about the same time as the appearance of infection.

If you will, our polymorphisms are largely the legacy of the cave, albeit different caves. It may be pertinent, however, possibly to mention a study which was conclusive in its main part, although suggestive in some of its lesser parts, and that was one conducted at the University of Michigan. Dr. Reed knows more about this than I do, but one of their conclusions indicated they could see no apparent role of infection. What they did was to consider many of the blood group polymorphisms as they were determined in a number of relatives of children who were suffering from potentially lethal disease—tuberculosis, leukemia, congenital heart disease, and some others. Some of them are not lethal now but were in the recent past.

They could see no very great differences between affected persons and their sibs. Intergroup comparisons did yield some differences; that is, comparisons between families where leukemia appeared and families where other potentially lethal disorders appeared.

In addition, concerning the possibility of infection itself, which I don't doubt plays a role at some loci, you must remember that we have no idea what was happening to bacteria a thousand years ago. They have gone through literally tens of millions of generations since that time, and what we call "*E. coli*" today may have comparatively little relationship to what we might have called "*E. coli*" a thousand years ago.

DR. BEARN: There was a study a few years ago in, I think, Scotland, in which there appeared to be an excess of infants of blood group A dying of bronchopneumonia (Struthers 1951). I wonder if anything more has been done along these lines?

I would also like to say that, in general, natural selection in man takes a fairly long time to operate because of man's long generation time. The whole question of the relationship of the environment to disease, and hereditary adaptive mechanisms is discussed very beautifully in the recent book by Rene Dubos entitled *The Mirage of Health* (1959). It may well be that with the rapid changes which are occurring in our environment today we will have to rely more on man-made biochemical adaption than on natural selection.

DR. DUBLIN: Dr. Bearn, since you have been working with Dr. McDermott, would you amplify the observation that Dr. McDermott recently reported in his study of the Navajo, on the occurrence of cardiovascular disease or lack of it among the Navajo. He has made, to me, the rather startling observation that the striking differences in expectancy of cardiovascular disease in the Navajo, as compared to the Caucasian, cannot be explained on dietary bases; that diet assays among the Navajo are essentially similar to those which one would find along the Eastern Seaboard.

And I think that this ties in with Dr. McKusick's reference to studies in Muskogee County, Georgia.

Would you comment briefly on that?

DR. BEARN: I would be far happier if Dr. McDermott himself were here to tell you about the Navajo project. Dr. Walsh McDermott and his colleagues (1960) have found ischemic heart disease in the Navajo to be extremely uncommon. The fat content of the diet is very similar to that consumed by the non-Navajo. (The protein is a little lower and the carbohydrate a little higher.) This was a surprise, at least to me. Detailed fatty acid analyses of the fats consumed have not yet been completed. I believe preliminary studies do not show any gross differences.

McDermott and his colleagues stressed in their recent article in *Science* that medical treatment which is good for one population is not necessarily good for another. The Cornell group have shown that congenital dislocation of the hip is about three times as common in the Navajo population as in New York City. Now, arthrodesis of the hip can often be very helpful for people with congenital dislocation of the hip because it helps to avoid traumatic arthritis in middle age. At one time, some of the Navajo with dislocated hips had been persuaded to have their hips arthrodesed. It was quite forgotten that the Navajo has his meals sitting on the ground on the floor of the hogan. With an arthrodesed hip this is a virtual impossibility. In addition, horse back riding is rendered extremely difficult. Here is an example where a treatment, perfectly valid for one population, is contraindicated in another.

DR. REED: I can give a small bit of information on the comments made by the two previous speakers. The blood group study done by Dr. Gershowitz at the University of Michigan, as Dr. Boyer said, did not find blood group frequency differences between the sick children and normal sibs, with one exception. For rheumatic heart disease, there is a significant excess of ABH non-secretors, which is a confirmation of a study in England by Glynn (1959) and so far is the only significant result of the Michigan study.

With regard to the relation of bronchial pneumonia in children and blood groups, the Glasgow study by Struthers (1951) found that an excess number of Group A children died with bronchial pneumonia and, in fact, bronchial pneumonia without other complications. This was repeated by Carter (1957) on a London child population, without confirming this excess of Group A children. But in the London study there was no bronchial pneumonia without associated disease. So the two populations are not comparable. The question of possible association is still up in the air.

DR. MOTULSKY: The point has been made about the relative roles of selection in microorganisms and of selection in man.

As has been hinted at by several speakers, since the generation time of the microorganism is much, much shorter than that of man, there are many more chances for mutations to occur. However, mutation in the host has been shown in several cases, as for instance in the field laboratory studies in rabbits. Rabbits have a longer generation time than the myxomatosis virus, yet they developed hereditary resistance factors against death from this virus. The human studies on tuberculosis, although not as clearcut, seem to point in the same direction.

By applying artificial selection in the laboratory, the emergence of resistant lines of mammalian organisms can proceed very rapidly. In Dr. Gowen's experiments, where natural resistance to typhoid was selected for, mortality changed from 80 per cent to 20 per cent in six or seven generations, just by artificial selection (Gowen 1948, 1951).

It has been calculated that if you remove the advantage of malarial protection of sickle cell trait carriers, the incidence of sickle cell trait would drop from a starting frequency of 30 per cent to 15 per cent in six generations. Some fairly rapid changes can occur in this type of microevolution even in man.

DR. APPLEYARD: I would like to remind the conference of one of Crow's (1958) contributions, namely, the expression for the ratio of the variance of family size to the square of the mean of family size, which gives an idea of the total potential selection available over a substantial fraction of the life cycle. One of the interesting approaches in this whole area might be to think about what fraction of that total variance is contributed by various sources in assessing their significance in the selection field.

DR. WITKOP: I would like to comment on a point alluded to by Dr. Motulsky. Man, because of his nature as a complex thinking animal may react to his environment in a sociological manner not seen in animal populations. The sociological aspects of man's society must be taken into account when we are dealing with genetic qualities. Man's reaction to disease may be just as complex in so-called primitive societies as it is in more modern populations. Sociological phenomena may change gene frequencies rapidly in a few generations. The recent war in Europe and the concentration camps are an adequate demonstration of this. Another example of a sociological phenomenon which has caused rapid changes in gene frequencies has been observed by us in several isolates located along the Atlantic Seaboard. These groups have shown rapid genetic drift from an unusual cause. In Halifax and Warren Counties, North Carolina, there is a tri-racial isolate. The Genetic Section of the National Institute of Dental Research, in cooperation with Dr. Graham of Chapel Hill have just completed a study of a new hereditary dyskeratosis of oral mucosa and conjunctiva. Many other genetic defects such as polydactylism, cleft lip and palate, deafmutism, and a peculiar neurological disease occur among these people. During our examinations of the dyskeratosis kindred portion of the isolate, we also found congenital heart disease and hemoglobin C trait. Dr. Politzer from North Carolina became interested in blood group frequencies and started with us on this kindred. In recent years, a successful attempt has been made by certain leaders in the isolate to organize a State recognized Indian Association for the purpose of obtaining an Indian school. Dr. Politzer continued his examinations among the children attending this school and their parents. We, in the meantime, continued to investigate the hereditary eye disease. Though we were not particularly looking for other conditions we did find numerous examples of these defects. Through a chance remark by the county nurse we learned that Dr. Politzer had examined about 600 persons and had found only congenital heart disease and hemoglobin C trait. This led us to investigate these members of the group who had and who had not been asked to join the Indian Association. It became obvious that the isolate of 4,000 people was rapidly splitting into two segments. Families with defects obvious to the lay observer, such as dyskeratosis, deafmutism, cleft lip and polydactylism, had not been asked to join the Association. Persons with defects not apparent to the casual observer were found among the Indian Association group and were seen by Dr. Politzer. When a part of an organism is injured or defective there is a tendency to eliminate or isolate the diseased tissue. It appeared that a similar effect was seen here—if you will, the social organism or community was attempting to rid itself of its defective members.

In a similar Delaware population such a schism took place twenty years ago, and as you approach the area where they reside two distinct groups of this once single population can be observed, bearing the same surnames but with marked differences in frequencies of certain hereditary diseases such as albinism and microphtalmia. Each segment of the group has continued to inbreed.

Dr. Neel (Ishikuni, et al, 1960) has observed an island population near Japan that has a fantastically high coefficient of inbreeding. Population control is maintained by the fact that the oldest son inherits the property and the younger sons are forced to leave the island and seek employment elsewhere. Although most defects have not been tolerated on the island, deafmutism does exist. The younger sons usually go to Hiroshima. So, in talking about the natural selective forces that have shaped the genetic composition of populations, we must also superimpose sociological forces when dealing with human populations.

Dr. Gibson: Social selection certainly is a factor that I think must be taken into account. I don't know off hand of any neat cases like those presented by the previous speaker in which a society has been split into two parts on the basis of a single inherited factor. But I do recall a few instances of the isolation of albinos.

Dr. McKusick: Listening to this interesting discussion of what has happened to infectious diseases in the past and what infectious diseases have done to human populations in the past, it appears to me that the example of leprosy and its distribution in Western Europe in the Middle Ages might be a useful one to examine. It is my understanding that leprosy was brought back by the Crusaders and had a relatively impressive frequency in Western Europe during that period. Yet it died out, as you all know, and one hypothesis for this, I suppose, would be the development of resistance, although right off the bat this would seem unlikely because it occurred over a brief period of time.

I recall that Dr. Henry Sigerist told us his own hypothesis, namely, that the "black death" wiped out leprosy. There was good historical evidence that leprosaria were converted to other purposes within the span of a few years, coincident with the occurrence of large epidemics in parts of France and also elsewhere in Western Europe. The Sigerist hypothesis was that lepers were particularly susceptible to the "black death" because of their other disease, and were just eliminated from the population.

Perhaps this is a useful example of an influence that might be inappropriately interpreted in genetic terms.

Dr. Motulsky: There was a paper by Aycock and McKinley (1938) which strongly suggests genetic factors in leprosy.

Dr. Witkop: Leprosy was introduced into Canada, as far as is known, quite some time after the Arcadian split in Evangeline's time. These latter people became the Cajuns of Louisiana. One of the reasons Carville Leprosorium was established in Mississippi was the high prevalence of leprosy among people of Cajun ancestry. Many of the surnames of patients in Carville and in Canada are the same.

To get back to the point of population dynamics and gene flow within populations, our studies covering about five generations indicate that only about 60 per cent of the people in generation one contributes genes to generation three. However, to put it into more quantitive terms about 30 per cent of the people in generation one contribute between 60 and 70 per cent of the genes in generation three (Witkop, unpub.)

We have been trying to determine whether or not certain hereditary diseases confer a reproductive disadvantage. We now have two studies completed on opalescent dentine, one in a single large family with over two hundred persons affected in Maryland and about 400 affected persons in 28 kindreds in Michigan (Witkop 1957.) Mutation does not seriously enter into the opalescent dentine picture, because thus far it is the only fairly common dominant disease in man for which no report of a mutation has appeared in the literature. Consistently when we examine completed sibships, where we have by direct examination, seen all or nearly all of the individuals in the sibship, we find that the affected individuals have one-third more offspring than their unaffected siblings.

I am a little bit leery that this is strictly a biological phenomenon. Opalescent dentine is esthetically unacceptable, but does not carry with it a serious biological disadvantage. People can get along fairly well without teeth. I wonder if this difference in reproduction is not a sociological phenomenon. Perhaps this is somewhat of the same thing as the compensated reproduction seen by Glass in his study of Rh mothers (Glass 1950). Do these people compensate by having more children? Some apparently do—as one woman said: "I just keep on having them until I have a normal one."

DR. BOYD: I have only a few rambling remarks. Some of the comments that were made showed me something I already knew, namely, how inadequate my coverage of the subject was.

The chemical similarity of blood group A and pneumococcus type 14 is possibly connected with resistance to pneumonia, so that there might be a connection between blood groups and resistance to pneumonia. I think this may operate and I think there may be many cases like this. We are beginning to realize the importance of the role of carbohydrates in blood group substances and in bacterial antigens, and they show considerable chemical similarities. I think it can hardly be doubted that ability to make antibodies to some of these bacterial antigens would be different in people of different blood groups, because if you have a blood group substance which is chemically similar to the antigen you are trying to respond to in the invading microorganism, it must be more difficult for you.

Examples of this are also found in parasites; in Ascaris there is a carbohydrate which cross-reacts with both the A and B blood group substances. It makes you wonder if people with these antigens would perhaps find it more difficult to produce an antibody to Ascaris. In salmonella they are beginning to find out the chemical structure of the salmonella antigens, and the monosaccharides, dideoxyhexoses, which form part of some of them. One of the so-called "unnatural" sugars, dideoxy-1-galactose, occurs, but we are beginning to realize these "unnatural" sugars can occur in nature. Streptomycin contains a derivative of L-glucose. And I have recently obtained evidence which suggests that the Rh D antigen contains either L-glucose or L-mannose or some related sugar as a terminal sugar. If this is so, you might well think there is a correlation between Rh and resistance to certain salmonella infections.

Something was said about fitness: that we should not think merely of death but of failure of people to pass on their genes. Of course fitness should be defined as reproductive fitness. I meant to imply that.

Then, Dr. Motulsky mentioned obesity in people with intake of calories and activity identical to those of normal weight. I wonder if that is actually true. I know that fat people like myself like to think that this is true, that we don't eat any more than other people; but I believe that in the case of mice, with hereditary obesity due to a single gene, where this has been studied, it has been shown that these mice are less active than other mice. And I wonder if this isn't true in general. Because I can hardly envision a mechanism that enables you to utilize a calorie more effectively than someone else.

It has been stated that the Navajo diet is the same as ours. I was surprised to hear that, because 12 years ago I spent a summer studying the Navajo and it was my impression that their diet was very different. One member of the expedition, exaggerating, said the Navajos lived on bread and coffee. Either their diet has changed or we didn't know much about their diet then.

About the evolution of microorganisms: they certainly evolve, but of course they have to adapt themselves to their host. If *E. coli* had evolved too much and become quite a different organism, this wouldn't have paid off because it wouldn't have found any hosts. These things must go hand in hand.

I think Burnet has been one of the best exponents of the concept of balance between host and infectious agent. He believes, if I understand him correctly, and if he hasn't changed his mind, that when a disease is extremely severe and causes a lot of mortality, this means it is a new disease, one which has arisen fairly recently, in geological terms at any rate, and has not yet fully adapted itself to its host. But when it has adapted itself to its host, it will not cause much disturbance. The classical example is herpes simplex, which gets along with its host so well its host doesn't know it's there, except when he gets exposed to the sun or something of the sort and gets an attack of herpes. Only then does he know he harbors the virus.

2

THE EVOLUTION OF MODERN MEDICAL ECOLOGY AS A RESEARCH DISCIPLINE

JOHN E. GORDON

TO APPRAISE PROPERLY the evolution of medical ecology as a branch of biology and to assess its usefulness as a research discipline (Gordon, 1958), it becomes desirable at the very outset to know how and when the parent discipline of general ecology came into existence. Along with many other workers, I long had the idea that ecology originated as a science with Haeckel in Germany somewhere about 1868. Rather recently I chanced upon record of a letter written by Thoreau many years before that date. He used the word, "ecology," as glibly and as readily as any of us today (Oehser 1959). In subsequent correspondence with Dr. Francis of Michigan on the origin of the term "ecology" the two of us have come to the conclusion that in all probability the word is a Hellenism. Nevertheless, the beginnings of the discipline remain as obscure as ever.

One thing that stands out rather clearly is that what we now call the science of ecology really started as the onetime Nature Study, with the end product a naturalist, a label which many ecologists, among them Marston Bates (1959), still find most satisfactory. In the course of time, Nature Study gained a more scientific atmosphere and progressed to what eventually became known as Natural History (Bates 1950). Under influence of this concept of natural history, it was common practice to speak of the behavior of disease in nature as the natural history of that disease, first advocated by Welch of Johns Hopkins many years ago.

Natural history was, in turn, the precursor of ecology; in its development, ecology has followed a continuing theme from study of plant life, through animal ecology to human ecology and ultimately to that specialized feature which is our concern today, namely medical ecology. As I speak now of medical ecology, I wish to leave no doubt that I view the term as synonymous with epidemiology. One other important consideration which applies equally to human ecology in general, is the need to appreciate that when these disciplines came into existence as a natural sequence in the study of animal ecology, something was added to ecology beyond a mere expansion of biological interests.

38

Evolution of Ecologic Principle

General ecology (Odum 1959) has to do with the mutual relationships between any one of the various species of living organisms of a universe and their animate and inanimate surroundings. More concisely stated, ecology deals with a host in juxtaposition to its environment. Human ecology follows the same pattern as general ecology. It embodies similar principles, but two new elements are added to the complex of the immediate parent discipline, animal ecology (Allee, et al, 1949).

In the first place, a social environment comes into play (Gordon and Augustine 1948) along with the other two features of the general environment, namely the physical and the biological components. A second factor is that man as the host possesses a culture, which markedly alters and enhances the fundamental genetic characteristics that ordinarily distinguish a host, to such extent that the part of the host in ecologic phenomena is much enlarged, particularly in relation to the production of disease. As a result, human ecology, along with its subdivision of medical ecology, turns out to be a much more complicated and complex discipline than general animal ecology. As would be expected, human ecology has expanded in a variety of directions.

Workers in a variety of sciences—the geographer, the social scientist, the psychologist, the anthropologist, and the demographer, in company with the physician—have turned ecology to their own particular purposes. In some instances, the development has been such that human ecology has become in reality an integral part of the individual discipline, to be viewed sometimes by workers in that field as their own private possession. Authorities of greater breadth and erudition recognize the interrelationships that exist between these various aspects of human ecology.

I am impelled without reservation to stress strongly the unity of human ecology, with emphasis on the holism of Jan Christian Smuts (1926). That is an important and a fundamental consideration. Even a casual familiarity with morbid processes will suggest that causality of most mass diseases has to do with just about all of the facets of human ecology that I have mentioned; with contributions from sociology, anthropology, and all the others. From the opposite standpoint, the numerous nonmedical features of human ecology have just as direct a dependence on health. Without a healthy population, economic development, social welfare or human behavior possess limited and restricted possibilities of developing their full potential. I would suggest then, as an impressive and a primary deduction, that human ecology, as well as ecology in general, is holistic in attitude, in development and in application. The concept of a unity of ecologic interests has practical implication in definition of the causes of disease; namely, that the pattern of causality is multifactorial. The factors responsible for disease in man, particularly in its mass relationships, stem from two main sources, an environment and an affected host. This has much significance, because the relative importance of the two sources tends to change with time. Many present day diseases arise from the things that man does to himself or does to his environment, to such extent that they truly are to be judged as man-made. The differences, compared with a century ago are striking; the important diseases of that era mainly had an origin in nature. The causes of the diseases characteristic of the present more advanced civilization are for the most part inherent in man himself and a part of his make-up. I admit to a generally recognized reputation among epidemiologists as a host man. A major gain from interpretation of diseases of man on an ecologic basis is the increasing appreciation that causes are multiple and that they arise from a variety of sources.

Evolution in Epidemiologic Activities

A second feature of an evolving medical ecology is the increased scope of its activities (Gordon 1954). When I was first introduced to epidemiology, that discipline was essentially a concern with epidemics and with communicable processes. In the course of years, interest enlarged, first to include chronic communicable disease, then problems of malnutrition and the intoxications, and finally to the present situation where, in this country, the main weight is on noncommunicable diseases. Concurrently an epidemiology of trauma has attained much importance, this in contrast to the medical ecology of disease. This field has to do with accidental trauma and planned trauma, which has been termed the epidemiology of war.

Evolution in Methodology

An evolution in methodology has occurred progressively and yet with the major development during relatively recent times. Not so long ago, the whole objective in epidemiology was the search for a source of infection, because communicable disease was the primary concern. Epidemiology was largely a descriptive science. In time it began to give attention to methods of measuring observed phenomena, and to the quantitation of results, to prevalence and incidence. Eventually the major concern came to be causality, because knowledge of the factors that determine a disease is the basis for prevention and control.

A more recent development is the planned experiment to establish the validity of a suspect or related causative factor. This matter will have detailed consideration later in this program, but it is well to emphasize here that the planned experiment may relate to conditions in nature or may be the experimental epidemiology employing animal populations (Greenwood, et al, 1936) of which Dr. Dublin spoke this morning. Under varying conditions, the field experiment may be long or short, retrospective or prospective. Controls are an essential feature.

A further development in field practice is in relation to the laboratory. Laboratory procedures have become increasingly a part of field method, so much so that almost every really satisfactory field study has its own particular laboratory facilities. The extent to which this need has been recognized was evidenced in our own studies in the Arctic. The first medical laboratory to be set up in that forbidding environment was established as a field station located at 70° north latitude. When a laboratory is transported by commercial plane to the last airport, then by multiple trips by bush plane to land on an unimproved beach on the Arctic Ocean, and finally by dog sled to where the work is to be done, that, let me assure you, requires a belief in laboratories. As the major effort in epidemiology turns from communicable disease to degenerative, neoplastic and metabolic conditions, and to the study of traumatic injuries, the need for laboratory services continues to be appreciated.

Year by year, epidemiologic methodology incorporates more and more of biometry, in such significant features as the design of field experiments, in sampling procedure, and in evaluating methods of measurement. Field study thereby gains exactness.

Field practice also has improved through incorporating modern skilled clinical procedure in the case finding effort, a procedure characterized most satisfactorily by John Paul (1958) as clinical epidemiology. The reason is evident—an adequate evaluation of the individual case is requisite to all population studies. Thus, it comes about in modern medical practice that the clinic has moved to the field, and the field in turn goes back to the laboratory, there to establish by methods of precision and experiment leads originally recognized under field conditions.

This interchange, this succession of emphases on procedure, demonstrates the need for a different sort of worker in epidemiological field work than was the case some years ago. The need is for a field worker having a broader and more comprehensive preparation (Bode, et al, 1949) than in the simpler situation where a source of infection was the sole objective.

If the causes of mass disease arise from the variety of sources indicated by an ecologic analysis (Gordon 1952), there is apparent need for a guiding discipline in field studies having as its objective a unification of effort deriving from a variety of disciplines that range from the social sciences to physics and genetics. Reference was made this morning to the difficulty in understanding each other's language. I would suggest that human ecology, and especially its component medical ecology, have the potential of serving that purpose: in the prosecution of research, in the education and training of medical investigators from a variety of fields, and in the evaluation of active public health measures. I shall speak of these three interests in the order given.

Public health and epidemiology draw increasingly on a variety of other sciences, each important in its own right and each as often as not having a highly sectarian viewpoint. The need in field study is to synthesize these various contributions to the common problem as they bear on understanding of mass disease processes. The usefulness of information from scientific disciplines other than clinical medicine is apparent. It becomes increasingly certain that field work in human disease and injury must seek anthropologists and social scientists as active participants, as well as having their aid in developing plans and methods of investigation.

In other words, active field investigation increasingly requires a variety of skills and yet I have, in another place (Gordon 1953) voiced my skepticism about the efficiency of the usual interdisciplinary approach to epidemiologic problems, largely for reasons already given, namely, the inability of workers in different fields to understand the common purpose.

Human Ecology in Action

I would like to feel that human ecology has the potential of such a unifying discipline. In illustration, I present now several examples of field problems, largely within my own experience, that emphasize first of all the need to bring these other methods of study into play if causation is to be developed fully and precisely; and second, to assure that the problem is explored in its various ramifications.

The first example relates to fungus diseases. Some years ago I was a member of a team of visiting scientists of the World Health Organization sent to India. We spent a month demonstrating the various established and newer methods and procedures of Western medicine. The local profession then offered to return the compliment by showing us some of the particular disease conditions common to Madras. The one day of that clinic repaid us for the three weeks of our own effort.

I sat by with no great surprise while cases of tropical eosinophilia and filariasis were demonstrated, but I was completely fascinated by the subsequent succession of patients with fungus diseases. Some of the conditions I had seen as isolated cases in temperate climates, but a ward full of patients suggested that the physical environment likely had some relation to differences in frequency and behavior as pronounced as those between Madras and Boston. Rather assuredly, the social as well as the physical environment was involved. The experience was capped completely when three patients were shown with maduramycosis, an exaggerated fungus infection such as I had never seen in the United States or in any other comparable country.

Scarcely was I accustomed to this procession of the bizarre in fungus diseases, when a second group of patients was presented. Offhand, they resembled those with fungus disease. This disease, however, was diphtheria of the skin, which I saw for the first time after an experience of faucial diphtheria that had run into thousands of cases, and included such other bizarre manifestations as vaginal diphtheria, conjunctival diphtheria and diphtheria of the lip. Here was a new clinical manifestation of an old and familiar infection, again related to the physical environment and very clearly a tropical environment. The frequency of diphtheritic infection is not materially different in the two regions, and yet the clinical disease takes on a decidedly different form, determined by environment.

A third example arises from a presumptive association between nutrition and coronary heart disease. Available records attest that coronary heart disease in various localities of Africa is far less frequent among the Negro than the white population. Various explanations included a difference in nutrition of the two groups, differences in reporting of the disease, differences in medical care, or an age differential, in itself illustrating the ecologic viewpoint that I take as my central theme. In other words, were these recorded differences real, and, if so, what were the factors responsible?

In a field reconnaissance having as its purpose the recognition of possible ecologic approaches to the problem, we visited a primitive village in Nyasaland where the diet was as simple as life itself. From that isolated country, groups of villagers periodically went to work in the distant gold mines of South Africa. There they had a different sort of diet and lived a barracks type of life, ordinarily for a term of one year. The physical and social environment was of another order from that to which they had been accustomed.

Other groups of young people from these same villages were drawn to an environment of contract labor in the copper mines of Rhodesia. The mode of living there was halfway between that of the village and that of the gold mines. The main differences were that men at the copper mines lived a family existence and subsisted on a mixed diet, incorporating the main elements of the original village diet along with substantial additions of a Western type from the mine commissary.

Alexandria Township, a suburban area some 18 miles outside Johannesburg, provided a Bantu population living under conditions essentially those of Western slum life as seen in America. The diet was that of the Western world, family life was the rule, and employment was in the nearby city, mainly as unskilled labor in industry or as domestic help.

The colored population in and around Capetown provided still another group of particular interest, characterized not only by a social environment that differed materially from that of the native villager, but with an added genetic factor. The Cape colored are a mixed race, of white and Negro, but also including Indian, Malay and others.

Causality in coronary heart disease apparently can be further explored ecologically as it relates to race, diet and social environment, by expanding the studies to Jamaica, with its predominantly Negro population living under the influence of a newly developing culture. The ultimate extension is to the United States, where coronary heart disease is of much the same frequency in Negro and white segments of the population; and increasingly so as social conditions approach equality.

A further ecological problem involving disease in populations of people relates to the association of nutrition and infection. In field studies on population dynamics in the Punjab area of India over the past six years, a decidedly high infant mortality rate was established for that particular locality, something better than 176 deaths per thousand live births during the first year of life. Health activities have centered on infant mortality, apparently to the exclusion of other important periods in early childhood. When deaths during the first month of life (neonatal mortality) were deleted from infant mortality for the year and adjustment made on a 12 months basis, death rates for the first and second years of life were much the same. A significant ecologic problem emerges, namely that the changes brought about as children pass from breast feeding to a mixed and essentially adult diet constitute a health hazard about as great as those so long recognized during infancy. The high death rate for the second year was largely due to acute gastrointestinal disease, a condition known locally as "weanling diarrhea." This past autumn I had opportunity to repeat these observations in Guatemala. Although cases were fewer and the observation time shorter, the results were much the same as in India. This circumstance is largely unappreciated. As for the ordinary bacterial pathogens of the intestinal tract, they were in these observations relatively unimportant in the direct ecology of the diarrhea so commonly found.

I cite as a final example an experience in the Arctic. In three years just past, studies were initiated in three Arctic areas. The first was in Alaska, in the village of Wainwright on the coast of the Arctic Ocean. By a curious chance, this audience today includes three persons who have worked in that isolated spot, Dr. Blumberg, Dr. Paul and myself. Other studies were made in Greenland and finally in Lapland. All three areas were about equally far north, approximately 70° north latitude. The physical environment of Alaska and Greenland contrasts sharply, however, with that of Lapland. Alaska and Greenland are what most people think of as the true Arctic, Alaska being tundra country and Greenland a glacier region. Scandinavia is taiga country and quite different from the other two. The difference is largely because of the warming action of the Gulf Stream. The result is a well-developed agriculture in Lapland. The people are mainly Scandinavian, the Lapps presently contributing only in minor degree to the population. Housing in general reminded me forcefully of my native Minnesota, which also has a dominantly Scandinavian population with customs and housing, climate and country in the two regions strongly resembling each other. There is real summer in Lapland, but little other than the calendar gives indication of that time of year in Greenland or Alaska. I once attended a whale feast in Wainwright. In the open water of the summer season, the village hunters one day caught a whale, which produced a holiday of feasting with a dance that night. The temperature was 42° F, and the dancing out of doors. I took a turn with one of the native belles, and as the drums stopped beating she said, "What a pity you came up here at this time of year. It's just too hot to dance."

At any rate, what differences did these variations in climate bring about in the intestinal infections we were studying? The physical environment that characterize Alaska and Greenland, with the social environment so distinctly modified by the physical, resulted in a high level of acute diarrheal disease, something between 500 and 600 cases per thousand population per year. The Lapland climate, so like Minnesota, gave a frequency of intestinal infection strikingly different from the other two regions, and indeed wholly comparable to that observed in Minnesota.

The intestinal parasites of man also had our attention in Greenland. To my complete surprise, 72 per cent of Eskimos in that Greenland population had intestinal parasites, a frequency rivalling that of most tropical countries. Viewed ecologically, the finding is not unexpected, because the crowding indoors in Eskimo houses matches that commonly seen in the tropics. Household temperatures also are maintained at close to tropical levels. Old pictures of life in Greenland show Eskimos in their huts in wintertime completely unclothed. Such indoor temperatures along with the crowding favor contact transmission. Despite the general frequency of intestinal parasites, and the good fortune to find for the first time a parasite of animals not previously recognized in man, no single case of ascariasis was observed, although that is one of the commoner parasites of man in almost every region of the world. The explanation is ecological, through adverse influence of the environment on the life cycle of the parasite; there is no soil in which eggs of the parasite may embryonate.

These illustrations support the view that an ecologic approach to causation represents sound principle and is a useful procedure in field investigation. Attention now turns to the part ecology has in promoting education and training of investigators from a variety of scientific disciplines having the common purpose of improved knowledge about health and disease, as manifested in populations of people.

An Ecologic Background as a Common Preparation for Medical Investigation

I believe in an interdisciplinary approach in preparation for field investigation, but I believe there is need to improve mechanisms. Medical ecology has an appeal as the discipline best suited to cultivate that common interest and understanding which workers from diverse disciplines must of necessity bring to the study of disease in Nature. If I may generalize, I should say that of the total body of workers in mass disease, some few should know a lot about medical ecology, and all should know something. There is need for the expert in medical ecology, whom you recall I accept as synonymous with the epidemiologist. The general Public Health worker and the investigator need an understanding of medical ecology if for no other reason than that epidemiology is the diagnostic discipline of public health (Gordon 1954). I see also a great advantage in cultivating an improved understanding among medical investigators other than the physician by command of a common language, that of ecology. Reference is to both the social scientist and the nonmedical biologic scientist. Finally, I am of the conviction that the medical student, with his increasing, if still limited, interest in preventive medicine, can find his greatest stimulus toward appreciation of preventive medicine as an integral part of modern medical practice if his understanding rests on a command of medical ecology—epidemiology—for it is the basic foundation of preventive medicine.

Evaluation of Public Health Measures

A practical evaluation of preventive measures and of public health programs for the control of disease and injury has become a necessity because of the many newly introduced and often incompletely assessed methods, and a present day demand for efficiency and economy. It is not generally appreciated that community health measures and public health programs currently are evaluated by what is in essence a clinical procedure, applicable to the individual person, and not by methods which determine the usefulness of these measures as applied to groups or populations of people. A new vaccine, or a new method of protecting a food supply, or assuring potability of water, is judged by what it does in terms of fewer deaths, or lesser disability, or the lesser residual defect produced by the particular disorder (disease) towards which the procedure is directed.

This is in terms of simple, direct effect, failing to appreciate that when a new element is introduced into a society—as Dr. Boyd brought out this morning in connection with genetics—that the system is disturbed as a whole and the quality and activity of elements already present is affected as well as that newly introduced. As a consequence, an evaluation of public health measures is desirably ecologic, with judgment based on the effect produced on the total system and not on an isolated selected element. That is the distinction I make between an ecologic as opposed to a clinical evaluation.

In conclusion, the chief contribution of an ecologic viewpoint in investigation of mass disease and in furtherance of preventive measures, seemingly rests in its unifying influence, the opportunity it has to bring together biologist and sociologist in a concerted attack on what are fundamentally problems common to both groups of workers.

DISCUSSION

DR. F. H. ALLEN: I would like to ask Dr. Gordon to define what he means by the ecological evaluation of treatment as opposed to the clinical evaluation of treatment.

DR. J. E. GORDON: Let us suppose that we have at hand a newly proposed method for controlling a particular disease. We set up a controlled field study, to determine whether or not this method decreases the number of deaths from the disease toward which it is directed. Does it decrease numbers of cases? Does it decrease days of disability? Does it decrease the number of patients with residual defects—permanent crippling for example?

That is the common approach in evaluating a new method. When I spoke of ecological evaluation, I implied that in addition to determining these direct effects we should study also the extent to which other diseases or other health conditions are affected by introduction of the particular method. The effect on the total health complex needs to be evaluated, rather than the effect of the measure on a specific disease.

An outstanding example is the decrease in crude death rates in Ceylon incident to an intensive malaria control program and the resulting problem that country faces in excess numbers of people. Clearly they have less malaria, but they have other troubles they never dreamed of before.

DR. DUBLIN: Dr. Allen, does that answer your question?

DR. F. H. ALLEN: Thank you very much. Yes, Sir.

DR. DUBLIN: I am reminded by Dr. Gordon's observation of a classic example of ecologic evaluation offered by one of my teachers, and perhaps one of yours, Dr. Allen,—Dr. Elliot Cutler—who, at that time, was Professor of Surgery at Harvard. Dr. Cutler held a surgical clinic for first year medical students in which he attempted to correlate principles of surgery with the fundamental course in anatomy. He would bring in a person with a severe traumatic wound of his hand and discuss the therapy of torn muscles, tendons and nerves. I remember his description of two surgical approaches which were not necessarily antithetical. One would provide a beautiful surgical and cosmetic result, but the man might end up as a cripple unable to earn his livelihood if he happened to be a manual worker. The other might result in a less cosmetic hand but with the preservation of optimal functional capacity. Earlier today, Dr. Bearn also offered as an illustration the therapy of congenital hip among the Navajo. Surgical treatment of the congenital hip by fusion might "cure" the dislocation, but as far as the ecologic requirements of the Navajo are concerned, the resulting stiff leg might make it far more difficult for that individual to survive.

DR. J. E. GORDON: These ecologic principles appear to me to have broad application; they enter into a system of genes as Dr. Boyd brought out, into a human population, or into a social system. I ask that you recall what happened when alcohol was prohibited in the American society. To a considerable extent society was freed of alcohol, but all manner of new and undesirable events were introduced, which permeated the whole sociologic and biologic and ecologic system of the country.

DR. BLUMBERG: I would like to add a comment to Dr. Gordon's paper which may or may not contribute significantly to the discussion. The whale eaten during your visit to Wainwright was the last one caught for three years. Do you think the feast discouraged them?

3

PRESENT DAY OPPORTUNITIES FOR RESEARCH BASED ON KNOWN GEOGRAPHIC VARIATIONS IN DISEASE

JOHN R. PAUL

THE previous speaker in this program, Dr. Gordon, has defined the task of the epidemiologist and has given us the term, "medical ecology." I might add to this concept a little by indicating that the task of the epidemiologist here is to find something he can measure to enable him to study medical ecology. One of his purposes therefore is to measure, with reasonable accuracy, all of the possible circumstances under which disease—any disease—may occur.

Most of the things which epidemiologists may wish to measure do not lend themselves to that kind of treatment, as those who have worked in this field well know. Certainly the character of the population, its ways of living, its diet, and various kinds of environment are not easily measured.

Dr. Gordon told us he is a "host" man and I would like to aspire to that also, because we are to be concerned in this brief review with methods of detecting and measuring host factors.

Obviously there are many things measurable and unmeasurable to be found in the human host, but I expect to limit myself to substances that can be found in blood. This morning there was discussion of how difficult it is to excise a piece of skin or some other tissue, while on the other hand, blood is more easily obtained. It contains many things: antibodies, electrolytes, lipids, plasma proteins, hemoglobins, etc. Such things can be measured in the course of a survey in which blood has been obtained from representative members of a given population, embracing members of different ages, and other groups which have different ways of life or ethnic backgrounds.

I doubt if all measurable substances in blood have ever been counted, but certainly at least 50 items can be measured from a single specimen of blood; perhaps there are even 100, each of which may have some bearing on the donor's phenotype or genotype.

I refer to the whole long list of antibodies, to proteins, gamma globulin, blood lipids, and to blood groups as well as many other features. Their study represents a kind of epidemiologic activity which some people have called *serologic epidemiology*—a new science still in its infancy.

Actually, however, it is not new, although some of its methods are. Surveys of this kind began more than a generation ago. Among early attempts were those designed to map out the number of individuals within urban communities who had positive Wassermann tests. We should also note that Schick test surveys (Frost 1928) and the tuberculin test surveys (Hetherington, et al., 1929) also employ this approach.

Perhaps one of the most important early serum surveys was on the prevalence of yellow fever antibodies, carried out in the 1930's in Africa and South America, largely through the work of Soper, et al., (1933) who was then with the Rockefeller Foundation. This among other aspects resulted in the demonstration of existence of jungle yellow fever.

Later, in the 1940's, serum surveys were used for mapping out the distribution of the arthropod-borne viral encephalitides in the U.S.A. (Hammon, et al., 1942) and in Japan (Sabin, et al., 1947). It was illuminating to some of us who went to Japan in the months immediately following World War II, to find that the Japanese had been using this method to map out the prevalence of Japanese encephalitis on their islands for at least ten years; (Paul and Hammon 1946). They had studied the serum of man, animals and birds, to indicate where the infection had been. It proved to be almost absent in their northern island of Hokkaido and most prevalent around the Inland Sea.

These studies have now expanded around the world. Arthropod-borne viral encephalitides represent an ideal subject for the study of global epidemiology. They include the viral diseases spread by insects: yellow fever, sand fly fever, dengue, and the many other kinds of viral infections in South America and in Africa. Russian, United States, Australian and British workers have been busy with this field.

Then again, poliomyelitis lends itself to such studies. The first paper that came from our own laboratory on this subject was in 1935 (Paul and Trask 1935). There is hardly a country in Europe today which doesn't know its own pattern of antibodies to poliomyelitis in the various age groups.

With influenza, important discoveries have been made by this technique. Drs. Davenport, Francis and colleagues (1953) showed that antibodies to swine influenza were present and limited to those individuals who were old enough to have lived through the great influenza pandemic of 1918, indicating that there may have well been a causal relationship between this particular virus and that epidemic, a suggestion which had previously been made by Laidlaw (1935) and later by Shope (1936). As another and more recent example, Mulder and Masurel (1958), in Holland, showed that the influenza epidemic which had occurred in 1889 and 1890 was probably caused by the same virus now in our midst— that of Asian influenza. This decision was based on the fact that antibodies to the virus of Asian influenza were fairly prevalent in the population among individuals who in 1958 were 70 years of age or older.

So, this kind of study has now been going on for some time, yet, a new development has come about, in that the W.H.O. has pointed out, through the work of one of its expert committees, that these collections of sera can be used for a battery of tests besides those of antibodies. Copies of their Report on "Immunological and Haematological Surveys"[1] are available, describing how sera may be collected for several purposes, and how such work could be done at relatively little cost. In this Report, it has been suggested that a number of serum banks be established, which would collaborate in this development and distribute the serum to those working in special fields.

Blood components that would be measured for the multipurpose survey might cover a pretty wide field. This has been divided into at least three categories:

1. Immunologic studies which concern infectious disease and its footprints. I say "footprints" because antibodies do represent footprints of infectious diseases that have passed that way, and which an individual may have experienced many years earlier.

2. Genetic surveys of which we have heard this morning, in which information regarding serum and red cells, and abnormal hemoglobins could be available from various collections of blood.

3. Biochemical surveys of plasma in which plasma proteins and blood lipids can be measured.

And so, from this multipurpose approach, serum which has been properly collected, properly stored, and properly distributed can be available for a variety of uses, the value of which is for future work to decide.

I could quote a few examples of the application of this method. In Egypt (Paul, et al., 1944), for instance, during World War II, local physicians in Cairo insisted that poliomyelitis was a very rare disease with them; to which their own local reports recording a mere half dozen cases a year bore witness—this in a population of about 17 million people. Argument would not persuade them that this was not correct, particularly at a time when British and American troops quartered in that area in

---

[1] "Immunological and Haematological Surveys", Report of a Study Group, W.H.O., Tech. Report Series, No. 181, Geneva, 1959.

1942-43 were having such a high rate for poliomyelitis. Local physicians claimed that poliomyelitis was an Anglo-American disease.

But it was not until 1950, when poliovirus antibody surveys carried out there indicated that Egypt was one of those countries whose population had the highest level of poliovirus antibodies among the youngest age groups of any of the countries that had been tested up to that time. In other words, the virus was widespread there. The population acquired immunity at a very young age and the disease was more or less masked because, as we all know, poliomyelitis is a much milder disease in infants than in children of school age or teenage or particularly in adult life.

So, the actual situation was that the disease in Egypt was under cover and it was no wonder that the United States and British troops acquired paralytic poliomyelitis at a rate far higher than they did in this country, even though local physicians insisted in 1942-43 that the Americans and British had brought this disease with them.

I have a slide to show illustrating the way the antibody patterns from these serologic surveys are expressed (See figure 1). This covers the age groups from 6 months to 40 years, and from the 250 sera tested in each series from Cairo, Egypt, from Miami, Florida, and from Alaska, one can see three different poliovirus antibody pictures. The ecology of polio-myelitis differs in these three populations, as do also the antibody patterns. Included is a population living on the North Coast of Alaska. The latter is an antibody record of some 250 representatives of a remote civilization, living far enough away from civilization so that common diseases pene-trated seldom.

One can learn several things from this chart. First, it is clear that prac-tically nobody under the age of 20 in the Alaskan population had anti-bodies to Type II poliovirus (Paul and Riordan 1950). This indicates that the infection had not been in this population for 20 years. But it also indicates that it had been there quite definitely 20 years prior to the collection of this material, obtained in 1949, because those over the age of 20 years possessed antibodies at rates of 75 to 90 per cent. This rather indicates that an epidemic had occurred 20 years before or actually in 1930—a Type II epidemic.

One could go on with a good many other interpretations that can be derived from this chart. One of them concerns the much discussed question as to whether poliovirus antibody levels are kept up by repeated infections. Some light has been thrown on the subject by this study. It seems very clear that this population had no repeated infections during a 20-year period—1930–1949—and yet the older individuals kept their antibodies pretty well (Paul and Riordan 1950).

This, then, was an unusual opportunity, and I am glad to say that Dr. Gordon's population from the village of Wainwright contributed half of this collection of sera. The collection of Eskimo sera has proved valuable

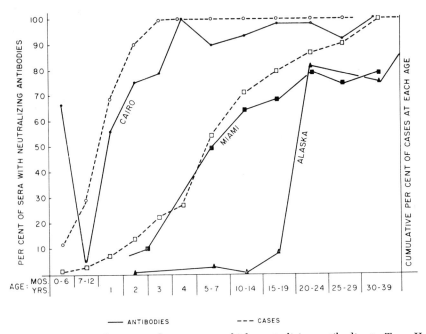

——— ANTIBODIES   – – – CASES

Fig. 1—Age-specific rates and patterns at which neutralizing antibodies to Type II poliovirus developed in these areas, compared with the ages in two urban populations (expressed as cumulative percentages), at which cases of local clinical poliomyelitis developed. The two cities shown—Cairo, Egypt and Miami, Florida—are located at about the same level of latitude, but in 1950 they differed considerably as to sanitary arrangements as well as the age composition of their respective populations. The Alaskan sera were from two Eskimo villages at the extreme north west of this state. Cario data from Paul, Melnick, Barnett and Goldblum (1952); Miami data from Paul, Melnick, and Riordan, (1952); Eskimo data from Paul and Riordan (1950).

from other aspects—for gradually as new tests became available they were applied to these sera until the last drop was used up.

In figure 1 we also have Miami (Paul, et al., 1952) just to show a middle-of-the-road situation, and an antibody pattern characteristic of an American city prior to the use of the Salk vaccine.

One other study in a North African group will be mentioned. This records the antibodies against epidemic (louse-borne) typhus in a population from French Morocco (Commission on Viral Infections, A.F.E.B., unpub. April 1954). These sera were collected in 1953. (See figure 2.) Under the age of five, no one had antibodies to epidemic typhus, the explanation being that for the previous five years, from 1948 to 1953, a heavy campaign of DDT dusting and antityphus activities had gone

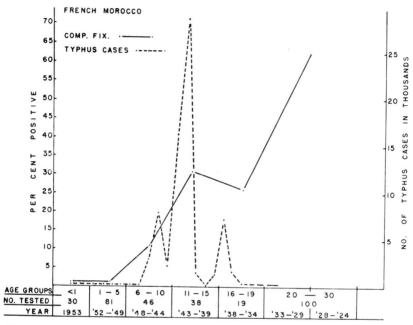

AGE GROUPS	<1	1 — 5	6 — 10	11 — 15	16 — 19	20 — 30	
NO. TESTED	30	81	46	38	19	100	
YEAR	1953	'52 —'49	'48—'44	'43 —'39	'38 —'34	'33 —'29	'28 —'24

Fig. 2—The chart shows age-specific rates for complement fixing antibodies against epidemic typhus in French Morocco in 1953 (see scale on left). Also shown is the annual number of local typhus cases which occurred between 1934 and 1948. (See scale on right.)

I am indebted to E. S. Murray of the Harvard School of Public Health for carrying out the complement fixation tests in this study (Commission on Viral Infections, A.F.E.B., 1954).

forward. On the other hand, some children born in 1948, prior to the campaign, had acquired antibodies to epidemic typhus. Here, during the war years and previously, Morocco had had a large epidemic of typhus, and obviously the people who had lived through that epidemic were more likely to have antibodies, and so in the adult age groups the positive percentages for this complement fixing antibody rises steadily.

These are but a few types of antibody analyses that can aid in the study of infectious diseases. However, a final word should be mentioned here as to what these measurements may mean—they are not necessarily a measurement of illness. In the case of measles, where about 100 per cent of infections are clinical, this would have been a record of illness, but most of the antibodies shown here are an indication of infection, not illness, for as many as 98 per cent of such infections may be inapparent or subclinical.

If we turn next to the *noninfectious diseases* and what can be learned through so-called hematological surveys, we can choose, as an example, the exploratory work being done with the rheumatoid factor, in an attempt to see if this can be used as a marker or as a measure of the prevalence of rheumatoid arthritis (Ziff 1958).

Another example is the level of blood pepsin as a diagnostic measure for those individuals who are liable to develop a duodenal ulcer. In our department we are bleeding all the freshmen who come to Yale College every year, a thousand of them annually, and storing away their sera, measuring blood pepsin levels on all of them, noting those with high and normal levels, and making a special effort to follow both groups clinically.

Now, as I go on, I shall be getting into fields of which I have relatively little knowledge, so I am treading on rather dangerous ground. The capacity to obtain information on *blood groups* from material of this kind is one concerning which there are others around this table who would be better qualified than I to discuss. The approach does lend itself to blood group surveys. In this connection, however, it is important to point out that any collections made on a multipurpose basis should carry with it ethnic and demographic data. Such surveys have a greater value when carried out in definable homogenous groups, whether racial or otherwise, than in sera which have been collected in a hit or miss fashion over a large area.

The abnormal hemoglobins obviously are another group which fall naturally into this type of study—and then the anemias, of which there are clearly many kinds. These anemias, associated with abnormal hemoglobins, are obviously to be distinguished from the iron deficiency anemia and from those due to infection or nutritional disturbances.

Plasma proteins represent a whole field which may include the percentage of plasma protein, their quality and the albumin/globulin ratios.

Vitamin A determinations and carotene levels represent still another group. And, perhaps more timely, will be studies on plasma lipids of which an example has been mentioned by Dr. Gordon. I understand that work is proceeding in South Africa on three population groups—the European descendants, the Bantus, and other native races. It calls for a comparison between the prevalence of coronary heart disease or ischemic heart disease among these various ethnic groups and the blood lipids.

Now, having painted perhaps too glowing an account of this approach, it is time to talk about its limitations. It seems hardly necessary to point out that there ought to be a very thorough knowledge on the part of the epidemiologic investigator with regard to the test that he is using, its significance and specificity. Many of these tests have relatively little specificity, although they may be useful as a screen, the decision also has to be made as to what is to be called positive test and what is to be called a high level or a low level. These are arbitrary decisions.

Furthermore, the tests should not be too complicated. They should certainly not be too expensive if one has to perform hundreds or thousands of them.

In interpreting the results of the hematologic survey it is important to point out that they give only a part of a story. Results have to be viewed in relation to the total ecologic picture. In this connection, I think it is an advantage for the epidemologist to collect his own sera, and witness the locale from whence they come, as well as to obtain an intimate view of the population. From this responsibility for the field work as well as the laboratory work, he can get a sense of the total ecologic picture which is helpful when it comes to an interpretation.

Now, I am going almost too fast. I should mention the fact that a great problem in this type of work whether it be a single or a multipurpose survey, is that of dealing with the techniques of *sampling*. Here one must weigh the chance of obtaining a truly random sample with the investigators' capacity to find those individuals who are willing to be bled. It is one thing to say, "We'll take so many here and so many there," and another thing to go into the homes, armed with a syringe and ask all the occupants to roll up their sleeves—particularly the young babies. You will have already noted how important in some of these surveys the blood samples of children and infants from three months on are. Difficulties arise in the bleeding of the very young children but they are not insurmountable.

There are several methods of sampling a large population. One is the random sampling of the whole region; another is based on a random method of choosing individual members from each of several population groups selected on a racial, social or environmental basis. These latter would not give results which would be valid only for the specific groups, although when taken together an overall picture can be estimated. The ideal sample is not often found. It can be a village where almost every member is bled. This has been done, but it is very unusual.

Then there is the question of what age groups to consider. If it is a multipurpose survey, the ages to be represented should range from infants right on up to the old age groups.

Next comes the question as to how many individuals there should be in the sample to make the tests statistically valid. Taking various factors into account, the usual survey can range between 300 and 600 individuals. About 25 samples from each of the annual age groups up to the age of four, and 50 samples from each of the five-year age groups beyond that have been felt to be advisable.

As to other technical details, and the actual size of the blood sample, I hope it is not going to grow larger. For the type of survey in which some of us have been interested, we take 26 ml. of blood from individuals over the age of six or eight and less from younger individuals.

This blood is immediately centrifuged, either as plasma or clotted blood, and the serum is separated. Various methods for storing have been tried often in small aliquots which are either frozen or lyophilized. The value of storage is that there are many things one cannot measure now, but which may be measurable in years to come.

In conclusion, I think that as this approach develops it may have an impact on public health thinking, as well as on epidemiologic thinking, possibly comparable to the impact which certain kinds of clinical investigations had on clinical medicine in this country in the 1920's.

DISCUSSION

DR. BOYD: One question I think may be one that you may have answered yourself—I wasn't sure. You are doing blood groups on these samples, I take it?

DR. PAUL: I am not.

DR. BOYD: But someone is?

DR. PAUL: Yes, there is a group in the Expert Committee that have dedicated themselves to this task.

DR. BOYD: Then in connection with that, is anyone looking for a correlation between blood pepsin levels and blood groups?

DR. PAUL: I know that we are studying such a correlation in our own study. I don't know about the others yet. This is an old correlation, of course.

DR. BOYD: Have you found it?

DR. PAUL: I am unable to report on it. I must say I don't think the results are too impressive.

DR. BOYD: And you preserve frozen serum. Are you preserving frozen cells for future reference?

DR. PAUL: This is in a stage of exploration. We have several techniques that are being tried. I would like to hear your comment about this. What has been your experience in an effort to preserve cells for your own purposes?

DR. BOYD: If they are frozen in glycerin, they apparently keep forever, as far as I know.

DR. PAUL: Satisfactorily?

DR. BOYD: Oh, yes. It's a little trouble to bring them out of it. Theoretically, so far as we know, they ought to keep for at least 50 years. It might be well worthwhile having them around, depending on what ethnic group you are taking blood from. Some of these populations are irreplaceable. Once they have died out, you'll never be able to get them again.

DR. DUBLIN: You did call attention, Dr. Paul, when you referred to the Expert Committee's report, that it stresses the need for methodologic and developmental research in connection with the storage of serum and blood cells in serologic banks. The report points out the limitations that presently exist in storing sera under lyophilized or other conditions.

DR. PAUL: This is the very kind of thing concerning which a subsequent meeting on methodology might be of great help.

DR. DUBLIN: In that regard, may I say that in planning for Thursday's discussion, you will notice that the program is relatively unstructured.

We hope that if the group wishes to discuss such things as the kinds of methodologic research that is needed, we could very well devote time to such a topic.

I believe Dr. Motulsky and Dr. Bearn both had questions.

DR. BEARN: Many of my questions have already been answered. Many of us are setting up serum banks and we are very concerned over the problem of the best method of storage. If serum is frozen in a conventional deep freeze, complement and probably many other substances will be lost. Perhaps we should store all serum at minus 75°C despite the expense. Ideally the serum should be divided into two or three small samples each of which should be stored separately. The problem, however, is not easy and I would like to have some guidance on these points.

DR. PAUL: You have put your finger on a pretty all-embracing question. Different antibodies have different lability, that's clear. Many of these other features are an unknown quantity. How well the blood lipids and how well the plasma proteins will keep when frozen or lyophilized is for the future to decide. In any event sera should be divided and kept in different aliquots. I doubt if frozen sera need to be kept at minus 75; the temperature in most general use is minus 20.

DR. MOTULSKY: When I saw the bulletin on epidemiologic blood sampling some months ago, I wondered whether this is an idea or whether it is already in practical use.

DR. PAUL: I think correctly it is the idea stage. Two serum banks are under consideration. But they have been recommended and should really come into existence.

We already have iceboxes bursting with all kinds of sera, but whether to actually dignify this situation with the name of bank, as yet, is questionable.

DR. DUBLIN: Chatting briefly with Dr. Payne of the W.H.O., when he was in Washington last week attending the International Conference on Influenza, he expressed his regrets that he could not be present for these discussions. It was his hope that the discussions around this table might help to foster the translation of the hopes and aspirations set forth in the Technical Bulletin referred to by Dr. Paul into actual programs.

4

EPIDEMIOLOGIC METHODS AND INFERENCES APPLIED TO THE STUDY OF NON-INFECTIOUS DISEASES

A. M. LILIENFELD

DRS. GORDON AND PAUL have, in a very wonderful manner, mapped out the broad field of epidemiology. What I would like to do is to limit myself to an operational approach, to the various methods being used in epidemiologic studies, with particular reference to noninfectious diseases and emphasizing the reasoning processes that epidemiologists use when they look at data.

As Dr. Gordon has indicated, epidemiology, or medical ecology, as he terms it, is concerned with the study of the distribution of a disease or a condition in a population and of those factors that might influence this distribution. Thus, the epidemiologist is concerned with the distribution of disease by age, sex, race, occupation, ethnic background, etc. Essentially, he is interested in determining what characterizes the diseased person as compared to the nondiseased person in a population. He makes use of this knowledge for various purposes, the primary one being the development of etiologic hypotheses concerning the disease.

I would like to illustrate this use with the results of studies of a disease problem, in which there is a great deal of current epidemiologic interest —leukemia. Hewitt (1955) reported the results of an analysis of the trend of mortality from leukemia in England and Wales in specific age groups. He noted that a marked increase in mortality had occurred in the third and fourth years of life during the period, 1931 to 1953 (figure 1). It was thought that these trends might be a reflection of the introduction of an environmental etiological agent either in the prenatal or postnatal period. Since previous work had demonstrated a relationship between x-radiation and leukemia, and since over this time period there had been an increased utilization of x-ray pelvimetries in obstetrical practice, it occurred to Hewitt and his colleagues that perhaps exposure of the fetus to antenatal x-rays might be of etiologic importance in childhood leukemia. To test this hypothesis, an investigation was carried out in which information was obtained on 1,299 deaths from malignancy for those under 10 years of age, as well as on a control group. The detailed results of this study are reported elsewhere, but in table 1 we have summarized the results of the study with respect to the relationship of these malignancies to antenatal irradiation (Stewart, et al., 1958). We note that a larger proportion of the leukemia and the other cancer cases had a history of exposure to fetal radiation than did the controls. It is of interest that the relationship of leukemia with x-radiation has been independently confirmed by two other investigators (Ford, et al., 1959)

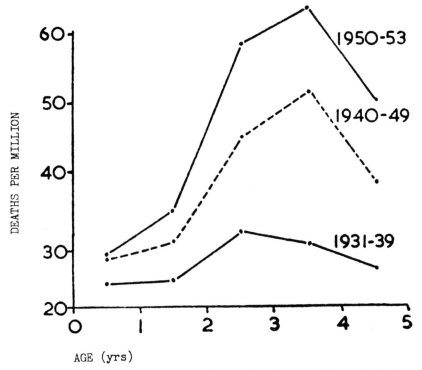

Fig. 1—Mortality from leukemia in children under five years of age, England and Wales (Hewitt, 1955).

(Manning and Carroll 1957). In interpreting these results, Stewart, et al., pointed out that the number of childhood malignancies accounted for by x-radiation is small relative to the increase of these deaths over the past two decades.

It is needless to point out that the results of these studies require further confirmation both by similar retrospective investigations and by prospective types of study, to be discussed later. However, these studies do provide an idea of the mode of investigation, the types of inferences made and the utility of knowledge of the distribution of disease in the population.

TABLE 1—*Comparative Frequency of Direct Fetal Irradiation Among Cases with Leukemia and Other Malignancies and Among Controls* (Stewart, et al., 1958)

Diagnosis		Irradiated in Utero	
	Total	Number	Percent
Leukemia, all types	619	79	12.8
Other types of malignancies	680	99	14.5
Controls	1299	93	7.2

A second use of epidemiologic data is to determine consistency of the population distribution of disease with various etiologic hypotheses. This can be viewed in two different ways, each of which will be illustrated. The term "consistent" is used in the sense that an etiologic hypothesis determined in the clinic or laboratory should be consistent with the distribution of disease in a human population. To the extent that it is not consistent, the hypothesis will have to be modified. An illustration is Holsti and Ermala's production in 1955 of bladder cancer in mice by the application of tobacco tar to the buccal mucous membrane (Holsti and Ermala 1955). The results indicated the existence of a relationship between tobacco tar and bladder carcinoma in mice. Naturally one is interested in determining if such a relationship exists in humans.

We were in the fortunate position of being located at the Roswell Park Memorial Institute where tobacco-use histories were obtained routinely over a number of years on all patients referred to the institute. We analyzed these data to determine if there was any association of tobacco use with bladder cancer (Lilienfeld, et al, 1956).

A summary of the results are presented in table 2. Clearly, there is an association between bladder cancer and cigarette smoking. Thus, a relationship determined by animal experimentation was confirmed in a human group.

Since then there have been several other studies on human populations, in Norway and Paris which have confirmed this relationship of cigarette use to the development of bladder cancer (Denoix and Schwartz 1956; Clemmesen, et al, 1958).

Interestingly enough, after Holsti and Ermala published their results, many investigators attempted to confirm the experimental work. Some of them did not succeed. About two or three months ago, this work was confirmed by Wynder (1960). This is a rather unusual situation since in most instances animal studies are more readily confirmed than are studies on humans.

TABLE 2—*Percentage of Men Aged Forty-Five Years and Over With History of Tobacco Use, by Class of Patient* (Lilienfeld, et al., 1956)

Class of Patient	No. of Patients	PER CENT TOBACCO USERS			
		Any Type of Tobacco	Cigarettes Only	Cigarettes Alone and in Combination with Other Types Of Tobacco	Any Type Other Than Cigarettes
		UNADJUSTED PERCENTAGE			
Bladder cancer	321	84.1	47.0	59.8	24.3
Benign bladder conditions	39	76.9	30.8	38.4	38.5
No disease	337	70.9	40.0	46.3	24.6
Prostate cancer	287	74.6	28.2	37.2	37.3
Lung cancer	306	91.8	67.3	84.3	7.5
		AGE-ADJUSTED PERCENTAGE			
Bladder cancer	321	84.7	48.7	61.4	23.2
Benign bladder conditions	39	77.9	32.8	37.1	40.8
No disease	337	70.8	35.8	44.1	26.7
Prostate cancer	287	77.8	32.6	42.3	36.1
Lung cancer	306	92.0	64.9	82.9	9.1

Consistency can be viewed in another light. Let us assume that we have knowledge of the distribution of a disease in a population and there are variations in the frequency of the disease by such characteristics as age, sex, race, geographic area, etc. Let us also assume that various studies have indicated a relationship between this disease and a certain individual characteristic. The question might then be raised as to whether the variations in frequency of the disease in different population segments is consistent with the variations in the frequency of people with the given characteristic.

To illustrate this approach, we will use various data from some studies on leukemia. Several years ago, MacMahon and Koller (1957) reported that the frequency of leukemia among Jewish residents in Brooklyn, New York, was about twice that of the non-Jewish residents. They considered the possibility that the Jewish population may have been exposed to more x-radiation, since there is evidence that Jews receive more medical care than other religious groups in Brooklyn. In 1956, a survey of the adult population of Buffalo, New York, was carried out with several objectives in mind, one of which was to determine the frequency of exposure to various forms of x-radiation by various population characteristics, including religion (Lilienfeld, 1959). Despite the fact that the data from Brooklyn and Buffalo may not be comparable, it was considered desirable to see

TABLE 3—*Age-adjusted Percentages of Persons Who Had One or More Diagnostic x-ray Examinations During 12 Months Preceding Interview and of Those Who Had x-ray or Radium Treatments During lifetime, in Upper Socio-Economic Group, by Religion and Sex* (Lilienfeld, 1959)

Religion and Sex	Number of Respondents	Per Cent Examined	Number of Respondents	Per Cent Treated
Jewish				
Men	59	54.1	61	13.6
Women	65	55.5	65	20.5
Protestant				
Men	341	46.8	347	9.4
Women	426	43.6	432	12.9
Roman Catholic				
Men	536	49.4	537	7.3
Women	634	39.7	640	12.5

if exposure to x-radiation differed by religion. The results are presented in table 3. Since the total number of Jewish people in the sample was relatively small, and since a majority of them were in the upper socioeconomic group, these comparisons were limited to this group. Clearly, for both sexes, the Jewish group had more diagnostic x-ray examinations and more x-ray therapy than the other religious groups. The differences were not large with respect to examinations, but the therapeutic procedures were almost twice as frequent among Jews as among non-Jews. These observations are clearly consistent with the variations in leukemia frequency. Needless to say, they require confirmation, particularly in the same geographic areas where information concerning leukemia frequency is obtained.

Consistency of the population distribution of disease and of the possible causative factor obviously increases confidence in the plausibility of an etiologic relationship between the two. In fact, the finding of complete consistency can be considered as being similar to "replication" in experimentation. In this sense we would interpret consistency as a replication of the relationship in different subgroups of the population, each of which differs from the others with respect to some characteristics.

A third use of the knowledge of our distribution of disease was alluded to by Dr. Gordon in that this knowledge is necessary and useful as a basis for preventive medical and control measures in a population. It might be well to give a few examples although simple ones. Data indicating that tuberculosis is very high in certain population groups, e.g., American Indians, Negroes, is of importance in providing a focal point for such public health measures as vaccination, chest x-ray surveys, etc. In the case of noninfectious diseases, such as diabetes, knowledge that there is familial aggregation is important in indicating that, when a case is diagnosed, it would be worthwhile to screen members of the diagnosed person's family as a means of finding cases early. For the remainder of our discussion we shall try to limit ourselves to a consideration of methods involved in trying to determine etiologic relationships in disease.

It is clear from our illustrations that the epidemiologic method can be considered as consisting of two general phases. The first phase is the development of a statistical association between a disease and a certain population characteristic, which we hope may be of etiologic importance. The second one consists of the derivation of inferences from the pattern of statistical associations, with respect to the biology of the disease. It is the totality of the series of statistical associations and the biologic inferences that we might call the epidemiology of disease.

How does one go about determining statistical associations? This might be best observed in terms of data types used for this kind of determination. I have classified them into two general broad categories and several subgroups as follows:

(A) *Study of General Population Characteristics*
    1. Vital statistics including mortality and morbidity data obtained on a routine basis.
    2. Special Population Surveys
(B) *Studies of Individual Characteristics*
    1. Cross Sectional Study
    2. Retrospective Study
    3. Prospective Study
    4. Experimental Study

We have already illustrated the use of routinely obtained mortality data by Hewitt's analysis of leukemia mortality.

A good example of the special population survey is obtained from the studies on the relationship between fluorides in the water supply and dental caries. Although some of you are familiar with this story, it may well be worth reviewing.

The possible relationship of caries to fluorosis developed from the clinical observations of dentists who examined children living in areas where there was a high natural fluoride content in the water supply. These children had developed mottled enamel as a result of fluoride exposure and those with mottled enamel had less dental caries. An association was observed and it was necessary to confirm it by a more definitive kind of study.

The Public Health Service carried out a special population survey in 21 cities of four states, of about 7,000 children, 12 to 14 years of age, who were examined with respect to their dental caries experience (Dean, et al, 1942). In each of these cities they also determined the fluoride

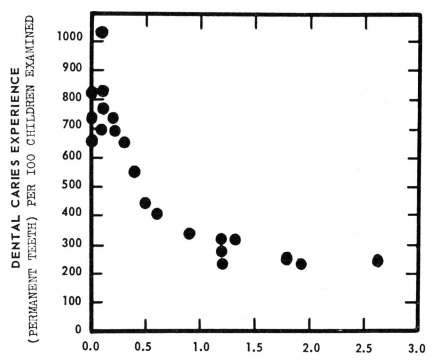

Fig. 2—Relation between dental caries and the fluoride (f) content in the public water supply in P.P.M., (*Dean, et al., 1942*).

content of the public water supply in parts per million. The results of this survey are presented in figure 2. You will note that as the fluoride content of the water supply increased, the dental caries experience of the school children decreased. There was a levelling-off point at about 1½ to 2 parts per million, beyond which there apparently was very little effect of increasing the fluoride content of the water supply. Thus, the clinical observation of the association was confirmed.

The next question that developed was: Is this association of etiologic importance? In this situation it was possible to carry out several experimental studies in which one would directly determine if the addition of fluorides to the water supply would decrease the dental caries rates among children in various communities. Several such experimental studies were carried out all of which confirmed the fact that the addition of fluorides to the water supply decreased the dental caries rates. This series of studies illustrates how from a clinical observation an etiologic hypothesis was developed, which was first confirmed by a special population survey, and then more definitively determined by an experimental study on human population groups.

The second general kinds of data are those concerned with individual characteristics. We shall discuss each of the subcategories listed above.

In the cross-sectional or retrospective kind of study, we try to obtain a group of individuals who have a disease, and determine the percentage of these individuals who have a certain characteristic, which we think might be a possible etiologic factor. Then we compare this percentage with the percentage found in a group of controls. An example of this type of study is that of the relationship of bladder cancer to cigarette smoking to which we referred earlier.

The distinction between the cross-sectional and retrospective types of study is in terms of the time element when the possible etiologic factor may have existed. We would regard a cross-sectional study as one in which, at one point in time, there is an association of a possible factor with the disease and we really do not know if this factor preceded the onset of the disease. On the other hand, in a retrospective study, we have affected individuals in whom we know that the possible etiologic factor existed prior to the onset of disease. For example, in the case of cigarette smoking and lung cancer, we know that people started to smoke in their twenties and developed their lung cancer at a much later age. In a cross-sectional study, the question of time relationships has to be resolved by other methods of investigation.

In both cross-sectional and retrospective studies, problems arise when one considers how the case and control groups are selected. Such studies are most commonly carried out by selecting both cases and controls from a hospital population. Practically all the retrospective studies indicating an association between lung cancer and cigarette smoking have been hospital studies (Cutler 1955). Control groups usually consist of patients with other diseases admitted to the same hospital or hospitals. This method's popularity results from the ease and inexpensiveness with which data can be obtained. In evaluating this method, several factors must be considered, and their relative importance judged by the investigator.

Probably the most frequent problem encountered in studies of hospital populations results from the influence of what is termed "sampling selection." Berkson has shown the possibility of obtaining a spurious association because of sampling selection resulting from differential rates of admission to the hospital of individuals with the disease, and those who serve as controls (Berkson 1946). However, Berkson (1946) and Kraus (1954) have also indicated that if a characteristic does not influence the admission of individuals to the hospital, the likelihood of a spurious association is negligible.

Deciding whether a characteristic does or does not influence admission to a hospital may be difficult at times. To a great extent, we are dependent on the judgment of the investigator and on our general knowledge of the specific situation, which makes evaluation of the results difficult. In many instances we may feel that a specific characteristic does not influence hospitalization, but this may result from ignorance of all of the related variables involved. For example, if we are interested in determining a possible relationship between eye color and a specific disease, and we find an association between blue eyes and a disease in a hospitalized series of cases and controls, it does not appear likely that individuals with blue eyes would be selected for hospitalization. However, if we are in a community in which the ethnic group with blue eyes is predominately in the lower social strata and if social class influences hospitalization, it is possible that sampling selection may operate to such an extent as to result in a spurious association of a disease with blue eyes.

In determining the importance to be assigned to the influence of sampling selection, another factor that must be considered is the strength of the observed association. In the extreme case, if we find that all the cases have the characteristic and all the controls do not, it would be very difficult to deny the existence of an association. Unfortunately, most associations are not this strong. Hence it may be helpful to judge the relative importance of sampling selection by determining arithmetically how much of an association could be expected for varying degrees of sampling selection. If the degree of the association is much greater than could be expected after taking into account what may be considered a reasonable influence of sampling selection, the association may be more readily accepted. Objections to this approach might be raised, since it is not as clearcut as is usually deemed desirable. However, an element of judgment is always present in the evaluation of any set of data, regardless of the source.

In many hospital studies, confidence in an observed association may be increased by the presence of internal evidence. For example, if several types of controls, each with a different disease or condition, are compared with the cases and the results with regard to characteristic are similar, confidence in the existence of an association can be greater than if only one control group is used. An illustration of this is afforded by the study of the relationship of bladder cancer to cigarette smoking, which we mentioned earlier. Also, confidence may be increased if there is a relationship between the disease and the amount of the particular characteristic, providing that it can be quantified. An example of this is the relationship of lung cancer to cigarette smoking where the degree of association increased with the amount of cigarettes smoked. In general, the more ways in which an association can be demonstrated, the greater can be our confidence that it is a real one and not a result of such a disturbing factor as sampling selection.

Hospital studies might be modified by the use of a control group selected from the general population and matched with the hospitalized cases according to certain characteristics. Usually, such a control group consists of individuals who reside in the same area and are similar in age, sex, and race to the hospitalized cases. Such a matched population control may diminish some of the difficulties resulting from the possible disturbing effect of sampling selection, but it is not completely clear how much really is accomplished. It is principally on intuitive grounds that such a control is regarded as better than a hospital control.

In some situations, it is possible that a matched population control group is worse than a hospital control group. If the characteristic under study is another disease or condition requiring medical diagnosis for its determination, the objection could be raised that matched population controls differ from hospitalized patients with regard to the amount of medical care received. For example, in studying the association of cancer of the cervix with diabetes, we would carry out a retrospective study with hospitalized cervix cancer patients from whom we obtain a history of diabetes. A matched population control may be completely inadequate for comparison with the patients, since the patients and controls would differ with regard to the amount of medical care received, and the matched control group may thus have an actually larger proportion of undiagnosed cases of diabetes. This situation will arise if the information concerning diabetes is obtained by interview. However, if the presence of diabetes is determined by examination, this difficulty will not be encountered. Consequently, if it is necessary to obtain the required information by interview, it may be preferable to use hospitalized patients as the controls in certain instances.

In the retrospective kind of study, one meets additional problems. For example, there is the possibility of subjective bias resulting from the fact that the person who obtains histories from cases or controls knows that certain individuals are cases or controls, and the way he asks questions may be biased by this fact. An association may appear as a result of bias. Many of you are familiar with this possibility but it is always worth emphasizing. In many hospital studies, it may be necessary to obtain the data before the diagnosis is made.

There is one general comment I would like to make with respect to retrospective studies. It is my feeling that probably the best way of doing such studies, even though it may be the most expensive, is to use cases from an entire community and take as a control group a probability sample of the population.

In view of the existence of these problems in cross-sectional and retrospective studies, it is the feeling of people working in this field that we utilize these kinds of studies essentially as a means of developing leads with respect to associations between possible factors and disease and to take care of some of the problems by going on to a prospective study to test the existence of the association in a more definitive manner.

In prospective, or follow-up studies, groups of individuals with and without the characteristic are obtained and followed for a definite period of time to determine the risk of developing the disease when the characteristic is present, as compared with the risk when it is absent. The prospective type of study is difficult, as I am sure you are all aware. First of all, it requires very large numbers; in fact, it is an impossible type of study in those cases where the risk of developing the disease is low. For example, in the lung cancer-cigarette smoking prospective studies information was obtained on about 200,000 people and these individuals were followed for a four-to-five-year period.

Just to bring the suggestion of a prospective study home; most of the studies on the relationship of blood groups to disease have been done on a cross-sectional basis. There is a need for studying these relationships in a prospective manner, to demonstrate more definitely the relationship and to determine relationships of individual blood groups to a number of diseases.

One additional advantage of the prospective method is that it provides a direct estimate of the risk of developing a disease, while in a retrospective kind of a study, all we can do is to make an indirect estimate of the relative risk by the methods developed by Cornfield (1951) and Woolf (1955).

In reviewing the various problems we have discussed with respect to epidemiologic studies, it is clear that they are present simply because we are dealing with observations of naturally occurring phenomena. They reflect the fact that we do not have direct control over the variables influencing these phenomena as an investigator has in experimental situations.

One of the major problems in any epidemiologic study concerns the selection of controls. This problem has been met many times in human genetics where one is interested in determining whether familial aggregation of a disease exists. These problems have been reviewed in detail elsewhere (Lilienfeld 1954). To date, family studies in human genetics have been retrospective studies. It seems to me that there is a real need to explore the possibilities of carrying out prospective studies of familial aggregation. We would select cases with the disease of interest from a community and a population sample as a control. We would then determine the status of the various family members at this point in time. Then, we would follow the relatives of the cases and controls for the next five or ten years to determine their risk of developing the disease. Such studies would provide more definitive data concerning familial aggregation than do retrospective studies.

In this relatively brief survey of epidemiology I have tried to provide some idea of the various methods used and of the various problems encountered. Clearly, there exists a real need for further development of study methods and for some rigorous thinking concerning the logical framework of the reasoning modes used. Many of the problems I have discussed are under investigation at present by many investigators, and perhaps in a few years some of these methodologic difficulties will be resolved.

DISCUSSION

DR. GILLIAM: Dr. Gordon, throughout his discussion, kept referring to "mass disease." I don't think he would want any of you to go away with the idea that the study of disease in human populations is done just for the fun of studying mass disease. It is done, of course, in the hope that it will contribute some knowledge of factors associated with the disease, and hopefully, some factors that govern disease occurrence in the individual. Or in other words, the object of studying the mass phenomena of disease is directed at trying to learn something about what happens in the individual.

Kipling, in another context, I think expressed it by saying that "the sins that we do by the two and the two are paid for one by one."

Of course, the ultimate objective is to find something either in the host or in the environment or what have you, that can be altered to the ultimate benefit of the individuals in the community.

All three speakers used the phraseology "noninfectious disease" while others use the term "chronic disease." Neither designation is satisfactory. With regard to chronic disease—some diseases we classify as acute continue for a long stage between recognition and termination, either with cure or death; and some of the diseases which we class as chronic, such as acute leukemia in children, or cancer of the lung, may progress quite rapidly between their recognition and death.

The "noninfectious" terminology is probably best, provided we keep very firmly in mind that some of the diseases now regarded as noninfectious may very well turn out to be actually infectious. After all, the concept of infectiousness and communicability is not a concept of microbiology. It is a concept of epidemiology, that is, the behavior of the disease in the human population. Tetanus is caused by an infectious agent. We know it is not communicable in the ordinary sense because of its behavior in the human population.

If we draw on analogies from communicable diseases, they vary tremendously in their apparent communicability. The fact that measles and chicken pox are catching is, of course, obvious to a layman. Paralytic polio may be less so than an outbreak of broken legs.

Dr. Paul, in his whole discussion, brings up a point we usually miss in our approach to the diseases we now class as non-infectious, and that is that you have, for most of this century at least, two tools in the infectious process. You have a way of directly measuring those people who become infected but not sick, and you also have a way, through serologic tests and other means, of identifying the people in the population who had been infected with the organism with resultant immunity.

In diphtheria, for example, in the days before serologic work was done, it was clearly shown by doing repeated Schick tests and repeated cultures that in the environment of Baltimore, infection was more likely to result in disease in the wintertime than in the spring. Similar observations in Puerto Rico showed that a large group of children who were originally Shick-positive and followed with Schick test every two weeks and cultures every week, that at the end of the period, none of them developed clinical diphtheria but 80 per cent of those who had harbored a virulent organism during that time had reverted to Schick negative status, a measure of immunity, as opposed to 10 per cent of those who had not had a recognized infection during the period of testing.

Thus, in the infectious diseases, we have measures, we have immune tests, and we have tests for those infected but not sick, which we can apply, as Dr. Paul has so well done in many situations, in drawing inferences about the behavior of the disease in the population.

I may say that in cancer we do have some evidence there is a counterpart to what exists in the infectious process without any implication of infection. There is evidence that there are "infected" people, whose disease process does not eventuate in what we call cancer. This is true in carcinoma of the uterine cervix and probably true in cancer of the prostate.

Dr. Paul mentioned blood pepsin determination. We have taken advantage of the tubeless gastric analysis because of the association between achlorhydria and gastric cancer and because of the demonstrated excessive risk to gastric cancer among Japanese males. We have applied this test at present to a really inadequate sample, and showed that there is no more achlorhydria among the Japanese tested than in the general U.S. population which was sampled. Though that is an inadequate study at the present, it does represent an attempt to use a laboratory test in study of cancer in human populations.

So that in the noninfectious diseases, we have to do the best we can and hope that in the future some of the tests, laboratory tests, about which Dr. Paul has been kidding me for our slowness in developing, will be available and can be applied to the population in the future.

I may say, with regard to blood banks, that about six years ago, when we started a study of leukemia, we contemplated setting up a bank of the proper kind of serum under refrigeration, which would enable us to test the relationship, or its lack, among viruses in this disease. At that time, it was not respectable to think of viruses in cancer, so we were unable to get the space for a deep freeze to store the sera, and the idea was dropped.

I would like to say in a little different way what all the speakers have said. The purpose, of course, of studying disease in the human population is to ascertain aspects associated with their occurrence, and, hopefully, aspects governing their occurrence. To do this we have to measure the disease in people with risk of disease in people of different characteristics. The measure of risk is the probability that one of the group will develop the disease in a defined period of time.

I'd like to throw in a word of caution to those of you who are not familiar with the use of the word "incidence" in medical literature, in the literature of pathology particularly. You sometimes encounter articles in which the word "incidence" is used to describe four totally different kinds of data in the same paper, none of which bear any relationship to incidence at all. This would only be a question of semantics except for the fact the author draws conclusions which would only be valid if the data represented incidence in fact. Thus, our problem is to measure risk of disease in persons with different characteristics.

Dr. Lilienfeld has shown four different ways in which this is approached. His use of the terms "retrospective studies" and "prospective studies"—these are the terms most popular at the moment, and in best standing for a number of reasons. I personally object very much to them. But regardless of the objection, what he did designate as retrospective study is an indirect measure of risk, and what he designates as a prospective type of study is a direct measure of risk.

In some of the data, Dr. Boyd showed, for example, this morning, with regard to blood group and cancer of the stomach and peptic ulcer, this is the familiar case-control type of study or indirect measure of risk. What you get by this method is the proportion of cases of cancer of the stomach of peptic ulcer in blood group A or B and compare that with a control group.

What you actually want to know is: out of a group of people with blood group A or B, what proportion get the disease. What you get is not incidence of the disease in people with A or B, but the proportion of diseased people with group A or B. From it you infer what the incidence is, and your inference is correct insofar as your cases are truly representative of all the cases and your controls are truly representative of the general population.

I may say, that, as Dr. Lilienfeld has said, in a little different way, in the case-control studies, in the indirect method of measuring risk, you may as well reconcile yourself to the fact at the start that—where your point of departure is a series of cases—that you will never get adequate and unimpeachable controls until you know all of the selective agents bearing on the occurrence of the disease. In spite of that, these studies will continue to be done, for they have been useful in the past. It is the time-honored method of medicine, and the only quarrel that I personally find with them is that, so often, on the basis of them, risk statements are made as though they were facts.

They may be regarded as evidence, very much as one would regard the evidence of the clinical impression, which in spite of its limitations is probably responsible for a good proportion of the advances in the medical field.

Go back again to this indirect method of estimating incidence that Dr. Lilienfeld mentioned, namely, the work of Alice Stewart, which showed that twice as many cases of leukemia gave a history of pre-natal irradiation as among those selected as controls. In one identical study in this country, a similar ratio was observed. The percentage of leukemia cases that showed history of prenatal irradiation was twice as great in the leukemia cases as in the controls. However, in this par-ticular study, the proportion who were said to have received prenatal irradiation was a little bit larger than in the case group in Britain. If one takes these and converts them on the basis of mortality from leukemia in the two countries, into direct estimates of risk, what that says is that, in spite of the higher rate of leukemia in those ages in this country, the estimated rate among those irradiated is lower in this country than in Great Britain. It is through tests of this kind that the significance of such associations and the validity of such associations are, in the last analysis, established.

Now, assuming that you have an irreproachable study that has defi-nitely established an excessive risk in some group, it is circumstantial from then on. This excessive risk does justify a hypothesis. But no mat-ter how attractive a hypothesis it might be, it is good sense to be slow to marry it. It is a good idea to get to know the hypothesis better, and then you reduce the odds of a painful divorce if a more attractive one comes along later.

Mr. Perrott: Today's discussion has been particularly interesting to me because of its relevance to the project on which I am now working. This is an undertaking sponsored by the Public Health Research Study Section. It is a survey of some of the past and current studies dealing with the health of groups of people. The genesis of the project was in the need felt for guidelines which might be of use to investigators contemplating projects of this kind and to the Study Section in its review of applications for such projects. As a first step in this project, we have compiled a description of some three hundred recent and current researches in this country and abroad. Information has been obtained in part from the literature and in part from persons currently or previously engaged in such studies. From this, a summary has been prepared of the kinds of population groups selected for such studies and the types of information obtained. It is believed that the range and variety of these studies will serve to furnish perspective for our subsequent efforts to evaluate particular types of research. We are planning a conference this fall to assist us in developing a final report.

DR. G. ALLEN: If a series of studies has compared a test group and another group, using different types of control selection, and they show, as in some of your cases, very different rates in the different types of controls, but all these controls had a lower rate than the test group, isn't it rather hard to believe that this difference is just a function of the methods of selecting controls, and that there is not an average difference in favor of the hypothesis?

DR. LILIENFELD: I think the more ways you look at the data and obtain the same results, the more confidence you have in the relationship. But as Berkson (1946) pointed out, since you are never really sure what selective bias or what agents were involved, you are never really certain that you may be getting different selective biases acting in the same direction. I think the more times you do this with different controls, the more unlikely this becomes; but how unlikely do you want this to be? This may be a matter of judgment, rather than of actual fact.

DR. GILLIAM: One of the studies in familial aggregation in breast cancer on Dr. Lilienfeld's list has a different kind of bias. I happen to know that in one it is not really a question of controls. Instead, it is a question of the fact that the cases were selected by physicians who submitted names of breast cancer patients who were not only willing to be interviewed, but the physician knew in advance the family had been riddled with breast cancer. When you stack the cards that way, you are certainly going to get more cases in the families with breast cancer than in the controls.

DR. LILIENFELD: The only way you can be certain of the data is to have very rigorous and unbiased sampling procedures. If you take a sample of the population as a control and a sample of cases in the population and do this in a rigorous manner, then you may feel fairly certain that the selective factors are minimized.

DR. GILLIAM: It is going to be pretty hard in a disease like cancer of the breast, where the lifetime probability of a woman developing the disease is about 5 chances in a hundred from birth, to have any re-course to anything but the case-control type of study. I think we may as well face the fact that these studies are going to continue to be used, and we have simply got to be as cautious as we can in their interpretation. The diversity of results in different studies will lead to further refinement, and replication will strengthen the security of generalizations made from them.

I am afraid we are hooked with them, and I for one do not look upon them with quite the jaundiced eye that some others do.

Mr. Perrott: When Dr. Gordon mentioned evaluation through using clinical indices, I thought about the other problem which the socio-logists call the Hawthorne effect: namely, the effect of the evaluation process on the phenomenon you are trying to measure.

The Hawthorne Effect was named after the Hawthorne plant of the Western Electric Company near Chicago, where a study was at-tempted of the effect of changing illumination on the daily output of women in a relay-assembling operation. The study was a failure because the favorable psychologic effect of being part of a special study group masked any effect of changing illumination. Production im-proved whatever the illumination. The same effect can happen in a healthy survey as a result of the interviewing process.

Dr. Lilienfeld: I think one problem we have in making inferences from these kinds of data and correlations and in trying to look at possible biases is that we are limited by the level of our biological knowledge.

For example, once you get an association and you want to distinguish between a biological relationship or whether it is just due to a common X factor, you are limited in terms of trying to define what this X fac-tor is. What one would like to do is to look for the common X factor. You may study a thousand factors that may be this common X factor, and all of these are the wrong ones because you just don't know what questions to ask at this stage of the investigation. You are limited by the kinds of questions that can be asked. If you could ask the right questions, the various problems, methodologic or otherwise, will dis-appear. Essentially, our problems really revolve around the fact that we are not asking the direct, right question.

But despite this you can, it seems to me, build up a body of infor-mation or a series of data obtained in different ways and integrate this with some experimental data, so that you might be able to obtain a fairly decent knowledge of the biologic situation, realizing full well that there is a certain chance in making erroneous inferences.

Dr. Paul: I was glad to hear Dr. Gilliam point out that we should not have preconceived notions whether a disease is infectious or not.

When you think of the story of pellagra which was mentioned earlier we have a disease originally thought to be hereditary in origin then considered by some to be an infection; and, finally, it ended up as a nutritional disorder.

Whether carcinoma is to be considered an "infectious disease" is one of the questions of the times. At a recent meeting in New York of virologists, the audience welcomed neoplasms into their fold. The Sloan-Kettering Institute for Cancer Research within the last few months has appointed a virologist as director. These are the signs of the times.

DR. J. E. GORDON: I would be sorry if my term "mass disease" brought confusion. I contrast mass disease to clinical disease, the one being disease in the group, the other disease as manifested in the individual. There is a further practical consideration in differentiating disease in the group. A group may result from the serial collection of a number of individuals; on the other hand, the group may represent a population as a whole, including both sick and well. The two are to be distinguished. Dr. Lilienfeld did that in his description of methods.

These two kinds of groups serve a particular purpose. I have the impression that with the disease of the moment, which we talked about mainly today, perhaps the first group is the most important, with the clinical differentiation pertinently in view. The second serves to my mind better for the communicable diseases.

I appreciate Dr. Perrott's addition to an ecologic concept of evaluation. It seems to me that the idea requires further acceptance and development. It is just like a pharmacologic attempt to test a drug's desired effect in limiting cases, duration of illness or deaths, with no attention to side effects. It may cause more cancer than it cures disease.

The last point I would make is that we have talked repeatedly, as I have seen so many times, about causality, almost to the point of its being a fetish. I always like to keep in mind that causality is a matter of concern for one single reason, what you can do about it, the practical application. And I thought we could learn much from the point that Dr. Paul made about serologic studies in poliomyelitis. I once was in Ceylon where great numbers of British sailors contracted poliomyelitis when they went ashore in the town. The townsmen were sure that the sailors were bringing poliomyelitis and passed a quarantine against the British Navy. They would have been much better advised to have quarantined the town.

5

POLYMORPHISM AND NATURAL SELECTION IN BLOOD GROUPS

T. EDWARD REED

INTRODUCTION

WHETHER I AM the first speaker this morning by accident or by design I do not know. I prefer to think it is in recognition of the fact that blood groups were the first genetic polymorphisms studied in man, other than sex and pigment color. Here, for clarity, I will define "polymorphism" as I, and other geneticists, use the term. It is the definition proposed by Ford (1940)—The occurrence in the same habitat of two or more discontinuous forms of a species in such proportions that the rarest of them cannot be maintained solely by mutation. This means that, to qualify by this definition, there must be at least two different forms, in our case, blood groups, each of which, in a given population, has an appreciable frequency, say greater than 0.1 per cent. If neutral genes are as rare as geneticists believe, some factor other than forward mutation must be responsible for the occurrence of polymorphism so defined and it is not a secret that this is usually natural selection.[1]

HUMAN BLOOD GROUP SYSTEMS AS EXAMPLES OF POLYMORPHISM

The eleven human blood group systems (ABO, MN, P, Rh, Lutheran, Kell, Lewis, Duffy, Kidd, Diego, and Js) all fulfill these criteria of polymorphism. Ford (1940) subdivided polymorphisms into two types, transient and balanced, according to whether the frequencies of the different forms were changing or were constant. Since the ABO blood groups have been known only for sixty years and the other systems for shorter periods, the absence of evidence for changing blood group frequencies is insufficient, by itself, for us to say that these systems are balanced polymorphisms. There is indirect evidence, however, which convinces many workers that this is the case for most, if not all, blood group systems. The best evidence is that red blood cell antigens similar to the

---

[1] There have been several reviews recently (Sheppard 1959; Mourant 1959) of natural selection and blood groups; I will try to consider some additional aspects in this review of the subject.

human A and B of the ABO system, c and D of the Rh system, and M and N of the MN system are present in certain anthropoid apes (Mourant 1954), strongly suggesting that these polymorphisms are of great antiquity.[1] Less convincing, but still persuasive, is the argument that, for any system, individuals of different blood groups very probably have different natural selective values and these values determine the polymorphism uniquely so that, in the absence of change in selection, the frequency of the blood group genes will remain constant. I do not think that these selective values are really constant but, on the other hand, I do not think they have changed grossly in, say, the last century. We can now consider some of these assumptions and implications of these beliefs.

GENETIC AND MEDICAL IMPLICATIONS OF POLYMORPHISM

I said that individuals with different blood group genotypes probably had different selective values, that is, different biologic fitnesses. Ford, in 1942 first stated this belief. By fitness I mean the number of children that a newborn individual will ultimately have; this is a measure of both viability and fertility over a life cycle and is what counts genetically (Reed 1959). Whenever a blood group system, or any other genetic system, is a balanced polymorphism, there will be differences in fitness among the genotypes. This is because the system is, by definition, in stable genetic equilibrium, and such stability can be maintained only by difference in fitness. In a stable equilibrium, any chance departure from the equilibrium frequencies is automatically opposed by the system and the frequencies are brought back to the equilibrium values for that system. For the case of two alleles, say the MN blood groups (neglecting the related factors such as S, s, Henshaw, etc.), a stable and balanced polymorphism requires, as is well known, that the heterozygote, MN, be more fit than either homozygote, M or N. The situation is more complex when there are three alleles, as in the ABO blood groups (ignoring the A_1-A_2 distinction), or when there are four or more, as is the case for the Rh system. The somewhat complicated relationships between the fitnesses of the different genotypes required for a stable equilibrium, when there are three or more alleles, has been investigated by several workers recently (Kimura 1956; Penrose, et al, 1956; Mandel 1959). A simple statement of these relationships is not possible, but several important consequences following from them can be given. One is that the fitness of each

---

[1] The persistence for a number of centuries in certain minority populations of blood group frequencies characteristic of their original parent population is further evidence for the stability of the polymorphisms.

homozygote is less than the mean fitness of all genotypes at equilibrium. For the case of three alleles, the fitness of one heterozygote at most may be less than the fitnesses of two homozygotes at most (Mandel 1959). To turn the problem around, given the values of relative fitness of the different genotypes, it is possible to determine whether the system is in stable equilibrium or not. The important thing in all this is that when a genetic system is a balanced polymorphism there are fitness differences between the genotypes. Since the blood group systems are quite likely balanced polymorphisms, we should expect to find, if we look hard, differences in fitness between the genotypes of any given system.

A few remarks about the ways in which fitness differences may arise or may be expressed are in order. Since the fitness we are discussing is the biologically effective fitness which can, potentially at least, alter gene frequencies, the fitness differences in question must occur before the end of the reproductive period of any individual. Differences in viability after this period, although of interest, have no influence on future gene frequency. Further, the obvious fact should not be forgotten that fitness differences can occur either through differences in viability or differences in fertility, or both. As we shall see, there are very likely situations where the relative viability of a given genotype may be less than average but is compensated for by a greater-than-average fertility. The reverse situation is also conceivable. Relative fitness may be thought of as the product of relative viability and relative fertility, so that a decrease in one can be offset by an increase in the other.

The medical implications of the fitness differences of balanced polymorphisms are, in general, not clear cut. Everything depends on the magnitude of the viability differences or fertility differences which occur and one's evaluation of these magnitudes. If they are, at most, of the order of a few per cent, it would be difficult to consider them an important medical problem for a particular individual, if that individual is still in good health. If they are of the order of 10 per cent, as claimed for certain mother-fetus ABO blood group combinations, it becomes quite meaningful. And, of course, if selection approaches or reaches 100 per cent, as in the case of sickle cell hemoglobin homozygotes, the medical importance is obvious. Even if the maximum fitness component (viability or fertility) difference in a given system is 2 per cent, say, this amount may still be considered important in an epidemiologic sense, considering that it may be present in a sizeable fraction of a population of many millions. Looking to the future, it may be that one of the important tasks for medicine will be raising the fitness of individuals who are the naturally less fit components of one or more balanced polymorphisms.

DIRECT EVIDENCE FOR NATURAL SELECTION IN BLOOD GROUPS

I will now review the evidence for the operation of natural selection in human blood groups and indicate its relation, if any, to the selection required by balanced polymorphism. I will consider first evidence on viability.

VIABILITY

Good evidence for selection

The clearest direct evidence that selection is occurring in blood groups undoubtedly is that of clinically important mother-fetus incompatibility, i.e., the occurrence of pregnancies in which the mother has an antibody against a red blood cell antigen of the fetus. The situation in the Rh blood groups is best known and, by serving as an example, makes it unnecessary to review this area in any detail. Here the mother, usually Rh negative, that is, homozygous for the gene *r* or *cde* (Fisher-Race) is married to a man who is Rh positive, that is, he is either heterozygous or homozygous for a gene, other than *r*, which produces an agglutinogen, usually D (or Rh_o) which, if transfused, could sensitize her. About 5 per cent of the time in the children from such matings hemolytic disease of the newborn occurs. In these cases the fetus has received the gene for the father's Rh antigen. The fetal antigen reaches the maternal blood stream, maternal antibodies against it are produced, and these antibodies in turn attack the fetal red cells. At worst the fetus dies *in utero;* at best there are no observable symptoms. The mortality from Rh hemolytic disease of the newborn is about 0.5 deaths per 1000 livebirths (Walker 1959).

The next most important type of hemolytic disease of the newborn is probably that due to incompatibility in the ABO blood groups. The frequency of this condition is poorly known because the disease is poorly defined (Zuelzer and Cohen 1957). The condition is potentially more common than Rh hemolytic disease because of the natural occurrence of anti-A and anti-B but, in fact, only O mothers of A or B fetuses are involved, and, of these fetuses, only about 10 per cent, at most, can be shown to have a hemolytic process (Rosenfield 1955). Of this 10 per cent, only perhaps 10 per cent have noteworthy clinical symptoms, and a much smaller fraction may terminate fatally. The mortality may be only 1 or 2 per cent of that of Rh hemolytic disease (Walker 1959). Hemolytic disease of the newborn due to incompatibility in other blood group systems also occurs but the mortality per 1000 livebirths is apparently less than that of the ABO disease.

The common feature of genetic interest in all these hemolytic diseases of the newborn is that the fetus being selected against is a heterozygote in the system concerned. Thus an A fetus in an O mother must be AO. If there were no selection in other parts of the life cycle, this elimination of heterozygotes would, in time, destroy the existing polymorphism. We may therefore confidently say that if the polymorphism is stable there must be selection elsewhere in the life cycle counterbalancing this fetal selection. The other point concerning this selection is that for any one system it is very small.

In addition to this late fetal selection just discussed, which may occur in most of the blood group systems, there is the very real likelihood of extensive early fetal selection in the ABO blood groups. Thus, significant deficiencies of A or B children with O mothers amounting up to 23 per cent have been claimed (Matsunaga 1955) by several workers. Other studies have shown an increased frequency of miscarriage in ABO incompatible matings (those which could produce a fetus incompatible to the mother). (See Reed 1956 for references.) The difficulty here is that some other studies have not found such selection. This is not a clear contradiction because the populations differ in time, place, and mother's parity (Reed 1956). The studies relying on newborns' blood groups suffer from the definite possibility of misgrouping which will resemble selection (Reed 1956; Kirk 1956). The point to keep in mind here, however, is that selection here, if it exists, is still selection against heterozygotes and cannot, by itself, maintain a stable polymorphism. We may summarize the general field of incompatibility selection by saying that there is no doubt of its existence but there is uncertainty regarding its magnitude. It is biologically effective since it changes future gene frequencies, but it cannot explain balanced polymorphism.

The other general area of blood group selection which is now clearly established is that of associations of blood groups and certain diseases. This field has been well reviewed recently by Fraser Roberts (1957, 1959). The well established associations all involve the ABO blood groups but this may reflect only the much more extensive data available for this system. The diseases showing clear associations are listed in table 1. Duodenal ulcer and group O, gastric ulcer and group O, cancer of the stomach and group A, and pernicious anemia and group A are the best established. These associations have been found in a number of different areas and at high levels of significance. The relative susceptibility to the disease in persons of the indicated blood group, relative to those of all other blood groups, varies from 1.19 to 1.38. Other associations, at signi-

TABLE 1—*Diseases Showing Strong Associations with the ABO Blood Groups* (Roberts, 1957)

Disease	Relative Susceptibility	
Duodenal ulcer	O/(A+B+AB)	=1.38
Gastric ulcer	O/(A+B+AB)	=1.19
Cancer of the stomach	A/O=A/B	=1.19
Pernicious anemia	A/O	=1.26
Diabetes mellitus	A/O	=1.16

ficant levels, but not so high as the preceding, have been reported. These include diabetes mellitus and group A and several others. It is reassuring that some extensive studies have failed to reveal any associations between certain diseases and blood groups (Roberts 1957). Enough has been said to indicate the general character of these associations. We must now consider what they imply for natural selection. First we must differentiate sharply between effective and ineffective genetic selection. To be effective genetically, selection must occur before the end of the reproductive period which, with negligible error, we may call 45 years. Any disease whose mortality or impairment of fertility occurs after this age will have almost no effect on future gene frequencies. We can exclude these from consideration when discussing polymorphism. If we now consider the age-specific mortality from the diseases just referred to, some interesting things are seen, as shown in table 2.

TABLE 2—*Proportion of the White American Population Dying Under Age 45 Years from Certain Diseases in 1955* (U.S. Vital Statistics)

Disease	Number dying		Proportion dying < 45 years
	< 45 years	Total	
Cancer of the stomach	689	19,815	0.0348
Gastric ulcer	348	4,352	0.0800
Duodenal ulcer	450	4,630	0.0972
Diabetes mellitus	379	22,956	0.0165
Pernicious anemia and hyperchromic anemia	27	1,039	0.0260
Total	1,893	52,792	0.0359

Total deaths from all causes: 1,350,869
Living U.S. population:
    Total 146.54×10^6
    < 45 yrs. 102.94×10^6

$$\frac{\text{Total deaths} < 45 \text{ years for above diseases}}{\text{Living population} < 45 \text{ years}} = \frac{1893}{102.94 \times 10^6} = 1.84 \times 10^{-5}$$

The data are for the year 1955, for the U. S. white population, taken from the *Vital Statistics of the United States*. There were a total of 1,350,869 deaths in the population of 146.54 million but only 52,792 of these deaths came from the five diseases discussed. Further, only 1,893 of these 52,792 deaths occurred under age 45 years. Since the total population under age 45 was 102.94 million, we can calculate that only 1.84×10^5 of the genetically functional part of the population has been removed through the action of selection on these five diseases. The fact that illness impairs reproduction, in addition to death, would tend to raise this figure, but this is more than offset by the occurrence, in this under 45 group, of most of these diseases at the end of the reproductive period. I think it is obvious that natural selection acting on these diseases today does not account for the ABO polymorphism. I think that a stronger statement can be made: in the past, selection against these diseases was also very likely unimportant relative to other selection. This is because I do not think that the basic biology of these diseases has changed appreciably. The age distribution of deaths from these diseases over the last 60 years clearly has not changed markedly. The possibility remains that many other current diseases are associated with particular blood groups and that the total genetic effect is appreciable. This cannot be disproved now, but if we consider only diseases important after childhood, it seems debatable.

The obvious disease categories to consider are those partly or largely of infancy and childhood since they have the greatest genetic effect. To date the only well established such disease is rheumatic fever, where an association with nonsecretion of the ABO substances is found (Glynn, et al, 1959), a polymorphism we are not now considering. Unfortunately, as some workers have noted, it may be too late to determine whether association with diseases is genetically important because of the great reduction in infant and child mortality in the last 100 years. This is illustrated by the fact that the lifetable probability that a liveborn white male child will die before the age of 15 years was 3.6 per cent in 1956 and 12.0 per cent in 1900. A genetically important disease association could have existed before 1900 but now, because of reduction in selection, be relatively ineffective. The possibility that susceptibility to diseases such as diphtheria, typhoid, influenza and pneumonia could vary between the ABO genotypes and that the present ABO blood group distribution may result from the recently important and genetically effective selection from these diseases has been discussed by Livingstone (1960). Significant associations between some of these diseases and ABO blood groups have been reported but need confirmation. Vogel, et al, (1960) present very interesting data showing serological similarity between (O) antigen (of ABO) and the plague organism and between A antigen (of ABO) and the smallpox organism. They suggest that these similarities can produce differences between persons having different ABO blood groups in susceptibility to these diseases and that the present ABO blood group frequencies may reflect differential mortality from these diseases in the past.

Before leaving this subject, I must mention that the distinction between phenotypic and genotypic selection must be kept in mind. Thus, a group A person may be AA or AO, homozygous or heterozygous for the A gene. It is quite conceivable that AA individuals differ greatly from AO in their selective values and that what we observe is the weighted algebraic sum of their different values. The difficulties resulting from this are obvious.

Possible evidence for selection

There are several other lines of investigation which suggest, to varying degrees, that the ABO blood groups are associated with viability differences. The most general approach is the comparison of blood group frequencies of a defined population at different ages. If a given phenotype, in a stable population, can be shown to be rarer at old age, this would be good evidence that selection against the phenotype is occurring. We can say at the outset that there are no data showing such a clear effect. Thomsen (1927) studied men and women in Copenhagen over age 65 and found a distribution which differed significantly from that in Copenhagen children (Rosling 1928), B being lower in the old people. Another Danish study (Hansen 1928) did not confirm this, however, nor did a German study of blood groups in 500 cadavers (Oppenheim and Voight 1926), although the mean age of B persons was several years younger than for other persons. Group B was implicated again when Hart (1944) studied 10,784 blood donors in northern Ireland. He found that the mean age of B males was about 2 years less than that of other males, significant at the .01 level. A very extensive study of blood donors in southwest England, made by Fraser Roberts (1948) on 85,438 donors of known age, did not reveal any significant age effects, however. It is clear that there is no simple consistent selection involving group B persons, but it seems possible that there may be some type of selection.

Another possible indication of viability effect of blood groups is the reported excess of MN children from MN x MN matings. This excess, which amounts to 4 or 5 per cent in some data, was first reported by Taylor and Prior (1939). The question has been considered by a number of workers since, most recently and in most detail by Morton and Chung

(1959). Using a more elaborate analysis, they find that there is also a significant excess of MN children from the mating N ♂ x MN ♀, so that both types of excess appear to require an MN mother. Various hypotheses alternative to selection, including technical errors, were considered and then excluded. They tentatively conclude that selective advantage of the MN fetus or child from these two mating types is the explanation for the excesses. It is clear that, if this is in fact the case, it is quite a special situation since it requires that the MN person have an MN mother. Various hypotheses for this might be considered but it hardly seems worthwhile to do this at present. Since the excess is in the heterozygote the genetic equilibrium should be stable.

There is an example in the ABO system where an excess of a heterozygote in the progeny of particular mating appears, but the evidence is contradictory. Matsunaga (1954), summarizing Japanese data, found 35 AB x AB matings from which 11 A, 19 B, and 57 AB resulted. Since 50 per cent AB were expected, the resulting 66 per cent was a significant difference at the 1 per cent probability level. However, the data on children from ABO matings summarized by Wiener (1943) show 129 children from AB x AB matings and of these 65 were AB. The agreement with 50 per cent could not be better, so there is a flat contradiction. We need not consider this further until more positive results are available.

A final possibility for viability selection is gametic selection, especially antigenic selection of sperm in the female reproductive tract. Although evidence for this selection is now lacking, the demonstration that uterine secretions may contain hemagglutinins (Gershowitz, et al, 1958) and that sperm have ABO antigens (Gullbring 1957) make it seem possible.

FERTILITY

Natural selection can occur through fertility differences as well as through viability differences but less attention has been given to this possible aspect of selection in the blood groups. Because of the necessary requirement that individuals or couples be ascertained independently of their fertility, only a few studies yield useful information. Fertility data do exist now, however, for the ABO, Rh, MN, and P blood groups.

ABO blood groups

As expected, the best data are for the ABO groups. The studies which have been made are shown in table 3. The first two studies, those of Bennett and Walker (1956) on individuals, and Reed and Kelly (1958)

TABLE 3—*Fertility Studies in the ABO Blood Groups* (Data ascertained independently of fertility)

TYPE OF DATA	POPULATION	NUMBER	SIGNIFICANT DIFFERENCES IN FERTILITY		STUDY
			LB	FD	
Individuals	English blood donors, ≧ 50 yrs., married	1290 ♂ 1319 ♀	No No	—* —	Bennett & Walker (1956)
Couples	U.S., mostly college graduates, reproduction completed	161	No	No**	Reed & Kelly (1958)
	Japanese, miners, low economic status, different ages	1429	Yes P < .001	Yes P < .001	Matsunaga & Itoh (1958)
	Japanese miners, fair economic status, different ages	915	No	Yes P < .001	Haga (1959)
	U.S. white Protestants, random sample, wife 30-39 yrs.	558	Yes P < .01	—	Reed & Ahronheim (1959)

LB=livebirths   FD=fetal deaths.
* The proportion of children dying under 10 years was much greater (P<.001) when the father was 0, Rh+.
** Probability that the difference in proportion of stillbirths in compatible and incompatible couples is due to chance is 0.0588.

on couples, are essentially negative. The small sample size of the latter should be noted. The remaining three studies, on couples, each show significant differences of some type. The two Japanese studies are especially interesting in that they are both on miners' families in the northern island of Hokkaido and were made only several years apart but show some marked differences. Haga (1959) attributes this to an appreciable difference in living standards, the families in his study, which show no difference in livebirths, being better off. His study, however, as does that of Matsunaga (1958), shows a very significant increase of fetal deaths in pregnancies of ABO incompatible matings. He estimates the mortality of incompatible fetuses to be about 0.05, compared to 0.21 in Matsunaga's data. If these differences between these studies are indeed due to difference in economic status, they are a remarkable example of sudden change in selective pressure. Matsunaga's results for livebirths paralleled those for fetal deaths, the mean being less for incompatible couples. The findings of Reed and Ahronheim (1959), however, were the opposite, incompatible matings being more fertile. As table 4 shows, the other American study also showed a higher mean for incompatible couples, but not significantly so.

TABLE 4—*Mean Number of Children* from ABO Compatible and ABO Incompatible Matings*

Population	Compatible	Incompatible	Significant Difference	Study
U.S.A.	2.390 ± 0.139	2.537 ± 0.182	No	Reed & Kelly (1958)
	1.689 ± 0.066	1.957 ± 0.097	Yes	Reed & Ahronheim (1959)
Japan (Hokkaido)	2.596 ± 0.064	2.173 ± 0.070	Yes	Matsunaga & Itoh (1958)
	2.590 ± 0.077	2.578 ± 0.085	No	Haga (1959)

* Livebirths in U.S. studies; children living at time of study in Japanese studies.

It would be tempting to say that incompatible couples are more fertile in favorable environments and less fertile in poor environments but I will resist this for a while longer. More important is the question of whether it is incompatibility which is really the important factor or is it certain mating types or individual genotypes which are included in this category. Reed and Ahronheim (1959) analyzed their fertility by a more general method, the analysis of variance, and found that significant differences between males' ABO groups alone, or females' ABO groups alone, did not occur. There were significant differences attributable to the interaction between males and females, i.e., the mating type. The most obvious explanation would be incompatibility effects, but we find the "incompatible" couples here to be more fertile. It begins to appear that something besides incompatibility is involved. Examining each of the separate mating fertilities does not help much. In the data of Reed and Ahronheim, the greatest significant departure from the mean is in the mating ♂ O x ♀ B, P being less than 0.005. This mating, in the two Japanese studies, however, does not differ significantly from the respective means of compatible matings. The same is true for the matings B x B and ♂ A x ♀ O, which are significantly different from other matings in our data, but not in the corresponding compatible or incompatible Japanese data. (I make comparisons within compatibility classes for the Japanese because there appears to be genuine incompatibility selection in Matsunaga's data.)

Interpreting what these results mean for balanced polymorphism is made still more difficult by our knowing the genotypes of only 0 and AB persons. There is one critical test which we can apply, however, based on Mandel's (1959) theoretical finding that the fitness of each homozygote must be less than the mean fitness of all genotypes at equilibrium. In table 5 we see the mean number of children for 0 (males and females together) parents compared to the mean for all parents. Since the differences are nonsignificant, all that can be said is that this test is inconclusive but suggests that fertility differences may not, by themselves, determine a stable polymorphism.

TABLE 5—*Fertility of 0 Individuals Compared to Mean Fertility*

Study	Mean number of children		Significance of difference
	0 parents	*All parents*	
Matsunaga & Itoh (1958)	2.395	2.414	Not significant
Haga (1959)	2.601	2.585	" "
Reed & Ahronheim (1959)	1.779	1.789	" "

There is an important gap here in any attempt to make a critical appraisal because we do not know that the children in these studies are born in the expected genetic proportions. If, for example, an O woman and an AO man consistently produce more than 50 per cent AO liveborn children, there could be selection favoring the heterozygote, even though the mean fertility of the couple is the same as the mean for all couples. Our conclusion with regard to the ABO fertility studies must be that fertility differences exist, but their relation to balanced polymorphism is unknown.

In table 6 the fertility data for Rh, MN, and P blood groups are presented. With regard to Rh groups, only one study, that of Reed (unpub.), found significant differences in fertility. These data are from the same population studied by Reed and Ahronheim (1959) for ABO blood groups. As indicated, this difference results from the incompatible matings being less fertile than the compatible ones. If this is the primary effect of

TABLE 6—*Fertility Studies in the Rh, MN, and P Blood Groups*
(Data Ascertained Independently of Fertility)

Blood group	Type of data	Population	Number	Significant difference in fertility		Study
				LB	FD	
Rh	Indi- viduals	English blood donors, ≥50 yrs., married	1290 ♂ 1319 ♀	No No	−* −	(1956) Bennett & Walker
	Couples	U.S. white Protestants, random sample, wife 30-39 yrs.	558	Yes† P < .05	−	Reed (unpublished)
MN	Couples	Japanese, miners, low economic status, different ages	1429	No	No	Matsunaga & Itoh (1958)
P (Jap. Q)	Couples	"	1429	No	No	"

LB=livebirths   FD=fetal deaths
* The proportion of children dying under 10 years was much greater (P<.001) when the father was O, Rh+.
† Mean fertility for (♂Rh+) × (♀Rh−): 1.541
Mean fertility for other three matings: 1.833
Difference: 0.292 ± 0.142, P<0.05.

selection, it is clear why the study of Bennett and Walker (1956) on individuals found no significant differences. If selection against Rh incompatible fetuses is important in the general population, as these data suggest, then there is selection against heterozygotes in this stage of the life cycle and such selection, by itself, would produce an unstable equilibrium. If the Rh system is in stable equilibrium, which may be debated, there must be selection elsewhere more than counterbalancing this heterozygote elimination. The fertilities of both Rh–males and Rh–females are less than the mean fertility but not significantly so. As in the ABO groups, we are hampered by not knowing the exact genotypes involved. The large number of Rh genotypes will make any critical analysis difficult.

The data on MN and P blood groups studied by Matsunaga and Itoh (1958), unlike those on the ABO blood groups, gave no evidence for selection. It is difficult to say how good these negative results are. It may be noted that their data include many young couples whose still low fertility will be confounded with the infertile older couples. It is clear that phenotypic fertility selection in the MN and P blood groups population is weaker than in the ABO groups. The fertilities of M, N, and P negative persons are all slightly higher than the mean fertility, so there is no evidence here for stable polymorphisms.

You will note that there are no data for the Kell, Duffy, Lewis, Lutheran, Kidd, Diego and Js systems, nor of the subdividsion of the previously mentioned groups.* It is clear that in fertility studies, as in viability studies, only the bare beginning of an understanding of the role of selection in determining the present polymorphisms has been made.

Prospects for Future Work

If we are to understand the relation between selection and polymorphism in the blood groups, there are certain obvious things which must be done. First, we must work with systems where genotypes can be determined serologically. This elminates the ABO blood groups, unfortunately. Second, we must obtain data over as much of the "life cycle" as possible, that is viability and fertility data to cover the cycle from zygote to adult to zygote again, since it is the overall selection which counts. Finally, we should, at first, concentrate our efforts on systems where the rewards seem greatest. For several reasons the MN system seems one of the best. It is the most stable in its world-wide distribution, suggesting a strong balancing selection, and its genotypes are simply determined. It remains to be shown, however, that presence of other antigens determined by genes at or near this locus, S, s, Hunter, etc., does not unduly complicate the investigation. The need for large samples is obvious and also discouraging. No one will be too optimistic, I think, about the likelihood of our understanding the blood group polymorphisms in the immediate future.

Conclusions

Summing up, we may say that it is very likely that some of the blood group systems represent balanced polymorphisms, and perhaps all of them do. Yet, in spite of the considerable amount of work done so far,

---

* Reed (1961) presents preliminary data on Kell, Duffy and Kidd blood groups which suggest an effect of Kell on fertility and of Duffy on stillbirths.

we still do not know the selective mechanism for maintaining any of these polymorphisms. This state largely reflects the fact that most data are for the ABO groups and, except for the incompatible fetuses, we do not know the genotypes of A and B individuals. Data continue to grow indicating that selection does occur, at least in ABO and Rh systems, but we cannot relate this to genotypic selection or to total selection over the whole life cycle. Yet we may expect to overcome these deficiencies in time.

DISCUSSION

DR. F. H. ALLEN: Dr. Reed, do you know if these Rh-negative women from the town of Jackson to whom you referred were sensitized to Rh?[1]

DR. REED: No, we do not. Our study there had certain remarkable strengths and weaknesses. The remarkable strength was that it was a truly random cross-section drawn originally from 72 per cent population sample of the town of Jackson which has a population 50,000. We have not, however, followed up by interview any of these couples for further medical questions or serologic examinations.

This is something, I think, that should be done and I think possibly may be already done, but I do not have that data now.

DR. LILIENFELD: Was the information on livebirths and fetal deaths in these studies obtained historically?

DR. REED: That is correct.

DR. LILIENFELD: Has this been true in other studies?

DR. REED: The two Japanese studies were cross-sectional surveys. The

---

[1] An apparent excess of type MN children born to couples one of which is type MN can sometimes be accounted for on the basis of technical errors, since it is easy to get false positive results with anti-N reagent and type M may be called "MN". The chance of errors of this type is presumably increased by the well recognized phenomenon that the red cells of newborns generally give somewhat weaker reactions with blood typing serums than do the red cells of adults, leading to the "over-reading" of these specimens. Actually, with respect to M and N, the difference between newborn and adult red cells is almost negligible, so that any over-reading is very likely to result in some type M's being labelled "MN". If both parents are known to be type M, an error will be detected; otherwise, it is very likely to go undetected. It is evident, then, that such testing must be done by experts, and readings of test results must be "blind".

We have been able to show in our laboratory recently that the common M genes produce a small amount of N factor in addition to the normal amount of M factor. This explains the difficulty in avoiding false positive reactions with anti-N reagent mentioned above. (Rare M genes produce no N factor that can be detected by present methods.) This observation suggests the possibility that some genes may produce large amounts of both M and N factor. Most persons having such a gene would have a large excess of type MN children. There is some evidence, I believe, that this is a common gene in chimpanzees, but no concrete evidence that it exists in humans. Concrete evidence would be almost impossible to obtain in the absence of the type M- N- (which has never been found). Statistical demonstrations would require many tests, and be most difficult to evaluate because of the technical serologic problems. If there were no serological problems, one could obtain good statistical evidence ($p < .01$) from testing 3,000 children of MN × MN matings if the frequency of the hypothetical gene were .02 or higher.

couples were interviewed, blood samples were taken, and a reproductive history obtained at the time.

My study in Jackson was a unique approach which needn't be recommended in all respects. We obtained the number of children resulting from a mating without consulting the parents. Some of you may know that the original data were on 48,000 individuals obtained in a mass blood grouping project in Jackson County. The data on these 48,000 individuals were put on punch cards. They were sorted by exact street address and number and the surnames were matched in the city directory to pick out couples. The age relationships were considered to pick out children. We therefore had assembled couples from individuals. We had literally "constructed families" from individual data. We did make a field check to see that we were in fact "making families" correctly, and were satisfied that we were.

DR. LILIENFELD: How did you determine the number of livebirths in Jackson?

DR. REED: I should say that the number of children here are the number of children who were blood grouped, which is about 80 per cent of the children born to the couples. We made these "families" without regard to parental blood groups. In other words, a couple, Smith, were matched. We picked out Mr. and Mrs. John Smith. They had certain children at the same address of certain ages. If those children were blood grouped we counted them as children of that couple. If a child of that couple was not blood grouped it was not present in our data to be counted. So we actually made a relative fertility comparison. We had religious classifications and we could distinguish between East Europeans and non-East Europeans by surname with considerable accuracy. We made our comparison then within religious and racial groups. We felt that the probability that a given child of a given couple would be counted in our survey was independent of parental blood groups. We did not use the parental blood groups to determine whether or not a given child was a child of a particular mating because you can see the bias that this would make. Therefore, what was determined was relative fertility; about 80 per cent of the total number of children were studied.

DR. LILIENFELD: In the studies where the information was obtained retrospectively, there is the difficulty that any historical enumeration of reproductive history even in terms of livebirths is fraught with a great amount of error. The Bureau of the Census has found this to be a problem in trying to enumerate the under-one age group in the population. People just don't consider someone under one year of age as being a member of the family. If a child is born and dies within a few days and you ask the mother about this event 30 or 40 years later, there is a good likelihood that she will not remember the child.

DR. REED: Yes, that is certainly true. But I think for our purposes, trying merely to establish whether or not there are significant differences, this would not be a source of error unless you assume that this recollection is dependent on the blood group.

DR. LILIENFELD: Except that, even if you have an equal amount of misclassification in the two groups you are comparing, this would tend to diminish any differences that may exist.

DR. REED: Oh, yes, this will make the analysis more difficult. A negative result is really perhaps less negative because of this error, but a positive result, I think, is still just as positive, if you assume the likelihood of forgetting is independent of blood groups, which, if we could eliminate racial differences, perhaps would be true.

DR. BOYER: When information is obtained concerning fertility, it usually centers on the female side. One can gain information from control figures from census information. Although the period of less than 45 years certainly encompasses the reproductive life of most females, it by no means limits the reproductivity of the male. MacArthur and Ibn Saud are cases in point.

Factors relating to the proportion of persons dying at less than 45 who suffer from a given disorder such as duodenal ulcer, a disease characterized by a male preponderance, are in a sense loaded figures because the male greater than 45 with duodenal ulcer may, for reasons best known to him, be more reproductive. This would tend to shift the observations in the direction of increasing O, let us say.

In any event, these comments simply point out we have *comparatively* little information about male fertility, and it may be of particular importance in those diseases to which the male is particularly prone and which were discussed this morning, such as duodenal and gastric ulcer, carcinoma, and several other examples.

DR. REED: Well, I would take some exception to that statement. Actually, we do have some good cross-sectional data on male fertility which we have got from several surveys in Michigan, primarily among the normal sibs of persons with Huntington's chorea, normal sibs of persons with neurofibromatosis and aniridia in the state of Michigan. And we do know well in these cases how the normal brother of an affected patient reproduces.

The other factor is that husbands are, on the average, three years older than their wives. In fact, this correlation is quite strong. And when we think of males with exceptional fertility, I think we tend to forget the general pattern. I would be happy to show some data in detail which will show that if you have a man who is, say, 46 years old, it is not likely that his wife is very far under the age of 40. In other words, his fertility is being limited by her fertility. The fact that we are considering couples whose ages are highly correlated is significant, and those few cases of old men with young fertile wives are not important in the population sense.

Dr. Boyer: I would certainly agree that this is true of this sort of disorder, but is it true of duodenal ulcer?

Dr. Reed: I don't think the error on the male side would be more than 5 per cent, say. I think that about 95 per cent of the ultimate fertility of men in our population today is achieved by the age of 45. This is largely because it is dependent on their wives' fertility.

Dr. Levine: Dr. Reed, you had one series in the chart on fertility in compatible ABO matings and incompatible ABO matings in which the fertility seemed to be greater in the incompatible matings.

Dr. Reed: That is true.

Dr. Levine: Was that a large series?

Dr. Reed: The significant finding is that on our Michigan population. That was based on 558 couples. The two-tail probability is one per cent.

My smaller study, which did not find a significant difference, nevertheless showed the incompatible couples to be more fertile than the compatible ones. That is on the 161 couples.

Dr. Levine: Did you take into account the total number of pregnancies?

Dr. Reed: The significant finding is on couples in which the wife is in the 30 to 39 age group. Therefore, it is not a completed sample. We did not have data on parity there.

The two Japanese studies shed some light here. In the second one with 900-some couples, the author asserted they were in good economic status and there was no significant difference between the fertility of the compatible and incompatible. In other words, it is approaching the American case. In contrast, the study on the miners (supposedly in poor economic status) found the incompatible less fertile. As I said, it looks as if in good environments the incompatible were more fertile than the compatible.

I want to emphasize that these findings are on studies unselected with regard to fertility. These studies include zero-child families. They are unselected with regard to fertility, and I think this is a vital difference. We include sterile couples in our data.

Dr. Gartler: Do you think this might be associated with reproductive compensation at higher economic levels?

Dr. Reed: I am not convinced there is reproductive compensation primarily because of our findings on Rh. Remember that the findings of Glass on Rh are again on women who are pregnant. His data are not a cross section of the population. He obviously did not have sterile couples.

DR. NEEL: There is one point we are all aware of: If you make enough comparisons something is bound to emerge at the level of statistical significance. And when we review findings of this nature, it is well to keep in mind the many negative studies that did not find their way to the final distillation. This raises the question of the appropriate significance level; I think the point of view is correct that it should be at least .001 before you get too excited about it.

DR. DUBLIN: It seems to me that Dr. Levine's question and Dr. Lilienfeld's question are quite intimately related. Dr. Reed did say he saw no reason why he should assume the reproduction rate in the two samples studied in Lansing should differ because of compatible and incompatible distinctions. But, Dr. Levine showed this is the one study in which the incompatible seemed to have a higher fertility rate than the compatible. Thus, there is justifiable basis for questioning whether the lack of historical information obtained about these couples is unimportant, or whether you can depend on the reported number of children in the household as a basis of getting the reproductive rate in the family.

DR. REED: Let me emphasize again that the Michigan study which found the significant difference was not based on recollection. We never saw the parents.

DR. DUBLIN: This is right. You have no history.

DR. REED: So we have no bias in this respect.

DR. NEEL: This was a Civil Defense project and history didn't enter into this, which is the unique feature of it.

DR. REED: From 30,000 individual blood groupings we extracted 558 records without consulting the couples. They never knew they were being investigated.

DR. LEVINE: In the Waterhouse study and all others, including my own, there was a factor of selection; we selected families with a large number of pregnancies.

DR. REED: Yes. You had to do that for your purposes. But if you want to analyze them for fertility you must remember that you do not have a population sample.

DR. LEVINE: Still, I think the findings of Waterhouse and Hogeben probably have some significance, especially if you have families with a large number of pregnancies.

DR. REED: I do not wish to leave the impression that my findings of incompatible couples being more fertile in any way means there is not strong ABO hemolytic diseases in some cases, because you can have both at the same time. You can have the incompatible couples having more stillbirths, more miscarriages, but in spite of that, having more liveborn children. And I am sure this is in fact operating. You saw that there is considerable evidence that there may be more stillbirths in the ABO incompatible mating, and I believe there are more miscarriages.

DR. LILIENFELD: There is an additional comment I'd like to make; actually all three of our comments are related.

The differences you are observing are small, and the chances of small differences of this type being a result of selective or biasing factors is fairly good.

This has been demonstrated numerically by Berkson (1946). Let us consider the way you sampled your couples in Jackson. If you took a larger sampling fraction of one kind of couple as compared to the other, which may have happened on a random sampling basis, you may obtain this kind of spurious association on the basis of association of sampling fractions. This could occur quite unconsciously without any particular bias in this type of study.

This relates, I think, to Dr. Neel's comment that you want to put probability levels of significance at the lowest possible level, but you are not quite sure at which level because you have no way of evaluating the number of biasing factors you have.

The same thing is true with respect to studies on the relationship of blood groups and disease. The relative risks are small. Consider that the relative risk for the lung cancer and cigarette smoking association is 9 to 10—that is, cigarette smokers have a 9 to 10 times greater risk of developing lung cancer than do non-smokers, and yet there is controversy as to whether this is meaningful in that the relationship may be a result of an indirect association. How much more can we feel this way when the relative risk is only 1.6 to 1.7? It seems to me the studies have to be refined to a much greater extent than they have been.

DR. REED: Let me be the first to ask for more data and higher significance levels. But let me also say that you have seen all the data on fertility here. There were four ABO blood group fertility studies made with couples. Three of them found significant differences. I don't know if you regard 15 per cent differences in the number of livebirths small or not. I don't think it is too small. But two out of the four studies found this value and the other two had indications of increased fetal deaths in ABO incompatible matings.

This is not making a large number of studies and finding just a few of them significant. Three of the four studies had significance probabilities of one per cent or less. I find this quite impressive.

DR. F. H. ALLEN: Do you recall how many of the women were Rh-negative?

DR. REED: About 16 per cent of 558.

6

THE GEOGRAPHY OF HEMOGLOBINOPATHIES[1]

JAMES V. NEEL

INTRODUCTION

I AM SURE THE REACTION of a good many members of this audience, when I get up to talk once again about hemoglobin, is that here is incontrovertible evidence for the ability of the human mind to get in a rut. To make my apparent preoccupation with this subject all the worse, I passed up a very pointed invitiation from Dr. Blumberg to discuss a much more general subject at this conference, in order to hold forth on hemoglobin once more. However, there is, I hope, a method in my apparently unshakable fixation. There have recently been a number of very exciting developments in this field. These very important advances have tended to create the impression that the hemoglobin polymorphisms are well understood. Without wishing for one instant to detract from these recent developments, I would like to try to draw your attention this morning to the many unsolved questions still surrounding the polymorphism so frequently quoted as the best understood of all the human genetic polymorphisms.

In some places I will seem to be bearing down rather heavily on the details, but field studies are after all composed of details, and I want to give you as much insight as possible in the allotted time to the kinds of questions and problems the geneticist encounters when he attempts to explain peculiar gene distributions.

BASIC GENETICS

There are now recognized some 20 inherited variations of human hemoglobin. This morning we will confine our attention mainly to only two of these, namely hemoglobins S and C. Each of these is inherited as if due to a single gene, which in the heterozygous condition results in 30 to 40 per cent of the hemoglobin being of an abnormal type, while in

---

[1] This presentation is modified from a review by D. L. Rucknagel and J. V. Neel, The Hemoglobinopathies (*in* Progress in Medical Genetics, vol. I, edited by A. G. Steinberg, Grune & Stratton, 1961), and is published here by kind permission of Grune & Stratton and Dr. Steinberg.

the homozygous condition, essentially all of the hemoglobin is abnormal. Figure 1 is a typical pedigree illustrating the inheritance of sickle cell hemoglobin. Observe that in the first generation the marriage of a person with the sickle cell trait (i.e., heterozygote) with a normal individual produces approximately equal numbers of normal and trait children, while in the second generation, a marriage of two individuals with the sickle cell trait produces several children with sickle cell anemia (i.e., homozygotes). The numbers in parentheses refer to the percentage of abnormal hemoglobin where this was determined. Although there are significant intrafamily similarities in this respect, the degree of constancy in this family is remarkable. Similar pedigrees could be shown for hemoglobin C. The genes determining these two hemoglobins appear to be alleles. We will henceforth refer to them as Hb_β^S and Hb_β^C, the subscript β referring to the fact that the ultimate biochemical change

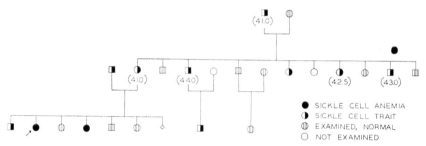

Fig. 1—A pedigree illustrating the inheritance of sickle cell hemoglobin.

responsible for the hemoglobin abnormality appears to reside in the β (rather than the α) chain of the hemoglobin molecule (Ingram 1956; Hunt and Ingram 1959; Ingram 1959; Vinograd, et al, 1959).

From the clinical standpoint, heterozygotes for these genes show no apparent ill effects, although there may be minor manifestations of the sickle-cell gene (review in Rucknagel and Neel, 1961). Individuals homozygous for the hemoglobin C gene characteristically exhibit a mild hemolytic anemia, but homozygotes for the S gene are the victims of a very severe, chronic hemolytic anemia which usually terminates fatally before the age of 20. Individuals heterozygous for both these genes suffer from an anemia intermediate in severity between the diseases of the two homozygotes.

PROBLEMS IN POPULATION GENETICS

The almost unique problems in population genetics presented by the abnormal hemoglobins were at once apparent following their discovery and the elucidation of their genetic control (cf. Neel 1951). In particular, with reference to the Hb_β^S gene, the early demonstration that in a broad belt extending across most of central Africa the frequency of trait carriers approximated 20 per cent raised many questions. If the results of homozygosity for this gene were the same in Africa as in the United States, then on the average 1 in 100 children would be expected to die of sickle cell anemia. If the populations concerned were at or near equilibrium, how was this gene loss compensated for? More specifically, to what extent were the gene frequencies in Africa the result of mutation pressure and to what extent of positive selection? Furthermore, in view of the occurrence of the Hb_β^S gene in such diverse groups as the "aboriginal" tribes of India and West Africa, as well as the inhabitants of certain areas in Greece, was there sufficient evidence for mutation to permit one to postulate multiple foci of origin for the gene, or was the mutation to be regarded as one of great rarity?

For a brief period, the possibility received consideration that the results of homozygosity for the Hb_β^S gene were much more serious in the United States than in the African populations, presumably because of the disruption of systems of genetic modifiers through hybridization in the former country (Raper 1950; Lehmann 1951). However, due primarily to the careful studies of the Lambotte-Legrands (1951; 1955), Foy, Kondi, and Brass (1951), and Vandepitte (1954), it quickly became apparent that in Africa the consequences of homozygosity were even more lethal than in the United States, while in the United States, no evidence could be found that sickle cell anemia was more severe in those Negroes with the greatest apparent degree of Caucasian admixture (Neel 1953). Attention was thus focused on the evidences for mutation and selection in favor of the heterozygote.

The collection of valid data on mutation presents many difficulties. There exist only four published, extensive series of observations in which the responsible investigators have examined routinely, where possible, both parents of children with sickle cell anemia of the type due to homozygosity for the gene responsible for hemoglobin S. None of these yields clear-cut evidence for the occurrence of mutation, i.e., one parent, preferably the mother, nonsickling, with other alternative explanations for the anemia in the child adequately excluded. The data seem adequate to exclude mutation pressure as the cause of the gene frequency. It should be pointed out that if the rate of mutation for this gene was 1×10^{-5}/gene/generation, then in areas where the sickle cell trait has a frequency of the order of 20 per cent, only 1 in 10,000 children would be expected, because of mutation, to be born of a mother who herself failed to sickle. The really prohibitive amount of labor involved in studying mutation rates by this approach, which is the best approach, is obvious.

It is important to recognize that on theoretical grounds alone, we may expect the rate of mutation resulting in any specific abnormality of hemoglobin to be well below the usual estimates. Thus, where we measure the rate with which mutation results in the absence of activity on the part of a particular enzyme, or in a specific phenotype whose biochemical basis is still imperfectly understood, we may be observing the end result of a change in any one of several hundred amino acids. But in studying the abnormal hemoglobins we are recognizing *specific* amino acid changes, which introduces an entirely different order of magnitude into the studies. Thus a mutation rate estimate of 1×10^{-5}/gene/generation which rests on *any* change in a 100-amino acid protein implies, if all the constituent amino acids are equally subject to genetic variation, a rate of 1×10^{-7} at the level of specific amino acid substitutions. The existing evidence suggests that not all of the constituent elements of a cistron are equally subject to mutation (Benzer 1959). With respect to that element involved in the $Hb_\beta{}^S$-$Hb_\beta{}^C$ mutation, then, it is readily conceivable that the mutation rate is of the order of 1×10^{-8}—in which case the responsible mutation might be expected to occur approximately once each generation in all Africa. The fact that two changes (the S and C) have been localized to precisely the same point in a polypeptide sequence cannot be used as an argument for a "genetic hot spot" since, in sampling a population, the findings reflect both mutation *and* selection, and we have abundant evidence that both these changes are subject to positive selection.

Essentially the same considerations as the foregoing apply to the two other hemoglobinopathy genes which have achieved relatively high frequencies in certain populations, namely, $Hb_\beta{}^C$ and $Hb_\beta{}^E$, the latter the gene responsible for hemoglobin E. In both instances, the homozygote suffers from a mild hemolytic anemia, which almost certainly confers some selective disadvantage, the magnitude of which cannot accurately be estimated at present. To what extent does mutation pressure offset this selective disadvantage? There are simply no data on this point at this writing. The developments shortly to be described make it clear that the answer to the relatively high frequencies of certain of the hemoglobinopathy genes is to be sought in selective mechanisms. However, any definitive understanding of the apparently restricted distribution of so many of the hemoglobinopathies would be greatly facilitated by mutation rate data. The considerations of the present section render it probable that, barring technical breakthroughs, such as the application to the problem of the methods of somatic cell genetics, it will probably be extraordinarily difficult to arrive at a reasonable estimate of the mutation rates concerned.

What is the evidence that the trait forms of the hemoglobinopathies are subject to positive selection?

The preceding considerations indicate that positive selection for the heterozygote must be the primary reason for the relatively high frequency of the $Hb_\beta{}^S$ gene, and, by inference, for the other Hb_β genes as well. Now, four of the inherited hemoglobinopathies—namely, hemoglobins S, C, E, and the thalassemia complex—occur with sufficiently high frequencies that studies on the manner in which the heterozygote is acted on by selection should be feasible. For one of these, hemoglobin E, no studies are yet available. The studies to date on the thalassemia complex have been inconclusive, with no significant progress in recent years. But for hemoglobins S and C, especially the former, there is available a considerable amount of interesting data.

Evidence for positive selection for the sickle cell trait in Africa

A two-allele system in which the frequency of a given allele is primarily maintained by a selective advantage of the heterozygote over either homozygote is the simplest example of a balanced polymorphic system. The gene frequencies attained at population equilibrium in such systems are of course primarily a function of the selective values of the three genotypes concerned. In the case of the $Hb_\beta{}^S$ gene, we know that the reproductive expectancy of homozygotes for this gene in Africa is virtually nil (Lambotte-Legrands 1955; Vandepitte 1959). We further know that in a number of different African tribes, trait (heterozygote) frequencies of 35 to 50 per cent have been encountered. If we assume that these are tribes in which the $Hb_\beta{}^S$ gene has its greatest selective advantage and in which the gene has been present long enough to attain equilibrium values, we can readily calculate the selective advantage the trait bearer must have over normal to offset the loss of $Hb_\beta{}^S$ genes through the early death of the homozygotes. This selective advantage may in essence be achieved by either one or some combination of two events, namely, differential survival and/or differential reproduction. Let us consider first what is required if differential survival is responsible for the maintenance of the polymorphism. In a population in which 35 per cent of adults have the sickle cell trait, the $Hb_\beta{}^S$ gene has a frequency, p, of $\frac{.35}{2} = .175$, and on the assumption of equal fertility of the two genotypes concerned, the zygote proportions in the next generation of the three genotypes, $Hb_\beta{}^A/Hb_\beta{}^A$, $Hb_\beta{}^A/Hb_\beta{}^S$, and $Hb_\beta{}^S/Hb_\beta{}^S$ are given by an expansion of the expression $(p + q)^2$, where $q = 1 - p$. If all Hb_β^S/Hb_β^S individuals die prior to the age of reproduction and if selection operates entirely through differential mortality, then in order for the gene frequency to remain constant from generation to generation, in each generation the relative frequency of heterozygotes must increase from 0.288750 at birth to 0.350000 at adulthood. If fitness be defined as the ratio of genotype frequency in the adult to that in the newborn, then the fitness of the Hb_β^A/Hb_β^A genotype is 0.955 and of the Hb_β^A/Hb_β^S, 1.212. The relative fitness of the heterozygote with respect to normal is 1.27.

The situation is somewhat different if equilibrium is maintained wholly by differential fertility. If one assumes a population with sickle cell trait frequencies as before (35 per cent), but with equal survival of Hb_β^A/Hb_β^A and Hb_β^A/Hb_β^S individuals, q, the frequency of the Hb_β^S gene in the population prior to the elimination of Hb_β^S/Hb_β^S individuals, may be determined from the relationship, $.65 = (1 - q)^2/1 - q^2$, from which q^2, the frequency of affected individuals at birth, is 0.044986. We are required now to estimate the fertility differential which must exist to off-set this loss of Hb_β^S genes each generation. The estimate varies according to certain assumptions which must be made regarding fertility, but where one assumes that the fertility of two individuals is multiplicative, at a value of 35 per cent for the sickle cell trait, f solves for .3684, i.e., the Hb_β^A/Hb_β^S individual must be 37 per cent more fertile than normal if this is the entire mechanism whereby the loss of Hb_β^S/Hb_β^S zygotes is offset.[1]

Studies on the evidence for differential survival ideally involve proper, age-stratified population samples of genetically homogeneous groups in areas where sickling rates are relatively high and mortality prior to the age of reproduction is upwards of 30 per cent, i.e., where the population may be assumed to be under the selective pressures responsible for high gene frequencies. Such samples are not readily assembled in Africa, and it is doubtful if any study thus far performed would meet the require-ments of the "census tract" approach. However, the literature contains some seven samples in which the ideal is approximated (field studies or an approach thereto, trait frequencies > 20 per cent) and in which the Hb_β^C gene, whose presence would complicate the calculations, may be assumed to be absent or to occur in negligible frequencies. All of the studies agree in showing a higher frequency of the sickle cell trait in adults than in infants. The unweighted average of the seven series is 1.15. Allowance for the inclusion of occasional surviving cases of sickle cell anemia in the figures for children exhibiting the sickling phenomenon would perhaps alter the estimate to 1.16 or 1.17. It may be tentatively

[1] I am indebted to Dr. T. E. Reed for helpful discussions of this subject.

concluded that differential survival is the major but not the entire factor in the sickle cell polymorphism, accounting for perhaps two-thirds of the advantage of the heterozygote.

With respect to differential fertility, significant data on this point have been slow to accumulate. There are now four series which meet the same general restrictions that were placed on the survival data. The data have been collected in a variety of ways, rendering the series difficult to compare. Data are for children ever born. Where possible, the comparison has been limited to the ratio of the fertility of trait x normal to that of normal x normal marriages. The unweighted average of the ratio in the four series is 1.13. This estimate is greatly influenced by the results of Allàrd's (1955) study, which appear at marked variance with those of the other three investigators. Be that as it may, this value of 1.13, which may be taken as a crude index to f, is about one-third the value necessary to maintain equilibrium, but yet does indicate that differential fertility may be of greater importance than assumed in most contemporary presentations of the subject. It cannot be too strongly emphasized how approximate are both the biologic data and its mathematical treatment in the derivation of these estimates.[1]

The manner in which selection favors the sickle cell trait in Africa

As a generalization, the action of selection on a genetically determined trait will, even in the simplest case, be found to be complex. The case of the $Hb_\beta{}^S$ gene may be unusual, in the extent to which one selective mechanism, differential susceptibility to P. falciparum malaria, overshadows all others. Although several investigators had previously mentioned the possibility of such a differential susceptibility (Beet 1946, 1947; the Lambotte-Legrands 1951, 1952; Brain 1952; Lehmann 1953), it was Allison (1954a, b, c) who first clearly formulated the hypothesis

---

[1] *Note added April 10, 1961:* Two important and well designed studies on fertility in relation to sickling in malarious regions have now come to our attention. Roberts and Boyo (1960) in studies on the Yoruba of southern Nigeria found sickle cell trait (or hemoglobin C trait) x normal marriages resulted in slightly although insignificantly more livebirths per fertile year of marriage than normal x normal marriages, regardless of whether the mother or father was the heterozygote. Firschein (unpublished thesis) finds that among the Black Caribs of British Honduras, with 23.3 percent sickle cell trait, the fertility ratio of sickle cell trait mothers to normal (whether based on mean number of children ever born or mean number surviving) is approximately 1.45—sufficient to maintain the observed gene frequencies even in the absence of any differential mortality due to malaria. Firschein suggests that the mechanism for this differential may be an increased number of abortions among the nonsickling mothers. The addition of these two studies to those already available leaves little doubt that both differential mortality and fertility are involved in the maintenance of the sickle cell polymorphism.

and introduced systematic attempts to prove it. The evidence adduced by him was of three types:

(*a*) Different rates of parasitemia in sicklers and non-sicklers, and lower parasite densities in sicklers once infection is established,

(*b*) Differences between sicklers and non-sicklers in susceptibility to experimental falciparum malaria, and

(*c*) The correlation between the distribution of severe (hyperendemic) falciparum malaria and the highest frequencies of the $Hb_\beta{}^S$ gene in Africa.

Evidence bearing on the malaria hypothesis may be of two types, for purposes of convenience termed "direct" and "indirect." The latter type of evidence is circumstantial in nature, tending to implicate malaria as a potentially more fatal disease in nonsicklers, whereas the former, admittedly more difficult to obtain, would consist of data on the relationship between actual death from malaria and the possession of the sickle cell trait. Allison's data were of the indirect type, as indeed were the data in most of the flood of publications on this point which quickly followed the appearance of Allison's three papers (Raper 1954, 1955, 1956; Mackey and Vivarelli 1954; Edington 1954; Moore, et al, 1954; Foy, et al, 1955, 1956; Beutler, et al, 1955; Archibald and Bruce-Chwatt 1955; Bezon 1955; Hiernaux 1955; Deliyannis and Tavlarakis 1955, 1956; Colbourne and Edington 1956; Lehmann and Raper 1956; Garlick and Barnicot 1957). An extended review of these papers would form an excellent documentary on the difficulties of establishing a correlation between a genetic trait and a disease susceptibility under field conditions, but such a review, while valuable, would carry us beyond the scope of this paper. The weight of the indirect evidence, and in particular the data on the younger age groups, favors the hypothesis that infections with falciparum malaria are less frequent and less severe in persons with the sickle cell trait, although there are several unexplained inconsistencies. However, it remained for Raper (1956), Vandepitte and Delaisse (1957), and the Lambotte-Legrands (1958a) to supply direct evidence, to the effect that among children dying of malaria, especially of the cerebral type, there was a relative deficiency of the sickle cell trait. There is now no doubt that malaria plays a role in maintaining the sickle cell polymorphism. However, because of the very high rate of malaria infection in hyperendemic regions and because of the fact that so many African children die of multiple causes, attempts to specify the precise extent to which malaria is responsible for the observed differential mortality seem unlikely to yield clearcut results.

With respect to the basis for the differences in fertility between sicklers and nonsicklers, no mechanism is known at present. It is conceivable that the greater malaria morbidity in childhood permanently impairs the reproductive capacity of the nonsickler. A supplementary explanation draws on the fact that in hyperendemic regions, the balance between the malaria parasite and its host remains precarious throughout life—there is no lasting immunity. Thus, Miller (1958) conducted daily blood examinations for a period of a year on 20 young African males living in a hyperendemic region for P. falciparum, and presumably with a very strong acquired immunity for falciparum malaria. Parasites were found in 20 per cent of all examinations; the members of the group averaged 1.5 mild clinical attacks during the year of the study. It is therefore conceivable that a greater frequency of subclinical or even clinical attacks of malaria throughout adult life play a role in the relatively impaired fertility of nonsicklers.

In a search for other selective advantages conferred by the sickle cell gene, a number of observers have correlated admissions to African hospitals by specific disease category with the frequency of the sickle cell trait (e.g., Beet 1946; Brain 1952; Lambotte-Legrands 1952; Raper 1956; Delbrouck (1958). Many of these hospital series suffer from a common defect, namely, a sample of mixed tribal origins, with the possibility of different disease patterns and sickling rates in the various tribes. Furthermore, most of the series are predominantly concerned with adults, whereas the genetically most significant segment of the population would be the children. Although no finding emerges as clearly significant at this writing, the following possibilities would seem to warrant further investigation: a decreased susceptibility to leprosy (André and André-Gadras 1957; Delbrouck 1958), a decreased susceptibility to hookworm anemia (Raper 1956, unconfirmed by the Lambotte-Legrands 1958b) but an increased susceptibility to typhoid fever (Lambotte-Legrands 1952; Raper 1956).

Evidences of pathological consequences of the sickle cell trait, from Africa and the United States

If in addition to its biologic advantages, there are also certain disadvantages to the sickle cell trait, these may be difficult to demonstrate in tropical regions, but more readily detected in areas such as the United States, where large numbers of Negroes are living under nontropical conditions. Surprisingly, there are only five sizeable series on age incidence trends in the U.S., these all unfortunately involving in whole or part hospital in- or out-patients (table 1). Four of the five series agree in indicating less sickling among older patients. The interpretation of the fifth series is complicated by the fact that the figures are based on studies of a racial isolate with a high frequency of sickling; in this isolate the rate of out-marriage (to individuals with a lower probability of possessing the Hb_β^S gene) has markedly increased in recent years. The overall results could be interpreted as compatible with less disease (and less cause for hospitalization) in older sicklers, or a higher death rate on the part of sicklers. Even when allowance is made for the probable inclusion of some cases of sickle cell anemia in the younger age group, the magnitude of the differential implied by these figures is really quite striking. Thus, for the combined series, exclusive of the last, assigning one-third of Pollitzer's (1958) "14-29" category to the "20 and below"

TABLE 1—*The Relation between Age and the Sickle Cell Trait in Some of the Larger Series of Tests for the Trait in American Negroes*

Investigator	Age group	Number tested	Number sickling	Per cent sickling
Diggs, L. W., Ahmann, C. F., and Bibb, J., The incidence and significance of the sickle cell trait., Ann. Int. Med., 7:769-778, 1933.	6-20	1,112	108	9.7
	21-50	1,102	96	8.7
	51-	403	28	7.0
Switzer, P. K., The incidence of the sickle cell trait in Negroes from the Sea Island area of South Carolina, South Med J., 43:48-49, 1950.	6-20	843	130	15.4
	21-50	1,233	165	13.4
	51-	302	42	13.9
Neel, J. V., The population genetics of two inherited blood dyscrasias in man., Cold Spring Harbor Symp. Quant. Biol., 15:141-158, 1951.	12-20	147	15	10.2
	21-50	703	67	9.6
	51-	146	7	4.8
Pollitzer, W. S., The Negroes of Charleston (S. C.); a study of hemoglobin types, serology, and morphology., Am. J. Phys. Anthrop., 16:241-263, 1958.	14-29	232	42	18.1
	30-	241	26	10.8
Rucknagel, D. L., Witkop, C. J., Jr., and Schmidt, R. J., Unpublished observations.	0-20	1,476	282	19.1
	21-50	530	101	19.1
	51-	176	46	26.1

group, and one-fourth of the "30-" category to "51 and older," the results are: below 20:12.25 per cent; 21 to 50:11.11 per cent; 51 and above: 9.22 per cent. These figures would seem to imply, on one interpretation, a roughly 25 per cent greater susceptibility to death between youth and the advanced years on the part of sicklers. This is an impressive figure, which is difficult to accept.

The need for clarification of this point for any final understanding of the dynamics of the Hb_β^S gene is obvious. Although on the face of it, most of this increased death rate occurs subsequent to the age of reproduction, and so is of relatively little importance in determining gene frequencies, there is some evidence for an increased death rate below the age of 50. If there is indeed intrinsically a selective disadvantage attached to the Hb_β^S gene, then the positive factors at work in a tropical environment must be even greater than calculated. Although it may seem an anachronistic stand in these days of biochemical excitement, in my opinion the outstanding gap in our knowledge of the population genetics of the Hb_β^S gene is this question of age-incidence trends under non-tropical conditions.

Evidence for selection with respect to the hemoglobin C trait in Africa and elsewhere

Knowledge concerning the dynamics of the Hb_β^C gene is meager—far less advanced than for the Hb_β^S. The maximum heterozygote frequencies thus far encountered are of the order of 20 per cent, but this is not a "pure" figure, since in these same populations there occur Hb_β^S and also the thalassemia complex (see following section). Thus, at the moment there is no observed equilibrium figure for the Hb_β^C heterozygote on the assumption of balanced polymorphism comparable to the figure of 35-40 for the Hb_β^S heterozygote. The two efforts to derive selective values for the Hb_β^A/Hb_β^C and Hb_β^C/Hb_β^C genotypes have yielded markedly contradictory values (Allison 1957; Edington and Laing 1957).

With the demonstration of the role of malaria in maintaining Hb_β^S gene frequencies, the question of course arises whether this same agent might be important to hemoglobin C. The only study to date on this point (Edington and Laing 1957) yielded no evidence that persons with the hemoglobin C trait were in any way protected against malaria; that same study provided suggestive evidence of the protection afforded by the sickle cell trait.

An even more striking failure to implicate hemoglobin C in the same selective system that regulates the frequency of the Hb_β^S gene emerges from a recently described "natural" experiment unwittingly performed in the days of the slave trade (Jonxis 1959; van der Sar 1959). In the seventeenth century the Dutch maintained a "factory" at Elmina on the Gold Coast. Most of the slaves transported to their New World possessions of Dutch Guiana or Surinam and Curaçao were probably derived from there. On Curaçao the slave found himself in a malaria-free environment, whereas in Surinam, malaria was rife. In both Surinam and Curaçao, some Caucasian admixture occurred. In Curaçao, blood group gene frequency studies on the inhabitants of the northwestern half of the island, who for various reasons are believed to represent the descendants of the original slaves to a greater degree than those of the other end of the island, suggested about 13-14 per cent Caucasian ancestry. No comparable studies have been carried out in Surinam, where the Negroes studied were to a large extent the descendants of slaves who escaped to the "bush" from the early plantations; the amount of white admixture would presumably have been less. Three groups of Negroes were studied in Surinam. All samples agree in sickle cell trait individuals being three times as frequent as hemoglobin C trait individuals. In Curaçao, on the other hand, the C trait is more frequent than the sickle cell trait. The difference between the two localities in the frequency of both the $Hb_\beta{}^S$ and $Hb_\beta{}^C$ genes is highly significant. Caucasian admixture cannot account for the results. There is of course no way to reconstruct the original gene frequencies, since even if the exact origins of the slaves were known, the $Hb_\beta{}^S$ and $Hb_\beta{}^C$ frequencies of 200-300 years ago are unknown. Jonxis (1959) interprets the findings as evidence for a selective value of the $Hb_\beta{}^S$ gene under "bush" conditions, presumably in consequence of malaria pressure. Equally interesting to us, and not commented on by the author, is the fact that if one accepts this conclusion, one is almost forced to the position that hemoglobin C is subject to different selection pressures. One alternative to this is the assumption that in a near equilibrium situation the $Hb_\beta{}^C$ allele is being "displaced" in Surinam by the more efficient $Hb_\beta{}^S$ gene, but this then conflicts with evidence summarized by Allison (1957) that in the Gold Coast area today higher frequencies of these two genes coexist.

West Africa

In bringing this presentation to a close, I should like to draw your attention briefly to the results of the studies to date in West Africa, as a practical example of some of the problems encountered in the pursuit of genetically determined, geographically localized pathology.

Hemoglobins S, C, G, K, and N, and the thalassemia phenotype, have all been reported from West Africa. Of these hemoglobin S, by virtue of numerous surveys of the frequency of the sickle cell trait, has been most intensively examined. However, the fact that hemoglobin C results from the presence of a gene allelic to that responsible for S means that conclusions regarding genetic equilibrium and tribal relationships which disregard hemoglobin C may be quite misleading. Accordingly, in this discussion we will confine our attention to surveys using electrophoretic techniques.

The basic data available for West Africa can be summarized in a series of figures. There are 301 tribes in West Africa. We have restricted our summary to those 48 tribes for whom 30 or more electrophoretic hemoglobin determinations have been performed on their members, the number 30 having been arbitrarily selected as the minimal figure necessary to provisional insight into the tribal composition. The findings may be briefly characterized as follows: As shown in figure 2, in the savannah country of the French Sudan, extending from the Lake Chad region in the east to the Atlantic in the west, and lying between the Sahara Desert on the north, and in the main, a tropical rain forest belt on the south, the $Hb_\beta{}^S$ gene attains a frequency in the neighborhood of 0.09. South of this band, the frequency of the $Hb_\beta{}^S$ gene is quite variable. In general, however, from Ghana east the frequency of the $Hb_\beta{}^S$ gene averages somewhat higher than in the interior, of the order of 0.12. Relatively high frequencies of this gene are also encountered in the Temne and Mende of Sierra Leone and also in the Banyun of the Gambia and adjacent areas. In view of the argument to be developed, it should be pointed out that these "highs," except in Sierra Leone, are the general regions in which the great rivers of interior West Africa—the Gambia, the Volta, and the Niger—break through to the Atlantic Ocean. The rivers of Africa have of course been major channels for trade and conquest.

By contrast, as shown in figure 3, the $Hb_\beta{}^C$ gene shows a striking restriction in its distribution which has been commented on by many investigators (Edington and Lehmann 1956; Allison 1956; Neel, et al, 1956). Although there are still critical deficiencies in our knowledge, the $Hb_\beta{}^C$ gene shows a clearly defined high, of the order if 0.10, in a region very roughly contained in the great bend of the Niger river. In all directions from this high, gene frequency falls off rapidly.

Finally, now, it should be pointed out that there are two areas in which both the $Hb_\beta{}^S$ and $Hb_\beta{}^C$ genes have negligible frequencies, namely, in the region of Portuguese Guinea (the Balanta, Pepel, and Bijogo) and in the region of southeastern Liberia and the southern Ivory Coast (the Kru, Ngere, Kran, Dan, Grebo, and Lagoon tribes). The recent report of Gibson (1958) of an $Hb_\beta{}^S$ frequency of only .007 in the inhabitants of some areas of that portion of the southern Cameroons under British administration raises the possibility of a similar "low" here. This latter frequency estimate is based on the results of sickling tests rather than electrophoresis, so that no estimates for $Hb_\beta{}^C$ are available, but in view of the known distribution of this gene, it would be highly surprising if it attained any appreciable frequency here.

Two other aspects of the hemoglobinopathies of West Africa are interesting. First, there is now evidence for a relatively high frequency of the thalassemia gene in Liberia, the Ivory Coast, and the Upper Volta region. Second, there is evidence, summarized in part in figure 4, for a

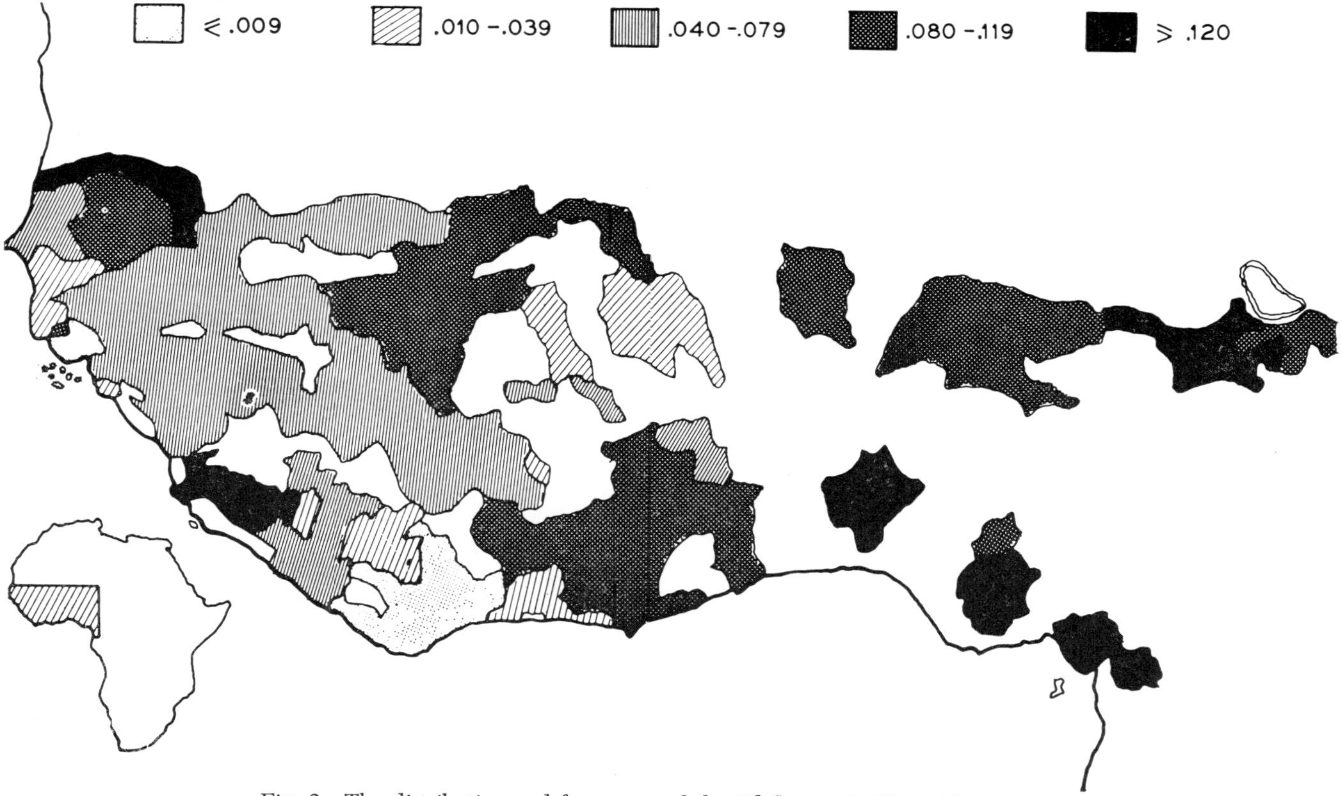

Fig. 2—The distribution and frequency of the $Hb_\beta{}^S$ gene in West Africa.

≤ .009

.010 – .039

.040 – .079

.080 – .119

≥ .120

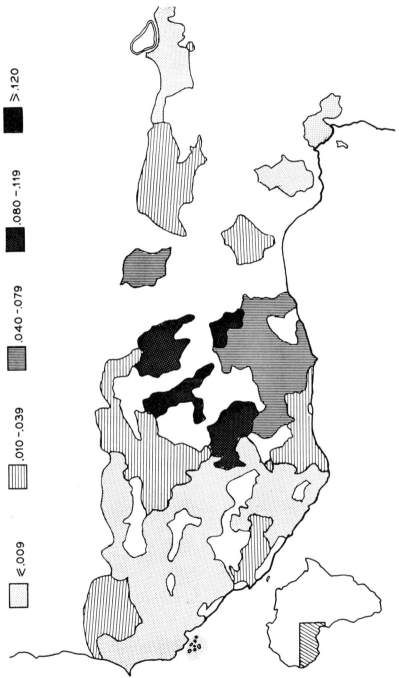

Fig. 3—The distribution and frequency of the $Hb_\beta{}^C$ gene in West Africa.

≤.009

.010 - .039

.040 - .079

.080 - .119

≥.120

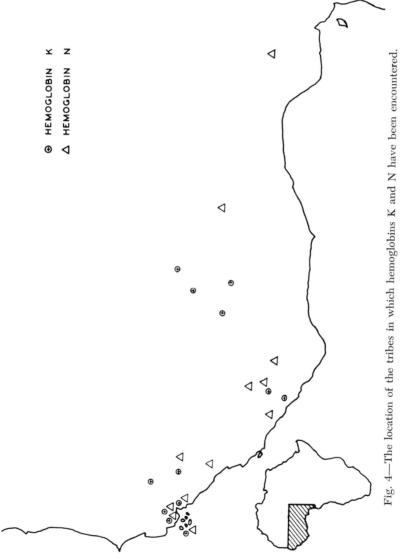

⊕ HEMOGLOBIN K

△ HEMOGLOBIN N

Fig. 4—The location of the tribes in which hemoglobins K and N have been encountered.

low frequency of hemoglobins N and K throughout many portions of West Africa.

How do we explain these findings? Livingstone has recently marshalled impressive evidence for the principal area from which the $Hb_\beta{}^S$ gene was disseminated throughout Africa being the Sudan region of the eastern two-thirds of West Africa. This is the area where iron and large-scale agriculture were first introduced to West Africa, only some 2000 years ago. Livingstone argues that these introductions set the stage for developments which greatly increased malaria mortality and morbidity, and so provided the selective pressures which built up sickle cell gene frequencies. Figure 5 is a rough map of the distribution of the most primitive or paleonegroid tribes of West Africa, occupying the tropical rain forest. Note the general correspondence between these areas and low frequencies of the $Hb_\beta{}^S$ gene. The sickle cell gene is still spreading to some of these tribes.

There is a remarkable correspondence between the area of relatively high $Hb_\beta{}^C$ frequency and the Gur sub-family of the Niger-Congo languages. These are the Voltaic peoples of Murdock (1959)—a collection of many culturally diverse, usually small tribes, whose agricultural practices are rather advanced, quite likely as a result of borrowing from the Mande to the west, but who otherwise, as a whole, exhibit a rather primitive culture. They appear to have been compressed into their present distribution by the more powerful tribes to the north, west, and east. The degree to which the $Hb_\beta{}^C$ gene is restricted to this group suggests—to the extent that language defines a genetic community—that this gene did not attain an appreciable frequency until the linguistic differentiation of Africa was well advanced. On these grounds, then, the gene, at least in its present frequency, would appear to be of relatively recent origin. Unfortunately, from the standpoint of establishing the genetic isoclines which could be of great help in understanding the history of this gene, there are, as figure 3 shows, very critical gaps in our knowledge of its distribution.

The question immediately arises, whether the $Hb_\beta{}^C$ gene attained appreciable frequencies before, at approximately the same time, or subsequent to the $Hb_\beta{}^S$ gene. A related question is whether appreciable frequencies of the $Hb_\beta{}^S$ gene first appeared in the same people as the $Hb_\beta{}^C$ gene or further to the east. In our opinion, these questions cannot be answered at this time, and, indeed may never receive definitive answers. In the face of constant selective pressures, the "older" gene should have attained equilibrium frequencies over wider areas. However, inasmuch as the only two studies of the selective value of $Hb_\beta{}^S/Hb_\beta{}^A$ as

Fig. 5—The distribution of the so-called relict, "paleonegroid," or indigenous tribes in West Africa.

versus $Hb_\beta{}^C/Hb_\beta{}^A$ performed in areas where their distribution overlaps to a significant extent have yielded conflicting evidence regarding the relative values of the two genotypes, we are scarcely in a position to reach decisions concerning equilibrium. Furthermore, although, as already brought out, a differential susceptibility to malaria is probably the major factor in maintaining the $Hb_\beta{}^S$ polymorphism, at the moment we have no really good clues as to what is responsible for the $Hb_\beta{}^C$ polymorphism. We are thus scarcely in a position to conclude which gene has been subject to favorable selection pressures for the longer period. The indirect evidence bearing on this point is confusing. Thus, the fact that the $Hb_\beta{}^S$ gene appears to have penetrated into areas not yet reached by $Hb_\beta{}^C$ (e.g., Liberia and the Ivory Coast) could be construed as an argument for the greater antiquity of the $Hb_\beta{}^S$ gene—but might also to some unspecifiable extent reflect a greater selective advantage of $Hb_\beta{}^S$. Likewise, the fact that the $Hb_\beta{}^C$ gene has a significantly higher frequency in Algerians as a group than the $Hb_\beta{}^S$ gene (Cabannes 1957) could indicate that the former has been diffusing into North Africa over a longer period of time than the latter, or, conversely that the selective disadvantage which may exist for the $Hb_\beta{}^S/Hb_\beta{}^A$ genotype outside of a tropical and subtropical ecology may have resulted in a more significant elimination of $Hb_\beta{}^S$ than of $Hb_\beta{}^C$ genes subsequent to their diffusion into North Africa. If the ecological developments favoring the attainment of considerable frequencies are roughly comparable for the two genes, then each might have been present in one or several populations at very low frequencies until the advent of malaria and other "new" selective agents, and then have increased in frequency at the same time.

It seems possible that the distribution of the $Hb_\beta{}^S$ and $Hb_\beta{}^C$ genes throughout West Africa prior to the advent of the selective pressures which result in their present frequencies was quite comparable to what we see today with respect to hemoglobins K and N. In this case, the present-day patterns of distribution for $Hb_\beta{}^S$ and $Hb_\beta{}^C$ reflect both the result of selection of a low-frequency allele by an advancing wave of changing selective pressures as well as the pattern created by the migration of individuals from an area of high gene frequency to one of low.

Dr. Allison has argued that much of West Africa has reached a genetic equilibrium as regards the multiple alleles at the S-C locus. While this point of view might have been tenable when he advanced it some three years ago, today the evidence suggests that large regions of West Africa are a far cry from genetic equilibrium. In our efforts to understand the factors responsible for this unstable situation, we are in a position to participate in a real exercise in genetic epidemiology.

CONCLUDING REMARKS

Although the general principles have been established that the $Hb_\beta{}^S$ and $Hb_\beta{}^C$ are members of a polymorphic system, and that falciparum malaria is an important factor in maintaining that balance, many of the details concerning this polymorphism remain exceedingly obscure. We have no satisfactory estimate of the mutation rates of the genes concerned. We do not know what handicap, if any, these two genes confer in a nontropical environment, i.e., the baseline against which the positive selection works. We are unsure how much of the polymorphism is due to differential mortality and how much to differential fertility, and, if the latter to any significant extent, i.e., the responsible mechanisms. We are actually not sure whether the $Hb_\beta{}^S$ or the $Hb_\beta{}^C$ gene confers the greater selective advantage—or whether the relative advantage may vary sharply from area to area. Finally, many important details regarding the distributions of these genes remain unknown, not only in West Africa but in other parts of the world, such as India, where the $Hb_\beta{}^S$ gene is rather widespread throughout the so-called aboriginal tribes but is also present in the "schedule castes" (Lehmann and Cutbush 1952a, b; Dunlop and Mozumder 1952; Bhatia, et al, 1955; Büchi 1955; Foy, Brass and Kondi 1956; Sukumaran, et al, 1956; Shukla and Solanki 1958; Shukla, Solanki and Parande 1958; Chatterjea 1959).

Clearly, the elucidation of many of these questions entails immense expenditures of effort. From the scientific standpoint, is the problem that important? In the author's opinion, yes. The demonstration of a role of malaria in maintaining the $Hb_\beta{}^S$ polymorphism is a fundamental advance in knowledge, but it would be unfortunate if the appeal of this advance discouraged full exploration of other possibilities. On the basis of our present information, here is perhaps the most favorable opportunity in human genetics today to gain detailed insight into the precise workings of a polymorphic system. In view of the current great interest in such genetic systems, this opportunity should certainly not be missed. This is true even though we can say with considerable assurance that this particular situation, with the loss at equilibrium of approximately 4 per cent of individuals prior to reproduction, cannot be typical of the genetic polymorphism of man or other animals. Thus, it is unlikely that many such systems could still exist undetected, while, on the other hand, the total known loss from birth through the first year of life in Western societies is not great enough to make allowance for many systems entailing a 4 per cent zygote loss. An unusual aspect of the $Hb_\beta{}^S$-$Hb_\beta{}^C$ polymorphism is that here we may be witnessing an early stage in the attempts in our species to evolve a genetic immunity to a new parasite, with the normal prospect that this would in time be superseded by a less wasteful polymorphism or genetic fixation of one or several alleles conferring a relative immunity. On the other hand, these latter genetic systems, simply because they are less wasteful, will be much more difficult to come to grips with in the requisite detail—it is these extreme systems which provide the insight and experience from the vantage point of which the less spectacular systems can be attacked.

DISCUSSION

DR. BLUMBERG: As Dr. Neel knows, there are essentially two Negro groups in Surinam. One group is the town Negroes or Creoles, whose affinities are with West Africans and Europeans. Many of the latter were, incidentally, Sephardic Jews. The second group is the Bush Negroes, or Djukas. According to everyone's belief, they have had very little mixture with the white settlers. On which group was the study done?

DR. NEEL: I'm sorry if I didn't make this clear. These were Djukas, approached through mission hospitals that are far in the interior.

DR. BLUMBERG: What is the evidence that the Surinam slaves and the Curaçao slaves come from the same place in West Africa?

DR. NEEL: This was essentially an indirect argument. The Dutch are known to have limited their slaving operations to a very small part of the West African coast. During the period that they were importing slaves into the New World, as far as is known, almost all of their shipments originated at a so-called "factory" that they held in what is now Ghana. However, it was apparently a matter of chance, as far as is known, whether a slave went to Curaçao or Surinam. So as far as we know we can assume that the original slaves of Curaçao and Surinam probably had the same frequencies of S and C.

Now, you are as familiar as I am with the sampling problem that could enter in here, in that slaves sometimes arrived in the Gold Coast after a 400-mile trek from points in the interior. But it wasn't as if there was only one boat that was sent to Curaçao, and another to Surinam. There were successive importations of slaves. So I think it's a fair assumption that the two areas were peopled by the same types of slaves.

DR. BLUMBERG: I have often wondered about the origins of the Djukas. When visiting in Nigeria I spoke a few words of Djuka talkie-talkie to my Yoruba assistant but he didn't recognize any of them. It might be possible to solve the problem by determining which African language is most similar to "deepie-talkie" the dialect of the Djukas which is said to contain many African words.

We will now call on some of the listed discussants. Dr. Levine, I wonder if you could discuss the preceding two talks.

DR. LEVINE: I'd like to make some comments regarding the selection against the heterozygote in Rh hemolytic disease and also on the effect of the ABO groups on Rh hemolytic disease.

With each fatally affected infant there is loss of one R dominant and one recessive and more frequent gene, r.

But actually, this is not a very important factor because in most cases the affected infants recover with replacement therapy. There is loss of genes in stillbirths, but there is a tendency as Dr. Glass (1950) has shown, for overcompensation with birth of normal Rh negative infants whose fathers are heterozygous for Rh.

The incidence of hemolytic diseases is low, about 1 in 25 of all pregnancies in Rh incompatible matings, and there are several reasons given for the failure for any Rh negative women to produce antibodies. One of the established protective factors is the effect of ABO incompatibility. But this cannot explain all of it. It can explain reduction of hemolytic disease by about 22 per cent. There remains a larger group of Rh negative women who, for one reason or another do not produce antibodies, and one theory that has been invoked is tolerance, which I would like to discuss. But in the final analysis we don't know the reason why a great many Rh negative women do not produce antibodies although the mother receives the antigenic stimulus in all pregnancies resulting in normal births.

I would like to discuss an observation which I made in 1943 (Levine 1943) because I hoped, in finding Rh hemolytic disease, I would quickly find other evidence of fetal neonatal mortality. And it was at that time that I arrived at certain figures in random Caucasoid matings of 65 per cent ABO compatible and 35 per cent ABO incompatible.

A compatible mating is one in which the father could give blood to the mother. O father by A mother would be compatible. A father by O mother would be incompatible. There are seven such incompatible matings and nine compatible.

In 1943 I was interested mainly in a group of cases with abortions and stillbirths. If I recall correctly my value, there were anywhere from 45 to 50 ABO incompatible and it was this which I stressed at the time. But I also found that in Rh hemolytic disease, the ABO incompatibility was reduced to 24 per cent. At present almost all studies show a value of about 17.7 per cent, so there is a considerable protective action from the ABO incompatibility.

We assume 50 per cent protection, i.e., the first pregnancy with an ABO compatible Rh positive fetus which almost always results in a normal infant, provides the antigenic stimulus. (We now have direct evidence from the studies of Cohen, et al., 1959a with fluorescein labelled antihuman globulin serum that in every normal pregnancy fetal red cells enter the maternal circulation.) One pregnancy with a group compatible Rh positive fetus is enough to start the immunization process. And once antibodies are produced and hemolytic disease occurs, then the ABO blood groups whether compatible or incompatible do not play any role.

ABO incompatible matings with homozygous (AA or BB) fathers are of course excluded; we cannot recognize them in our serologic testing. Another mating which would be excluded is AB by O, because although not homozygous for A or B, this mating cannot result in a group O fetus which would be compatible with the mother.

Of the 35 per cent incompatible matings, 6 per cent are matings with homozygous husbands. Of the remaining 29 per cent, 50 per cent of them will be heterozygous fathers, and the first pregnancy could provide a fetus which is either AB compatible or incompatible.

The sources of Rh hemolytic disease are 65 per cent from compatible matings and 14 per cent from the incompatible matings. This gives us 79 per cent of all sources of hemolytic disease with ABO compatible and ABO incompatible matings. If you bring this to 100 per cent you get 18.2, a value which does not differ much from the 17.7 observed in more than 5,000 cases of Rh hemolytic disease reported in 11 independent studies. And the interesting thing is that, if we study hemolytic disease due to anti-c (hr'), we obtain the value of 18.2 ABO incompatible matings.

I would like to indicate that the most striking differences in Rh hemolytic disease are in incompatible matings AB by O and compatible matings O by AB, i.e., O and 59 matings, respectively.

If one studies whole families, one finds an excess of group compatible pregnancies in the first or the last healthy child which starts the immunization process. Once you have immunization started, then the ABO compatible or ABO incompatible makes no difference. The expected 50 per cent is obtained in the affected infants, since all husbands are heterozygous.

I would like to make some remarks about the possibility of tolerance as an explanation of selection. Following the work of Burnett and the work of Billingham on tolerance to grafts—the view has been suggested that possibly hemolytic disease is limited to those Rh negative women whose mothers are also Rh negative, that is, the former have not been exposed in utero to the Rh antigen.

This was put to the test in several studies, including the study by Owen, et al, (1954), and an Australian study by Walsh and Kooptzoff (1954), but it was found that in determining the Rh status of the maternal grandmother of the affected child, there was no difference from the expected incidence of Rh positive and Rh negative except in one small series of Owen, et al, in which there seemed to be a very nice correlation. When there were antibodies with hemolytic disease, the maternal grandmother was more frequently Rh negative. When there were no antibodies, the maternal grandmother was more frequently Rh positive.

Now, there are only 51 cases in these two groups, 34 without antibodies and 17 with antibodies. I had occasion to see the records of these cases with Dr. Sturgeon. We found that in the series with antibodies there was a very high incidence of ABO compatible pregnancies which would permit the fetal cells to get into the maternal circulation and immunize. Where there was no hemolytic disease there was an excess of ABO incompatible matings.

So here we had an observation which was statistically significant, indicating that the Rh status of the maternal grandmother was important, but which we consider is probably accidental and it is the protective action of the ABO incompatibility which is the more likely explanation.

I'd like to mention one or two other points briefly. That is, that in Rh hemolytic disease there is a suggestion that in certain Rh genetic combinations, i.e., those involving Rh_2 infants there was more severe hemolytic disease and also higher incidence of stillbirths. But this should be investigated more thoroughly. It has been suggested that Rh_2 may be more antigenic than Rh_1.

Of course, another point which may be pertinent to this discussion is the occurrence of hemolytic disease due to ABO incompatibility. This condition is very frequent in its milder forms, but more severe forms are rare. It almost always occurs in group O mothers.

One other point with regard to tolerance. There was a recent study in Australia which would indicate that the group O fetus exposed to a group A mother is less capable of making antibodies than a group O born to a group O mother. This effect was observed naturally or on challenging the group O individual with material containing A. I refer to this because the possibility of tolerance in any question involving fertility may perhaps come up in the future.

Dr. F. H. Allen: I thought it was of more than passing interest to mention something of great current interest in respect to different frequencies of blood groups in different populations. This is the very marked change in frequency of the blood factor Diego as one goes north. The gene has a frequency of approximately 20 per cent in parts of northern South America, and the frequency decreases steadily and becomes essentially zero when one gets to the Indians of Alaska and the Yukon (Corcoran, et al, 1959).

Similarly, the frequency of the Diego gene is very low among

Eskimos who, although they are not closely related to the Arctic Indians culturally and in other ways, are related in the fact that they presumably both came from eastern Asia and they both live in cold climates. One can't help wondering if the cold climate has anything to do with the low frequency of Diego in Alaska, but this is obviously pure speculation.

I wanted to make another comment about the Rh-negative women in Jackson, Michigan, Dr. Reed. Some quick and rather rough calculations would lead me to expect that in a population of this size there would have been, perhaps, two or three erythroblastotic still-births and neonatal deaths due to Rh incompatibility—a number so small that it could not possibly have resulted in the probability figure of .05 or less that you gave for a relation of Rh incompatibility to decreased fertility. Therefore, I would assume there must be some other relation between Rh incompatibility and decreased fertility if this really is a true bill.

There is the tendency not to report curious correlations that one cannot understand. I would like to make just one observation in this regard, which Dr. Giblett and others also have made. And that is with respect to the frequency of anti-K and anti-c. There are unpublished data, as far as I know. When sensitization is the result of transfusion, there is a relatively high incidence of anti-K and relatively low incidence of anti-c. Where it is the result of pregnancy, there is a low anti-K and relatively high anti-c frequency. There is no question whatever of the significance of this huge difference, but any possible explanation of this escapes us, so nobody has published it.

Another important factor that has to be taken into account in statistical analysis is the tendency to bias in the sampling. I would like to mention very briefly that some years ago we attempted to confirm Dr. Levine's early findings that there was an increase of early abortions in ABO incompatible matings. We only did the bloodtyping tests: the materials were sent to us by a clinic in Boston.

We got a fair amount of data and were about ready to conclude that ABO incompatibility did indeed result in a high incidence of early abortions. Then, in checking up one final time as to the composition of the material sent us, it turned out that when they knew the man and woman had compatible blood groups, they didn't bother to send the samples.

One final thing that I would like to mention has to do with the blood groups of mothers and their newborn babies. We have been testing consecutive cases at the Boston Lying-In Hospital for the past four months and have accumulated so far 502 mother-child combinations which, of course, is far too small a number from which to draw independent conclusions.

However, there has been a relative excess of type O women and a relative excess of type A children, which would appear, so far as it goes, to confirm what Dr. Reed said about a possible increased fertility in these ABO incompatible matings.

When we analyzed for sex of the child, we found in the group where the mother was type O, 79 type O male babies and only 61 type O female babies, whereas type A infants consisted of 36 males and 36 females.

Again these figures are far too small to allow independent conclusions. However, some years ago Dr. Sanghvi in India found a similar disproportion of type O males born to type O mothers, and found that this excess of type O males entirely accounted for the excess of males in the newborn population. He came over to this country and did a similar study at the Presbyterian Maternity Unit in New York and found exactly the same thing.

No one has any idea why this should be so. Obviously, it might have an effect on the blood groups of the population. I don't know how it is in the rest of the country, but in Boston an excess of type O males would certainly lead to an excess of type O children in the next generation, since in Boston we don't have enough males to go around.

DR. BLUMBERG: We're sorry to hear that, Dr. Allen.

DR. REED: Dr. Levine's comments on the interaction of Rh and ABO are certainly pertinent in understanding the overall selection picture. I did point out in my recent note on this analysis of the ABO blood groups and fertility in Jackson, Michigan, that this interaction between ABO and Rh did not account for the difference between our results in Jackson, Michigan, and the first big Japanese study on ABO blood groups and fertility, because if we pick out from the Jackson, Michigan, study only those couples which are Rh compatible, ignoring the Rh incompatible, and then look at the ABO blood groups in relation to fertility, the ABO incompatible matings are still more fertile than the ABO compatible as they were without regard to the Rh blood groups. In fact, the difference is slightly more striking when we throw out the Rh incompatible couples.

He mentioned compensation with regard to the Rh blood groups, that is Rh negative women perhaps having more children than positive. As you saw in the data that I had, this does not occur. Rh-negative women appear if anything to be less fertile. Remember that these data are on populations selected without regard to fertility, whereas the data of Glass were those in which the mother at least had to be pregnant. I think the question of compensation is at least open.

With regard to Dr. Allen's statement on negative findings not being reported, for the case of fertility studies I think that objection is not important as I indicated earlier. For the disease indications it may be, but I have the definite impression that most studies that have been made, looking for a possible association between disease and blood groups, have tended to be published whether they are positive or negative.

As you well know, there are a number of clear negative findings now established: Cancer of the colon and rectum, cancer of the lung— I think cancer of the breast—and toxemia of pregnancy, have all been shown not to be associated with the ABO blood groups. And my small knowledge of studies going on has suggested that people are anxious to put negative findings in the literature now, too. They realize the problem.

DR. GIBLETT: The point has been raised, and very aptly I think, that it is necessary to know the genotypes as well as the phenotypes when doing this type of blood group study. However, from a practical standpoint, I think this is a very difficult problem when you consider not only how little we know about the nature of the antigens and their respective genes, but also the limited availability and the poor reproducibility of results with some of the antibodies. Also, serious errors in interpretation of serologic tests can occur when we assume certain alleles exist when they, in fact, do not.

I think a good example of that was the testing of Negro red cells with anti-Fy^a. There wasn't a sufficient amount of anti-Fy^b to test these individuals. So it was assumed that because their cells failed to react with anti-Fy^a, the large proportion of the Negroes tested were $Fy(a-b+)$; whereas they are actually $Fy(a-b-)$. If you consider every one of the blood group systems, you encounter a number of objections on a purely theoretical basis that make it very difficult to determine the genotype in each case.

DR. MOTULSKY: I'd like to ask Dr. Neel one question. This refers to possible protective advantages of hemoglobin C against malaria. We know that sickle cell anemia is a very lethal disease in Africa—more so than in this country. The mortality of patients homozygous for hemoglobin C is considerably less. To balance the hemoglobin C system as a balanced polymorphism, therefore, the protective advantage of the hemoglobin C trait would not have to be as great as that required to balance the sickle cell system. The study you quoted was based on parasite density in relation to possible hemoglobin C protection against malaria. If there is only a small advantage, a parasite density study might not be sensitive enough to detect it. We really would have to look for much more detailed mortality figures of the kind you have discussed, which are so difficult to get.

DR. NEEL: I agree.

DR. SUTTON: I would like to extend Dr. Giblett's comments a little by saying that we rarely *know* what the phenotype is, either. One can only apply a limited number of criteria, and by these criteria a given variable may be assigned to one of several categories.

In the case of the hemoglobins we know this is a very artificial differentiation. Hemoglobin D has been recognized to consist at least of three different molecules depending on the source of the sample (Benzer, et al, 1958). There is no reason to think that the biologically important property is the one which we happen to measure. Furthermore, studies done in different populations may yield quite discordant results simply because trait A in one population may not be the same as trait A in another.

DR. GARTLER: Dr. Neel, since you brought the mutation story up again with regard to sickle cell anemia, I wonder how you would account for the fact that there appear to be no S's or C's in other populations.

DR. NEEL: If the sickle cell trait is actually selected against in temperate climates, do you think our present day information excludes the possibility of a 1 in 10,000 frequency of Caucasians with the sickle-cell trait?

DR. GARTLER: My mistake, I thought you were arguing that the polymorphism in Africa is balanced mainly by mutation.

DR. BLUMBERG: In connection with the question of the occurrence of inherited traits in some human populations and not in others, it is of interest to determine the presence of such traits in lower animals. For example, in a study of approximately 200 lower primates (170 *Macaca mulatta* monkeys, 4 chimpanzees and 34 baboons) it was found that none had haptoglobins corresponding to the human 2-2 or 2-1 phenotypes, and all had a single protein with approximately the same mobility as a human type 1-1 haptoglobin (Blumberg 1960). Of course, this does not rule out the presence of the product of the haptoglobin 2 gene in the *Macaca mulatta*, but if present in this species it must occur in fairly low frequency; presumably if mutation to this gene did occur, the selection pressures to maintain the gene in the *Macaca mulatta* population were not as great as in humans.[1]

---

[1] Patterns similar to haptoglobin type 2-1 modified have been reported in *Macaca irus* (Beckman and Cedermark, 1960).

DR. WITKOP: I would like to add one idea about blood group data on small samples. Where you had a small number of samples, 30 to 50, how were these collected? Was it strictly a random sort of thing or did you go into homes and get complete families? I would suppose that different frequencies might be obtained in small populations, if a sample of the population was selected from not closely related individuals rather than selecting families or school houses where numerous siblings might be found.

There are populations which are in the throes of disappearing, in which we are trying to obtain our samples from marriage partners not more closely related than first cousins rather than by families where numerous siblings might be included in the sample. Would someone comment on the best method of sampling for such small populations?

DR. BEARN: There have been a number of individuals who appear to be homozygous for the sickle cell gene and in whom the hemoglobin level is about 11 grams. I wonder if you would care to discuss this Dr. Neel?

DR. NEEL: This phenomenon was encountered, independently, by Edington in the Gold Coast and by ourselves in Liberia. There are known individuals who upon electrophoresis appear to have all hemoglobin S but whose hemoglobin levels are about 11 grams per cent and who clinically are well. It has now been shown that a substantial fraction of these individuals owe their electrophoretic pattern to the combination of one hemoglobin S gene and a gene responsible for an elevated proportion of fetal hemoglobin. They are genetically not the classic sickle cell anemia but a different entity.

DR. LILIENFELD: Concerning the question on estimating gene frequencies from family data, there are a series of papers by Finney, Fisher and Cotterman in which they have developed methods for gene frequency estimations from related individuals.

It is interesting that even though these methods were published 15 or 20 years ago, I have rarely seen them actually used in practice, even though most investigators take these kinds of samples of the population.

7

HAPTOGLOBINS AND TRANSFERRINS

ELOISE GIBLETT

THE TWO SERUM PROTEINS, haptoglobin and transferrin, have in common the fact that they both have molecular variability under genetic control, and also they are concerned either directly or indirectly in iron metabolism. If these proteins have any functions other than the few I am going to discuss, it would be very helpful to know what they are, since at present we do not have any clues concerning any role they might play in the process of selection.

Polonovski and Jayle (1938) published the first of a series of articles describing a glycoprotein constituent of the serum alpha-2 globulin fraction which they called haptoglobin because it had the property of binding hemoglobin.

The formation of a stable hapto-hemoglobin complex may be demonstrated by a method which was first described by Laurell and Nyman (1947): one simply adds increments of hemoglobin to aliquots of a given serum specimen in a series of tubes, and then subjects those specimens to electrophoresis at pH7. At that pH, the free hemoglobin does not move forward, but the hapto-hemoglobin complex migrates a little more slowly than the uncomplexed haptoglobin would if there were no hemoglobin present.

As shown in figure 1, when one adds a small amount of hemoglobin, a rather faint but broad band (representing the complexed proteins) appears. The breadth of this band diminishes as one increases the concentration of hemoglobin. This is presumably due to the fact that at first, there is unequal saturation of the haptoglobin molecules by the hemoglobin, resulting in unequal mobility. As the haptoglobin becomes more saturated, the band then becomes narrower and more concentrated.

When the hemoglobin-binding capacity of the serum is exceeded, free hemoglobin appears, and from that point on, the concentration of the hapto-hemoglobin complex is constant. All of the additional hemoglobin accumulates as free hemoglobin. The haptoglobin content is then expressed as the hemoglobin-binding capacity of that particular serum specimen.

Jayle and Polonovski had shown, prior to Dr. Laurell's studies, that the complex of haptoglobin and hemoglobin has a very high peroxidase ac-

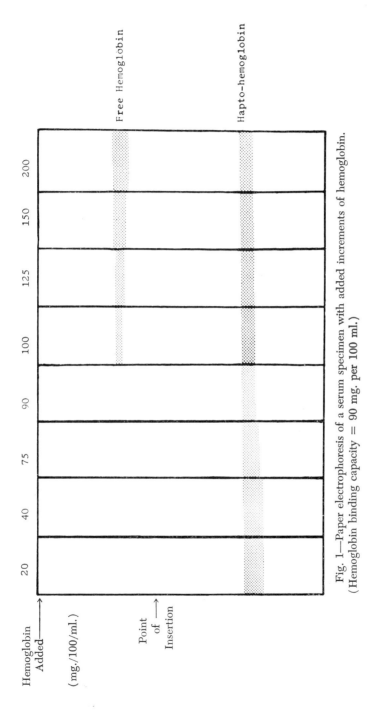

Free Hemoglobin

Hapto-hemoglobin

Hemoglobin Added ⟶

(mg./100/ml.)

Point of ⟶ Insertion

20   40   75   90   100   125   150   200

Fig. 1—Paper electrophoresis of a serum specimen with added increments of hemoglobin. (Hemoglobin binding capacity = 90 mg. per 100 ml.)

tivity as compared with hemoglobin alone. Measurement of that activity forms the basis for the other method of haptoglobin quantitation. The modification of Connell and Smithies (1959) is particularly well suited to the performance of large numbers of determinations.

The normal haptoglobin level, expressed in terms of the milligrams of hemoglobin bound per 100 ml. of serum, is about 50 to 150 milligrams per 100 ml. This level is usually increased in diseases associated with an inflammatory process or tissue necrosis. Thus haptoglobin quantitation is not a specific diagnostic aid, having about the same significance as the erythrocyte sedimentation level.

Laurell and Nyman in Sweden (1957) and Allison and ap Rees (1957) in England pointed out that in diseases associated with increased red cell destruction, the haptoglobin level is either decreased or entirely absent.

Laurell injected two normal subjects with hemoglobin in amounts calculated to equal but not to exceed their hemoglobin-binding capacity.

As shown by the two lower curves in figure 2, the level of hapto-hemoglobin in the serum decreased over a period of about seven or eight hours at a constant rate. This hemoglobin did not appear in the urine, and was presumably removed by the reticuloendothelial system.

The next to the top line on the figure represents the results we obtained after giving a large amount of hemoglobin to a patient with a very high initial level of haptoglobin. She, too, showed the same rate of removal of bound hemoglobin, probably indicating the amount of functional reticuloendothelial tissue.

When the haptoglobin binding capacity was exceeded in our patient, free hemoglobin, in addition to the hapto-hemoglobin complex, appeared in the serum. This is shown by the top line in the figure. Under these circumstances, only the free hemoglobin appears in the urine. Thus, the so-called renal threshold of hemoglobin is actually an indication of the amount of haptoglobin present in the serum to which the hemoglobin can bind. It is doubtful that there is tubular reabsorption of hemoglobin to any appreciable degree in the normal person.

After the individual has been depleted of his hapto-hemoglobin complex, as shown in figure 3, haptoglobin begins to reappear in the serum in the unbound state. Several days are required before the preinjection level is attained. This probably represents *de novo* synthesis of haptoglobin rather than a return of previously bound haptoglobin to the serum.

As suggested by Allison and ap Rees (1957) the major function of haptoglobin may be to conserve iron. In other words, as red cells are destroyed, the hemoglobin released may be bound to haptoglobin. The resulting haptoglobin-hemoglobin complex is taken up by the RE system so that iron is retained in the body. This series of events undoubtedly does

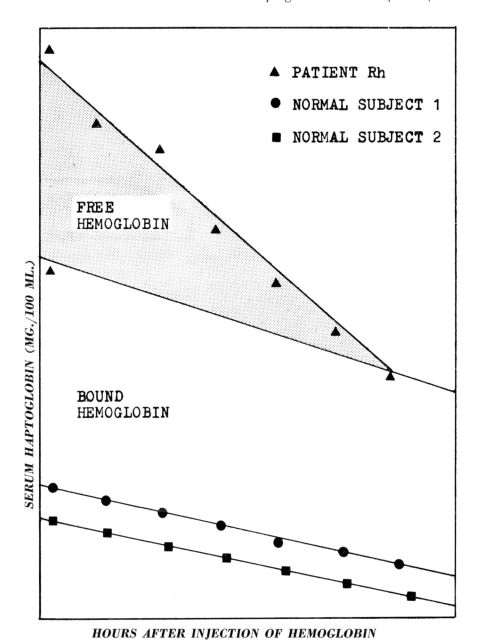

Fig. 2—Serum hemoglobin in patient Rh and two normal subjects after injection of hemoglobin, as reported by Laurell.

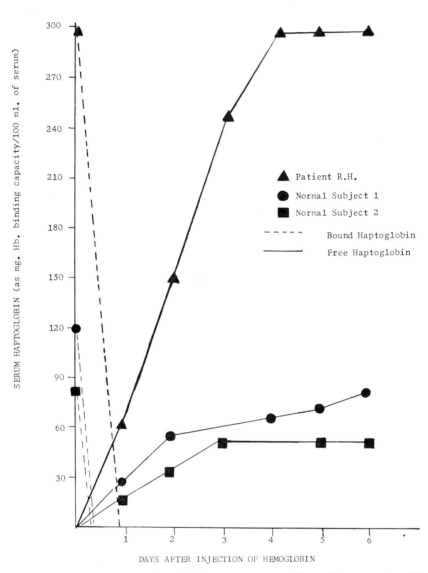

Fig. 3—Serum haptoglobin levels following injection of hemoglobin in patient Rh and two normal subjects, as reported by Laurell.

occur in patients who have a hemolytic process. Whether it is functional in normal physiology is more difficult to determine.

It is intriguing to believe, however, that haptoglobin might have some other properties. For example, it might be able to bind some other protein or proteins such as hormones, enzymes or toxins.

Interest in the physiologic role of haptoglobin has been greatly increased by the researches of Dr. Oliver Smithies in Toronto. Smithies (1955) found that if serum is subjected to electrophoresis in starch gel at pH 8.5, many more protein bands are visible than one sees in the classic paper or starch grain type of electrophoresis.

This is presumably due to the fact that there is increased frictional resistance in the starch gel which, as it were, holds back the large-sized molecules. Thus, proteins with different molecular sizes but the same electrical charge migrate in the same position on paper, but become differentiated in starch gel.

When Smithies had subjected a number of sera to starch gel electrophoresis, he found that in the area between the so-called slow alpha-2 globulin and the beta-1 globulin, haptoglobin proteins with three distinctly different patterns could be identified.

As shown in figure 4, the first pattern was characterized by a single heavy band migrating not quite so fast as the beta-1 globulin band. The second was characterized by a number of bands, each of which appeared to increase in intensity with its mobility, with the exception of the fastest-moving band, which was always quite faint.

The third pattern had a faintly straining band coinciding with that in the first pattern, as well as additional bands which had somewhat the same appearance as those in the second pattern except that they consistently migrated a little bit faster.

Smithies (1956) was able to show that these three basic patterns were inherited in a manner consistent with the existence of two allelic autosomal genes of equal dominance, called Hp^1 and Hp^2. A number of other investigators, notably Galatius-Jensen (1957) and Harris, et al. (1958a), have substantiated this mode of inheritance.

These findings were disturbing, because they apparently indicated that a single gene (that is, Hp^2) was capable of producing several different proteins. Furthermore, the product of the combination of the two genes, Hp^1 and Hp^2, was not the same as a mixture of their individual products, Hp 1-1 and Hp 2-2.

Drs. Bearn and Franklin (1958, 1959) complexed the various haptoglobins with hemoglobin C so that they could be separated from the other nonhaptoglobin proteins. These purified complexes were tested by starch

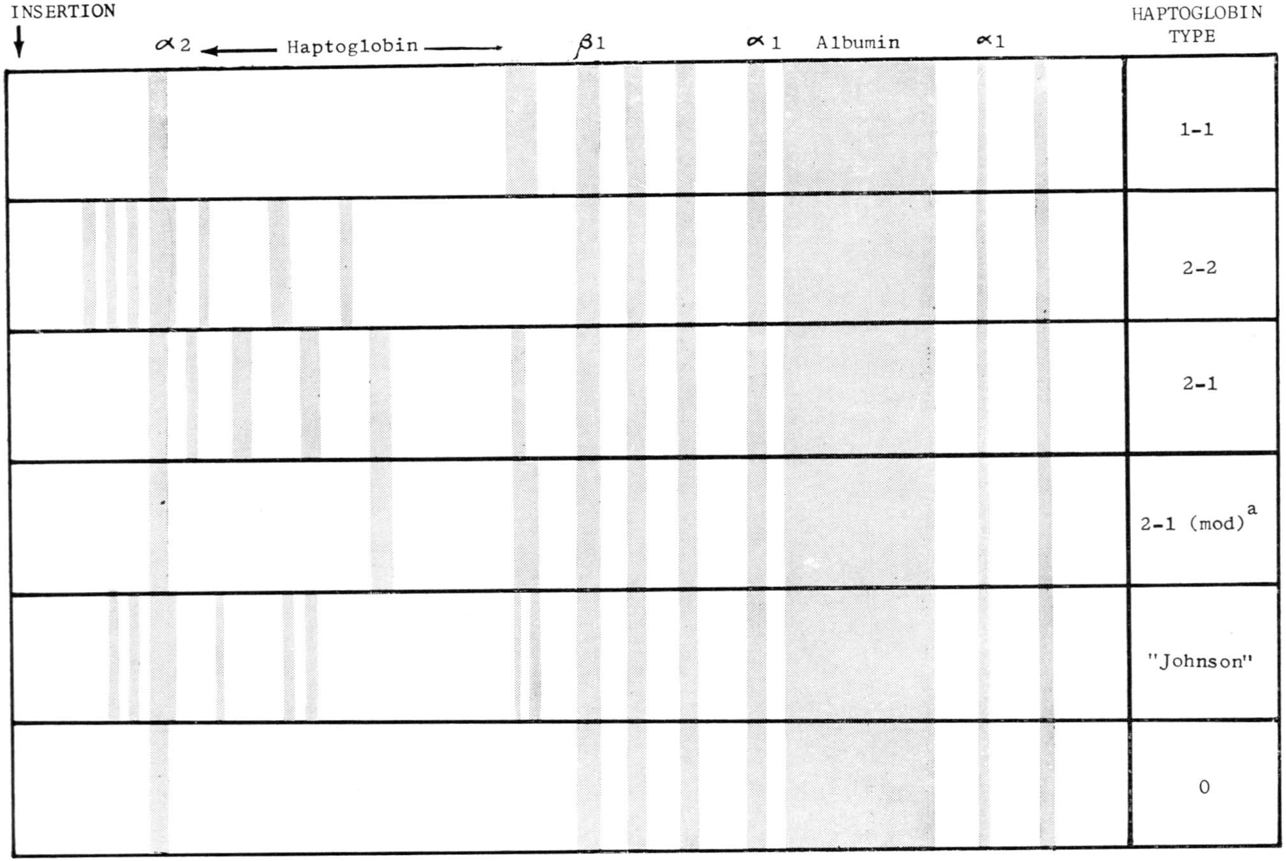

Fig. 4—Haptoglobin patterns obtained by starch gel electrophoresis of human serum containing added hemoglobin.

block electrophoresis. As shown in figure 5, Hp 1-1 had the fastest mobility, followed by 2-1 and 2-2.

When Bearn and Franklin subjected these protein complexes to ultra-centrifugation, they showed that the haptoglobin 1-1 complex gave a symmetrical pattern with a single peak, the sedimentation coefficient being around 6S. Hp 2-1 had a three-peaked appearance, the middle peak being the largest in quantity. Hp 2-2 had a very asymmetric pattern, indicating a number of components. The sedimentation coefficient was about 9 or 10. This suggested again that the Hp^2 gene was capable of producing more than one protein.

Then, when they mixed the purified haptoglobins 1-1 and 2-2 they obtained a pattern that was not the same as that of the heterozygous 2-1.

This information, coupled with other similar studies done by Dr. Connell (unpub.) in Toronto and Dr. Guinand (1956) in France, led Smithies (1959) to the following hypothesis:

(A) The haptoglobin 1-1 homozygote produces what one can call haptoglobin-1 protein. This basic protein material has a molecular weight of about 100,000; it migrates as a single band.

(B) The haptoglobin 2-2 individual produces what can be called the haptoglobin-2 protein. This basic protein material has the ability to polymerize. Therefore in the Hp 2-2 homozygote, it forms a series of stable polymers which have an average molecular weight of about 400,000.

(C) The heterozygote produces both of the basic proteins (haptoglobin-2 and haptoglobin-1). These form a series of stable polymers with an average molecular weight of about 200,000. They migrate more rapidly than the Hp 2-2 polymers but less rapidly than the protein produced by Hp 1-1 individuals. There is some residual haptoglobin-1 protein in the 2-1 pattern, showing that not all of the haptoglobin-1 protein has been polymerized with the haptoglobin-2 protein.

This hypothesis fits very well, if one considers only the three basis haptoglobin phenotypes. Unfortunately, the situation is not quite that simple.

As shown in figure 4, there is a pattern called Hp 2-1 (mod) which is very rare in Caucasians but occurs in about 10 per cent of American Negroes (Giblett 1959) and a variable percentage of native African Negroes (Robson, pers. comm.). It is characterized by a much heavier band in the 1-1 position, as well as the fastest moving of the 2-1 bands.

With Dr. Arthur Steinberg (Giblett and Steinberg, 1960) we have performed a number of studies on Negro families and have obtained good evidence that the haptoglobin 2-1 (mod) pattern actually represents the genotype Hp^{2m}/Hp^1. The gene Hp^{2m} is thus allelic to Hp^2 and Hp^1. The current studies of Smithies (not yet published) tend to indicate small but definite differences between the proteins produced by the Hp^2 gene and the Hp^{2m} gene.

There are other complications. One is an aberrant, very rare phenotype which Dr. Galatius-Jensen (1958) has found in two unrelated Danish families. Dr. Smithies says this looks as if one took two parts of Hp 2-2 and one part of 2-1 and mixed them together. The mechanism of its inheritance is unknown at present.

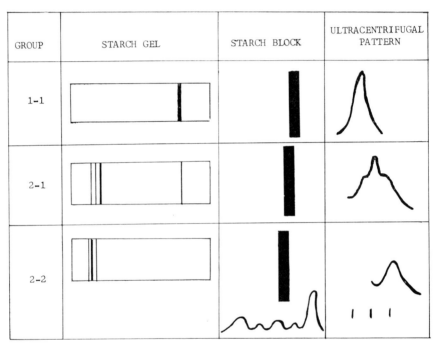

Fig. 5—Comparison of the starch gel, starch block, and ultracentrifugal patterns of the haptoglobin-hemoglobin complexes from the three main genetic groups. (*Taken from Bearn and Franklin, 1958.*)

There is another modification called the "Johnson" type, which has been found in a Negro family in Seattle (Giblett, unpub. obs.). Both the mother and her daughter have this very strange pattern shown in figure 4. The location of the haptoglobin bands is not the same as it is in any of the other patterns.

An even more puzzling complication is the apparent absence of haptoglobin (or ahaptoglobinemia). When an individual is born, he rarely has any haptoglobin present in his serum, but he begins to form it almost immediately. In Caucasians who do not have hemolytic disease, it is rare to see an individual who lacks, or apparently lacks, haptoglobin. However, in all the African Negro populations that have so far been studied, (including American Negroes) there have been a certain percentage of ahaptoglobinemic individuals. I use that word with great reservation, but at least in repeated specimens obtained from some of these individuals, it has been impossible to demonstrate the presence of any haptoglobin. Furthermore, we (Giblett 1959) were unable to show that such subjects have unusual hemoglobins or glucose-6-phosphate dehydrogenase deficiency or increased reticulocyte counts.

Drs. Allison and Blumberg and Mrs. ap Rees (1958) found this phenomenon in a very large percentage of Nigerian natives. In the studies reported by Sutton, et al, (1959) and Harris, et al, (1959b) and from our laboratory on various populations of the African continent, ahaptoglobinemia has always been present in a variable degree.

In 92 Negro families (Giblett and Steinberg, 1960) we found that the preponderance of ahaptoglobinemic children were born to matings in which at least one parent had the phenotype Hp 2-1 (mod). However, the exact mechanism of ahaptoglobinemia inheritance remains to be delineated.

A number of people have performed studies on the distribution of the haptoglobins in various populations of the world. These have been ably summarized in a recent paper by Dr. Sutton and colleagues (in press).

Figure 6 shows the approximate distribution of Hp genes in Seattle blood donors of various racial groups representing over 600 Negroes, 200 Orientals (mostly Japanese) and 200 Caucasians. In Orientals the Hp^2 gene is predominant whereas the most prevalent gene in Negroes in Hp^1. In the Caucasian group there is a more intermediate distribution, which is seen throughout the areas of Europe that have been tested as well as in the United States. These and other studies indicate that Asiatics (including Japanese, Chinese and Indians) have the highest frequency of the Hp^2 gene.

The observations of Blumberg, et al, (1959) and our own (Giblett, unpub. obs. [b]) on the Eskimos show that they too have quite a high Hp^2 gene frequency.

The American Indians need to be studied further. There are some indications that as one goes from north to south, there is a marked increase in the Hp^1 gene frequency, which approaches that seen in certain areas of Africa (Sutton, et al; 1959; Sutton, et al; 1960; Blumberg, et al; 1959). However, much more data need to be obtained before a really clear picture about haptoglobin gene distribution finally emerges.

The second protein, transferrin, has a very important physiologic func-

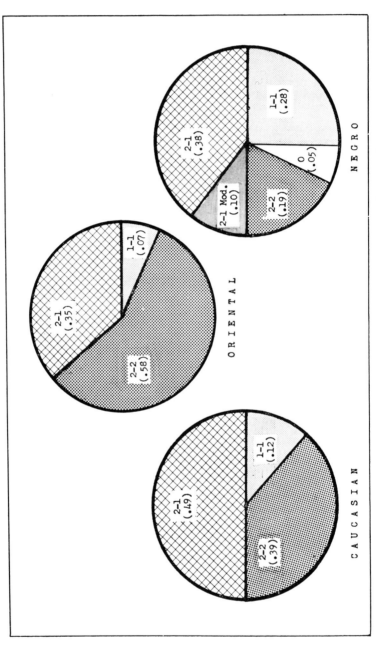

Fig. 6—Seattle blood donors: incidence of haptoglobin types in three racial groups.

tion. It is the iron-binding protein which transports iron to the iron stores and to the marrow. The normal individual has about 250 milligrams of transferrin per 100 ml. of plasma. Since the usual plasma iron concentration is around 100 micrograms per 100 ml., the transferrin present is normally only about one-third saturated. The concentration of this protein is increased fairly regularly in iron deficiency anemia, in late pregnancy, and in some cases of acute hepatitis. It is decreased in a number of chronic disease states, particularly those affecting protein metabolism.

There is an indication that transferrin may have an additional function. Martin and Jandl (1959) reported at the Atlantic City meetings last year, that transferrin has the ability to decrease the multiplication of viruses and bacteria. In other words, it may be a virostatic and bacteriostatic agent.

When Drs. Poulik and Smithies (1958) performed two-dimensional electrophoresis on serum specimens, they showed that there were usually four fractions of β globulin. The largest component was the third in mobility, so it was called β globulin C. In addition, a small number of serum specimens obtained from American Negroes and Australian aborigines contained another β globulin, subsequently called β globulin D (Smithies and Hiller 1959). Studies with radioiron showed that both of these fractions (C and D) were capable of binding iron, and thus were transferrins. Six more transferrins have been found in human subjects, and the mode of inheritance of four of these has been clearly established (Harris, et al., 1958b; Smithies and Hiller (1959); Giblett, et al, 1959). Figure 7 diagrammatically represents their appearance on starch gel. Transferrin C, the most common of the transferrins, is represented in its homozygous state and also as it appears in individuals who are heterozygous for one of the other seven Tf genes. At present it appears that there are at least eight allelic autosomal transferrin (Tf) genes occupying a single locus on homologous chromosomes. Most people are homozygous for the gene Tf^c. The other transferrins are named in accordance with their mobility rates. Thus, those transferrins which migrate more rapidly than transferrin C are Called B_2, B_1 and B_0. Those that migrate less rapidly are called D_0, D_1, D_2, and D_3.

Dr. Turnbull and I (1960) were interested in finding out whether individuals who are homozygous or heterozygous for unusual transferrins have an altered ability to bind and transport iron. The plasma of recipients who had transferrin C was tagged with Fe^{55}, and the plasma of donors who had aberrant transferrins, with Fe^{59}. The two tagged plasmas were then injected, and their radioactive disappearance curves were measured. The rate of disappearance was nearly identical in four different individuals, using transferrin CD_3 and B_1 (apparently from a homo-

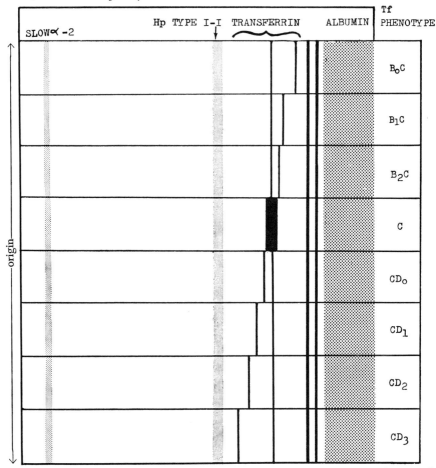

Fig. 7—Transferrin phenotype patterns obtained by starch gel electrophoresis of human serum.

zygote). Rates of iron utilization were also much the same. From these experiments, we were unable to detect any differences in the transport and utilization of iron bound to those transferrins which were tested.

The distribution of the Tf genes in various populations has been reported by only a few investigators (Sutton, et al, 1960; Giblett, et al, 1959; Barnicot, et al, 1959; Kirk and Vos, pers. comm.; Robson, pers. comm.; Giblett and Zoutendyk, unpub.). Table 1 summarizes the results so far obtained. No population has so far been found which has a high incidence of the fast-moving transferrins. Two populations studied have a fairly high frequency of slow-moving transferrins. This is particularly startling in western Australian aborigines. According to Kirk and Vos (pers. comm.), 37 per cent of 150 natives tested had patterns indicating the transferrin phenotype CD_1; and nearly 4 per cent were apparent D_1 homozygotes. In Africa the incidence of the transferrin D_1 gene appears to be somewhat higher in the northern part than in the south, with the exception of the Kalahari desert. The Bushmen there have an increased transferrin D_1 incidence, as recently shown by Barnicot, et al; (1959).

The few studies performed on American Indians, Asiatics and Western Europeans indicate that these populations probably have a low frequency of abberant transferrins. However, the paucity of data does not allow any absolute statements at this time.

TABLE 1—*Distribution of Serum Transferrins*

NATIVE ORIGIN	TRANSFERRIN PHENOTYPE				
	B	BC	CC	CD	D
Asia (307)	.003	.003	.991	.003	
No. and So. America (1027)		.005	.990	.005	
Europe (945)		.011	.989		
So. Africa (798)			.948	.051	.001
No. Africa (1760)		.001	.926	.073	
Australia (154)			.591	.370	.039

From this brief summary, it is obvious that a large number of questions pertaining to the polymorphic proteins, haptoglobin and transferrin, remain to be answered. First of all, a much larger segment of the world's population needs to be sampled in order to obtain a better idea about gene frequencies. Second, we need to know something about the actual differences in molecular structure. Smithies is currently attempting to clarify this problem with the haptoglobins; similar work should be done on the transferrins.

Third, we should find out what, if any, relationship exists between the incidence of these genes and various diseases throughout the world. The few studies so far attempted have been on a very small scale.

Fourth, more investigations on gene linkage are in order. We know that the Hp and Tf genes probably are not closely linked to the genes determining blood group specificity, but little information presently exists concerning relative linkage with these and other human genes.

Finally, as an aid to determining the possible role of the Hp and Tf genes in selection, we need to have further information on their physiologic functions. Whereas these unknown functions (if any) may not be directly related to the mechanisms of balanced polymorphism, they might provide some valuable clues for detecting the selection processes.

DISCUSSION

DR. BLUMBERG: Thank you, Dr. Giblett, for your clear and concise discussion of a difficult topic.

We have completed a study of sera collected from the nomadic Fulani of northern Nigeria. Of 84 sera, 40 were ahaptoglobinemic, 24 were type 1-1, 13 were type 2-1 and only 4 were type 2-2. Three were rare types (Blumberg and Gentile, 1961). Ahaptoglobinemia appears to be fairly common in West Africa. It is now clear that some individuals may be ahaptoglobinemic at one point in time, but have detectable haptoglobin at another (Galatius-Jensen 1958; Blumberg and Gentile, 1961). We studied sera of two individuals from Micronesia who, in 1957 were type 2-2, but in 1959 had no detectable haptoglobin. In collaboration with Dr. N. R. Shulman of the National Institutes of Health, we have studied a patient who suffered from paroxysmal cold hemoglobinuria apparently due to Donath-Landsteiner cold hemolysin. Immediately after the hemolytic attack, he had no detectable haptoglobin. Within less than a month there was detectable haptoglobin in the blood. Within three months the patient had a normal 2-2 haptoglobin pattern and bound approximately a normal amount of haptoglobin. Subsequent studies showed that his haptoglobin had again disappeared, and this was independent of any clinically detectable hemolysis.

The Fulani had 15 per cent transferrin types CD, an extremely high frequency.

DR. BEARN: Dr. Blumberg and Dr. Giblett have so admirably summarized the situation there is very little I can add.

When this technology was first introduced by Dr. Smithies, it was immediately recognized as an enormously powerful tool. There were, however, a number of features about the technique which were, initially, regarded as disquieting. For one thing, the ionic strength of the buffer appeared frighteningly low. It was, in the range where one might imagine that binding of small ions to proteins might occur and one couldn't but wonder whether some of the bands observed might not be due to interaction. I think the evidence that these fears were unjustified was in the genetical studies.

I do think, however, that we should always bear in mind that the gels reveal qualitative differences. The main value of starch gel electrophoresis is when used in conjunction with other more preparative techniques such as starch block electrophoresis and chromatography.

One of the ways in which one can decide whether a line in a gel is an artifact is to isolate the protein from the gel and re-run it to see if the electrophoretic mobility remains the same. One of the few dis-advantages of the starch gel is that, so far, it has not been possible regularly to get adequate recoveries of protein from the gel, except when the protein is present in fairly high concentration. Whenever it has been possible to re-run the proteins, however, they have migrated in the same position.

Now there are a few things I might say about the chemical consti-tution of the haptoglobins. Dr. Giblett has mentioned most of them. They will bind many variants of hemoglobin, both normal and ab-normal, and in addition animal hemoglobins.

It was Laurell, I think, who first showed that it was the globulin part of the hemoglobin molecule which binds haptoglobin. You can block the binding of haptoglobin if pure globulin is added first. The amount of hemoglobin bound to haptoglobin type 1 and haptoglobin type 2 appears to be the same.

We have looked for immunologic differences between the hapto-globins, but thus far have not been able to detect any. The quantitative precipitin curves are identical within the error of the method.

Clearly there are differences in the molecule (at least one) and per-haps better techniques will reveal true, immunologic differences. The results are reminiscent of the failure to find immunologic differences between the hemoglobins.

In many ways the haptoglobins behave like an acute-phase protein, for they go up, early in the course of acute infection. Nyman and Laurell (1959) have reported that the concentration of haptoglobin decreases markedly with the administration of estrogens.

Now if this is so, and there is no real reason to doubt it, one wonders whether some of the individuals in Africa with low levels of hapto-globin (ahaptoglobinemics), perhaps, be due to environmental (hor-monal) causes. I am not sure of the estrogen dose—perhaps they were pharmacologic rather than physiologic—and this would of course be important in judging its relevance.

Both Dr. Giblett and Dr. Blumberg have emphasized something with which I entirely agree—one has to examine several samples of serum from ahaptoglobinemic people before we can be sure that the ahapto-globinemia is truly genetic.

The observation that the heterozygote appears to have molecular species not present in either homozygote makes one wonder whether the proteins present in the heterozygote might confer some kind of advantage. This is the kind of mechanism that Haldane suggested might play a role in the phenomenon of heterozygous advantage. Per-haps the haptoglobins are an example of this.

As far as the transferrins are concerned, I wondered whether any work had been done on the inhibition of viral multiplication by different transferrins. I also wondered whether any comparative studies have been made with some of the substituted benzimidazoles which are powerful inhibitors of viral multiplication.

There was a report some years ago now, in which a patient was said to have no transferrins. I am not sure of the details (Riegel and Thomas 1956). If the haptoglobin locus was on chromosome 21 one might have observed a different phenotype in Mongols, but we and others have looked at the haptoglobin pattern of Mongols and have not noticed anything grossly abnormal.

DR. SUTTON: There is not too much more to say, obviously. In terms of the function of haptoglobin I think that it would be premature to conclude that hemoglobin binding is the whole story. The conservation of iron by haptoglobin may be very beneficial. However, from what we know about the rate of haptoglobin synthesis (Laurell and Nyman 1957) haptoglobin could hardly bear the sole responsibility for recovering iron or hemoglobin from defunct erythrocytes. In my discussions with Dr. Giblett, It is apparent that she has come to the same conclusion that Dr. Neel and I have. The amount of circulating haptoglobin is not enough to take care of just the normal daily turnover of red cells and the time required to synthesize that much haptoglobin is too long.

This suggests we must not look upon haptoglobin as the normal mechanism of recovering iron. This does not mean it cannot prove useful when hemolysis occurs intervascularly, and in certain types of blood diseases this may be the case.

So far as the selective factors involved in haptoglobins are concerned, there seem to be several possible ones. In addition to the possibility of iron recovery, there is also the question of the protection of the kidney from free hemoglobin. If one looks at gene distributions around the world, there is evidence there may be two different selective factors operating. Among Western Caucasians, the gene frequency simply does not vary much from .40. All the studies in the United States, England, Scandinavia, and Continental Europe arrive at very nearly the same value, suggesting that the system is balanced in these populations.

On the other hand, there is a marked cline from Southeast Asia up through North America and down to South America (Sutton, et al, 1960). The Values for the Hp^1 gene in Indian have been variously reported from .09 to .18, and there is a regular increase of .25 from Japan, .30 for Alaskan Eskimos, .42 for North Athabascans (Alaska),

.59 for Apaches (New Mexico) and Central American Indians, and .73 for Peruvian and Brazilian Indians. This cline is characterized by tremendous gaps in our knowledge, and perhaps as more information becomes available, it will prove to be not so interesting.

But I think one should consider the possibility that there is more than one selective factor operating. Areas of high Hp^1 frequency may reflect the fact that type 1-1 individuals have a greater hemoglobin binding capacity than do the other types, whereas the other selective factors may not be hemoglobin binding but some other trait that we do not recognize.

The only other comment I'd make at the moment is in regard to the transferrins. It is just a matter of emphasizing what Dr. Giblett said regarding the occurrence of transferrin polymorphism in other species. Two years ago, we did electrophoresis of sera from about ten monkeys which Dr. J. Buettner-Janusch supplied. Within that group we found four different transferrin phenotypes. It has been everyone's experience that this is the one protein system, recognizable as such, which seems to vary in almost all higher organisms.

DR. H. GORDON: Yesterday when Drs. Lilienfeld and John Gordon referred to themselves as "host men," I wondered what the opposite was and the only term I could think of was "pest men." It is as such that I felt that I might enter the discussion at this stage and draw attention to the role of environmental factors in Africa, South of the Sahara and to the presence there of a very high incidence of liver disease. I won't go at all into the types of liver disease or their etiology, but suffice it to say that all workers there agree that there is a great deal of liver disease in African populations and that this may or may not express itself clinically. I am concerned about the possible effect that this might have on Dr. Giblett's data on serum haptoglobin and transferrin patterns in African populations.

Much of the comparative interracial research in Southern Africa is bewitched, bothered and bewildered by this hepatic factor. For example, in our studies on blood lipids, considerable differences were found between the White and Negro races. We find much lower mean serum-cholesterol levels in the Bantu than in the Whites and while genetic influences probably play a part in determining these differences, the importance of environmental factors (particularly the dietary fat content) is more clearly established (Brock and Gordon 1959). Moreover, we cannot completely ignore the possibility that liver disease in the Bantu also contributes to these differences. Similarily, the plasma of the Bantu shows more rapid fibrinolytic activity than White controls (Merskey, et al, 1960) and this difference may also partly be due to hepatic dysfunction (Kwaan, et al, 1956). Although we went to great pains in these studies to ensure that only healthy subjects were included, short of liver biopsy it is not always possible to detect some cases of liver disease.

Porphyria is another case in point. You will doubtless have heard that porphyria is common in the Bantu (Barnes 1955). Until recently this had been regarded as an "inborn error of metabolism" like the porphyrias in America and Scandinavia; but now it has been demonstrated that many cases of Bantu porphyria are merely symptomatic of underlying liver disease (Mentz and Bersohn 1959; Dean 1960).

This brings me back to the question of the haptoglobin polymorphisms. Serum-globulin levels tend to be high in African populations and in some cases the elevation may be due to liver disease (Bersohn, et al, 1954). Fluctuating serum-globulin levels are characteristic of the fluctuating course of liver disease. The chronic infections which are so common in Africa may also contribute to elevated and fluctuating serum-globulin levels. In the same way, some of the variability in the haptoglobin pattern in Africans which Dr. Giblett has described may be due to environmental and hepatic factors.

In this connection, Dr. Bearn's comment on the effect of estrogen on haptoglobin levels is interesting. The South African Bantu has been shown by Bersohn and Oelofse to excrete higher levels of total estrogen (mainly estradiol) than White controls (Bersohn and Oelofse 1957). The reason for this, be it hepatic dysfunction, genetic trait, etc., is not known, but such increased estrogenic activity may also be important in relation to the differences in haptoglobin patterns in Africa.

I would therefore question the purely genetic interpretations put on serum samples which are sent across the Atlantic without some consideration of the health of the subjects. It might be advisable in such cases routinely to perform some sort of liver function test on these samples. I wish that I could suggest a suitable test to you, but I know of no simple one. A BSP retention test would be adequate, but of course this has to be done on the subject and not on a sample of his serum and is not practicable for field studies.

May I add a comment about liver siderosis which is so common in African populations (Higginson, et al, 1953)? Most authorities agree that this is distinct from the hereditable disorder, hemochromatosis, and that environmental factors predominate in its pathogenesis. Walker and Arvidsson (1953) have suggested that liver siderosis is merely the result of a diet habitually overloaded with iron. The Gillman brothers (1951), on the other hand, have postulated that malnutrition produces pancreatic and hepatic dysfunction, with disturbed synthesis of transferrin; the intestinal mucosal mechanism for blocking excessive iron absorption fails, iron-transport is disorganized and excessive deposits occur in the liver. I mention this as another possible example of environmental factors modifying a genetic marker trait, in this case, transferrin.

In conclusion, then, I would urge that close attention be paid to environmental factors which seriously may distort the pattern of genetic markers in certain populations.

DR. GIBLETT: All I can say is I think it's doubtful that 4 per cent of presumably healthy Negro blood donors in Seattle would have significant liver disease, but one would have no way of proving this.

DR. H. GORDON: The figure of 4 per cent wouldn't surprise me in the least.[1]

My concern about the possible role of malnutrition and of subclinical hepatic dysfunction in modifying the pattern of disease incidence and the biochemical picture in the South African Negroids, was sufficient to encourage me to come to the United States where I hope to carry out similar clinical and biochemical studies among the American Negroes who are comparatively free from these complications. I do not think that we can lightly dismiss the influence of these environmental variables. I will reiterate that the studies which were made in South Africa on the Bantu in relation to blood lipids and blood coagulation were on individuals carefully selected by all clinical criteria as being healthy men—mine workers, quarry laborers —men selected for their excellent physique and apparent health. Nevertheless we did encounter biochemical evidence of apparent liver dysfunction in these people.

DR. GIBLETT: There are two recent studies of haptoglobin levels in people with liver diseases (Nyman 1959; Owen, et al, 1959). In both instances the degree of liver dysfunction associated with ahaptoglobinemia was quite severe.

DR. LILIENFELD: Do you get ahaptoglobinemia in Negro infants of about 6 months of age?

DR. GIBLETT: I have no data on this, except to say that in general 6 month-old infants would probably have less haptoglobin. In Caucasians, there are, for some reason, more children with ahaptoglobinemia than adults. The percentage of such children is much lower in Caucasians than in Negroes.

DR. BLUMBERG: Despite the fact that the individuals you examined were ostensibly healthy, Dr. H. Gordon's point could still obtain.

[1] In fact, most reports from Southern Africa indicate a much higher incidence of liver disease (Higginson, et al, 1957; Berman 1951).

DR. GIBLETT: Yes.

DR. BOYER: Dr. Harris in London recently observed some very interesting findings of urinary levels of haptoglobin of various types in children with nephrosis. When children with a 2-1 phenotype are considered and the nephrosis is very severe, all of the 2-1 components appear in the urine. With improvement of the nephrosis there is gradual disappearance of first the slow, fairly large polymers in the 2-1, and finally, and almost with complete improvement, protein falling in the urine, only the one band remains.

This suggests another role of haptoglobins which is intimately tied up with the speculation which has been offered by Drs. Giblett, Bearn and Sutton, that is, another role for haptoglobins. One of these roles may be intimately related to the ability of these substances to pass cell barriers, particularly in states of inflammation. One would expect that the lightest compounds, the lightest polymers, would pass the most easily.

So far as I know, the presence of haptoglobins and transferrins in the ascitic fluid of infection or heart failure or hepatic disease has not been investigated. It may be of interest to do this.

Insofar as the fact that it might bind something else, we looked long and hard last fall for something else that it might bind. We knew that it did not bind at the heme moiety of the protein. Yet, we nevertheless thought that the presence of the heme moiety might be important, and with this long shot in mind we endeavored to see if it would bind other hematoproteins and it did not, such things as biological peroxidases.

Concerning another case with paroxysmal hemoglobinuria, even though the patient did not have a hemolytic crisis while on the ward, we were unable to demonstrate any haptoglobin, despite a careful search.

Concerning the bacteriostatic role of transferrins, I'd like to ask: Was any of this related to the iron content of the transferrins, or were they stripped of this iron before this was attempted? In the case of *Corynebacterium diphtheria* the metabolism of iron by this organism is well known from the earlier studies in Labrador.

I believe now Ashton has demonstrated some five alleles in cattle. The cattle provide a rather interesting point about the physical structure of transferrins, in that, if one looks at any particular animal serum, one finds even in the homozygote, homozygote by genetic test, that there are faint leading bands, usually four in number, and finally, that closest to the origin is the darkest band of all.

Now, we have observed this in a great variety of species, that is a number of bands, one dominant band or two dominant bands, and a succession of faint bands.

Our experience is similar to Dr. Sutton's. In one species of primate, cynomologous monkeys, all of the animals examined showed the same kind of transferrins, whereas chimpanzees show seven phenotypes. We suggest that the transferrins like the haptoglobins may represent polymers in the serum. If they do, it is a question of how many base blocks are getting polymerized. This is analogous, if you will, to the different chains of hemoglobin, where apparently different parts are made at different loci and then stuck together in the body. Endeavoring to get at this problem, we have been following Dr. Smithies' technique first applied to haptoglobins, namely, fractionation of radioactively labeled transferrins, in urea gels. We have some results.

We do seem to break down the bands, but how many bands we are getting we are not sure yet. A byproduct of this has come from the fact that when we leave our apparatus turned on for a long period of time, we observe an additional faint band in the CC phenotype. We have observed this faint band in CC's repeatedly. We have observed it in very fresh sera, the run of which in the electrophoretic apparatus began some 45 minutes after it left the patient's body and entered our syringe. The point I wish to make is that this possibility of polymerization of some basic unit may extend to man. It is sufficiently ubiquitous in the animal kingdom that we see no reason why man should be an exception.

DR. BLUMBERG: In collaboration with Dr. L. Warren of the National Institutes of Health, we are completing preliminary studies of some of the carbohydrate components of the transferrins. We have found that sialidase digestion results in splitting of human and lower primate transferrins into subunits which may bear a regular relation to each other. Some of the breakdown products are common to two or more of the phenotypes. The biochemical and genetic significance of this work is under study (Blumberg and Warren 1961).

DR. SUTTON: I would question how important the haptoglobins are in nephrosis. Guinand, et al, (1956) found a single patient who excreted haptoglobin out of a large series of nephrotics. I have looked and looked at nephrotic urine because this is an ideal place to isolate haptoglobin. As yet I have found none. It may be that the cases of Harris which Dr. Boyer reported were more severe than these others. If true, then it would seem unlikely haptoglobin and nephrosis are related.

DR. BLUMBERG: Dr. Bearn, are you satisfied that there is no antigenic effect of a haptoglobin protein of one type transfused into an individual of a different haptoglobin type? It is probable that this could not be a very striking effect since, because of the relatively high frequency of both of the genes in most populations, such transfusions must have taken place frequently. Could you discuss the possibility that there might be an effect which is not readily detectable.

Dr. Boyer is shaking his head.

DR. BOYER: Yes, there is some very recent work on this just published last week.

DR. BLUMBERG: Please tell us about it.

DR. BOYER: Dr. Clausen (1960) used an immunochemical technique. He found that rabbit antihaptoglobin reacted apaprently equally well with human and mouse haptoglobin.

Hirschfeld (1960) reported no evidence for serologic differences within the haptoglobins. He investigated against about 40 different immune rabbit sera and one immune horse serum. There may be fine differences which are not demonstrated.

DR. BLUMBERG: Would some of the others like to enter into this general discussion? This question is pertinent to all the human intraspecies protein differences; that is whether transfusion of an individual with human blood which contains proteins which are different from his own can have any clinical consequence.[1]

DR. F. H. ALLEN: I have no information. I think there is a lot of evidence that haptoglobin isn't a critical factor in erythroblastosis fetalis because these babies exhaust the haptoglobin very fast and they never, never develop iron deficiency.

DR. BOYD: Why do you think it would be a hazard? The amount of this protein is small. Suppose the individual does produce an antibody for it. What difference will that make in subsequent transfusions?

DR. BLUMBERG: I'd rather ask you that question.

DR. BOYD: I would like to suggest it might not make any difference.

DR. BLUMBERG: Your reason is that the amount of antibody produced would be small.

DR. BOYD: Yes.

DR. BLUMBERG: Could you conceive that there might be some clinical

---

[1] Note added April 1961. We have recently found an antibody-like material in the serum of some multiply transfused patients which reacts to form a precipitin in agar gel with a globulin present in the serum of some individuals but not in others (Allison and Blumberg 1961). Twin and family studies are consistent with the hypothesis that the presence or absence of the "antigen" is under genetic control (Blumberg and Bernanke 1961). It does not appear to be related to the haptoglobin, group specific substances or the common blood groups. An antibody-like material has been found in the serum of five multiply transfused individuals, of approximately 100 studied. Among these are at least two different kinds of antibodies (Blumberg and Bernanke 1961).

conditions which result from the production of small amounts of antibody? Is there a precedent for this?

DR. BOYD: I don't know. We don't know about the amounts present in some cases. It was only a suggestion.

DR. BLUMBERG: Does this have any relation to the so-called autoimmune diseases?

DR. LEVINE: Dr. Giblett, didn't you discuss a case like that in Chicago?

DR. GIBLETT: No, I just brought up the possibility. We have looked for it in a very superficial way without success, but we feel there is a possibility it can occur.

There is certainly good evidence that there are other proteins besides haptoglobin and transferrin that exhibit polymorphism. These might be the cause of antibody formation in blood recipients. Subsequent antigen-antibody reactions might be responsible for some of the febrile reactions we see so commonly during blood transfusions.

DR. BOYD: The sort of reaction you see in transfusion is usually due to reaction with the red cell. If you were to inject soluble blood group A or B substance into a person you will not see the sort of reaction that follows the injection of incompatible cells, I think.

DR. GIBLETT: There is a skin reaction.

DR. NEEL: One of the bothersome aspects of haptoglobins is that when you need them they are not there. The renal tubule seems to be able to handle small amounts of hemoglobin. It is in the face of massive hemolysis you need protection and by that time the haptoglobins are shot. The same with malaria.

If they are so important, why hasn't natural selection stepped up the level to where it is useful when we need it? There is something about this that is missing our attention right now.

DR. MOTULSKY: I can answer one question Dr. Boyer asked. That relates to the bactericidal action of transferrin. It has shown that the bactericidal action of this substance relates to tying up the iron which is required for normal bacterial metabolism (Schade and Caroline 1946).

I do not think that this aspect has been carefully worked out for viricidal action. However, transferrin does inhibit viral growth (Martin and Jandl 1959).

DR. BEARN: Do you know how much protein in terms of micrograms of nitrogen are necessary to do this?

DR. MOTULSKY: I don't know.

DR. GIBLETT: They stated it was within the physiologic range but the specific amount was not given.

I think, looking over the abstract again, they implied that it was binding of iron that was important.

DR. BLUMBERG: I think we should bear in mind that certain of the high polymer sugars will precipitate viruses.

DR. GIBLETT: Yes.

DR. BEARN: In this connection one could try the alpha-1 glycoprotein.

DR. BLUMBERG: Dr. Gartler, do you have any contribution?

DR. GARTLER: I have one question. What are the results of matings between ahaptoglobinemics?

DR. GIBLETT: That is the one mating we haven't been able to get.

DR. NEEL: Are we agreed that there is ahaptoglobinemia primarily the result of concomitant disease, and ahaptoglobinemia primarily due to genetic factors?

DR. GIBLETT: We had 92 families out of which we have 38 children with ahaptoglobinemia. The preponderance of these children have one or both parents with Hp 2-1 (Mod.). So this indicates to us there is a genetic significance but we don't know what it is.

DR. REED: I'd like to raise this, since we have strayed so far from selection: Is it known that the frequency of haptoglobin genes in the young children is the same as in adults?

DR. GIBLETT: Yes, in Caucasian subjects.

DR. REED: And for transferrins?

DR. GIBLETT: There is very little evidence for this. Among the 92 families I mentioned earlier, the frequency of the Tf^D_1 gene was about the same in parents and children. However, this is a small sample.

DR. DUBLIN: In his presentation earlier, Dr. Neel emphasized that the S hemoglobin opened up some fascinating epidemiologic inferences, and there is one that I thought this group might like to speculate on.

If you remember, he discussed the equilibrium of the hemoglobin polymorphism that has arisen among African Negroes. He then mentioned that they had carried on parallel studies among American Negroes, pointing out there were striking differences of an ecologic nature between the two populations. In Africa, the equilibrium is maintained by virtue of the fact that the normal hemoglobin homozygotes were subjected to a high incidence and mortality from malaria, whereas the heterozygotes were protected. Then he referred to the American situation where the Negro has not experienced the same exposure to malaria.

What happens to the polymorphism in a population where this equilibrium has been established with malaria being a very important balancing factor, and an intensive antimalarial campaign is conducted as has been done in Greece and perhaps in other parts of the world? What happens to this equilibrium?

DR. NEEL: I hesitate to express an opinion about the malaria parasite as a Johnny-come-lately on the parasitic scene in the presence of some-one like Dr. Gordon. But what reading I have done has tended to suggest that the malaria parasite, as parasites go, is not as well adapted as some. It kills its host too often. And this isn't the hallmark of the successful parasite. You can argue from this that perhaps malaria has assumed its position of relative importance only within fairly recent times in terms of human evolution. As a matter of fact, I tried to de-velop this morning the thesis that in Africa it may be only, say, some two or three thousand years that malaria has been the scourge that we know it for, and that in an effort to meet this the human species is only now evolving certain genetic mechanisms. The abnormal hemo-globins happen to be one such mechanism.

Actually, my own thinking is that the sickle cell story may be what we call an evolutionary fluke, in that the protection afforded by the hemoglobinopathies may not involve any immunologic principles as much as a happenstance, namely, that red cells that contain the falciparum parasite tend to adhere to capillary walls where the oxygen tension is reduced, with premature destruction in persons with the sickle cell trait. The result is mechanical interference with the life cycle of the parasite. This does not invoke any immunologic principle at all. It is only a fortuitous happenstance.

If one changes the conditions under which the polymorphism arose, as can be done by malaria control, you can upset the polymorphism and upset it badly. Actually, however, this doesn't mean an increased loss of life. Children with sickle cell anemia will continue to die just as before but in decreasing numbers as the gene is eliminated. The normal people being killed by malaria before will now live, so there is no increased loss of life in this particular instance.

DR. DUBLIN: What would you expect to observe in ten or fifteen years, or whatever the period has been since intensive antimalarial campaigns have been conducted on a nation-wide basis? Obviously, this is too short a period to pass through a full cycle of genetic reproduction, if you will.

DR. NEEL: Dr. Sheila Smith in an appendix to one of Tony Allison's 1954 papers has very nicely worked out the mathematical consequences of suddenly stopping the selection. Actually, in the case of a lethal homo-zygote, that is to say, sickle cell anemia, one starts with an initial gene frequency of 40 per cent, it is going to go down pretty fast, and inside of, I believe, eight generations you will halve the gene frequency.

Dr. MOTULSKY: At 30 per cent you get down to half in seven to eight generations.

Dr. NEEL: Right. In Curaçao, the hemoglobin S carrier frequency is down around 4 per cent now. If the natives at the time of their introduction possessed, say, 20 per cent, there have elapsed about the right number of generations to demean it to 4 per cent, in the absence of positive selection.

Dr. J. E. GORDON: It is rather well demonstrated that in countries such as Ceylon where malaria has been controlled, even close to eradicated, in a rather brief period of time—fantastically, in two or three years in Ceylon—important influences have been introduced in the behavior of other communicable diseases, and in respect also to the general death rate.

With all due respect to my characterization of myself yesterday as a "host man," any interpretation of the broad ecologic effect of malaria control measures, or of reduction in frequency of malaria itself, must of necessity take into consideration a variety of environmental factors.

8

POPULATION GENETICS OF GLUCOSE-6-PHOSPHATE DEHYDROGENASE DEFICIENCY OF THE RED CELL

ARNO G. MOTULSKY and JEAN M. CAMPBELL-KRAUT

TEN YEARS AGO, Dr. Boyd predicted the polymorphism under discussion. He pointed out that the British, in contrast to Mediterranean populations, never develop hemolytic anemia on ingestion of fava beans and suggested a genetic difference as explanation (Boyd 1950). Workers at the University of Chicago noticed that approximately 10 per cent of Negro soldiers and some white soldiers developed severe hemolytic anemia when given conventional doses of a new antimalarial drug: primaquine (Hockwald, et al, 1952). Red cells of susceptible subjects were tagged and transfused to compatible normal individuals to whom primaquine was administered. Only the tagged cells were hemolyzed, indicating an intrinsic defect of the red cells as the basis of drug hemolysis (Dern, et al., 1954). When tagged, normal cells were transfused into suceptible subjects and the drug was administered, no destruction of normal cells occurred. Studies with radioactive iron showed that the hemolytic action of the drug in susceptible subjects affected only the older segment of the red cell population. Young red cells were spared from hemolysis (see Beutler 1959a). When red cells reached an age of approximately 50 days, they were destroyed by the drug (normal life span 120 days). These data explained the selflimited nature of the hemolytic reactions noted with primaquine and the many other drugs (Beutler 1959a) which can provoke this type of reaction. When one of these drugs had been administered to a susceptible individual, one-half of the red cells were destroyed and the hemolytic reaction stopped. The younger red cells were not affected.

Studies performed at the University of Chicago, attempting to relate the intrinsic abnormality of the cell to some of the known red cell traits such as blood groups and hemoglobin variants, were negative (Beutler, et al., 1954b). It was found, however, that the red cells of susceptible individuals had a slight deficiency of nonprotein glutathione (Beutler, et al, 1955a). Although there was overlap between normals and susceptible subjects, the mean glutathione level of abnormals was significantly lower than that of normals. Further studies resulted in the discovery that the enzyme glucose-6-phosphate dehydrogenase, operative in the shunt or oxidative pathway of red cell metabolism, was markedly deficient in individuals susceptible to drug hemolysis (Carson, et al., 1956). Figure 1

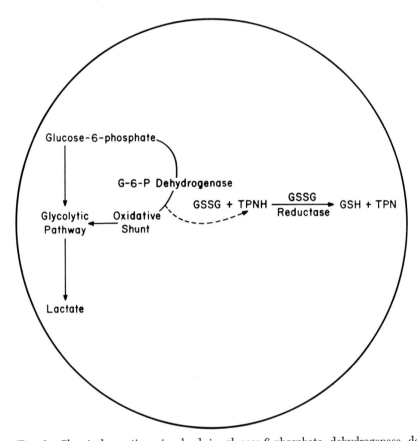

Fig. 1—Chemical reactions involved in glucose-6-phosphate dehydrogenase deficiency of the red cell.
GSSG=oxidized glutathione. GSH=reduced glutathione. TPN=oxidized triphosphopyridine nucleotide. TPNH=reduced triphosphopyridine nucleotide.

summarizes the relationship of glucose-6-phosphate dehydrogenase and glutathione metabolism. Glucose-6-phosphate dehydrogenase catalyzes the first step of the shunt pathway and releases TPNH. TPNH is required for reduction of oxidized glutathione (GSSG) to reduce glutathione (GSH). This relationship of TPNH to glutathione metabolism provides some indication of how deficient glucose-6-phosphate dehydrogenase activity might lead to abnormalities in glutathione metabolism of the red cell. The exact nature of the glutathione abnormalities is not yet fully understood.

Further studies by Beutler showed that incubation of red cells from susceptible subjects with acetylphenylhydrazine depleted the slightly depressed level of glutathione to markedly low levels (Beutler 1957). Normal cells under these conditions only showed an insignificant loss of glutathione. This difference is the basis of the glutathione stability test which has been frequently employed to detect susceptible individuals.

Soon after these discoveries were made, workers in Italy, Israel and the United States independently demonstrated that hemolytic anemia induced by fava bean ingestion only developed in individuals with glucose-6-phosphate dehydrogenase deficiency (Szeinberg, et al., 1958a; Sansone and Segni 1957; Zinkham, et al, 1958). Such individuals will also develop hemolytic anemia on exposure to the offending drugs (Larizza 1958). It is of interest that not only eating of fava beans will produce hemolytic episodes, but that walking past a flowering field of fava beans has precipitated blood destruction (Sansone, et al., 1958). Volatile products from the plants apparently may react with susceptible red cells to produce hemolysis.

Genetics

Studies among Negro, Mediterranean and Jewish populations using either glutathione stability or glucose-6-phosphate dehydrogenase activity as testing parameters indicate that the defect is inherited as a sex-linked trait (Childs, et al., 1958; Gross, et al., 1958; Szeinberg and Sheba 1958; Siniscalco, et al., 1960). Figure 2 indicates the genetic mechanisms underlying a sex-linked trait. Males, with only one X chromosome, will be either affected or normal. Studies done with glutathione stability tests and enzyme assays have indicated a clear bimodal pattern in males with no overlap between normals and abnormals. Three genotypes are found in females; normal homozygotes, heterozygotes and abnormal homozygotes. On theoretical grounds, one would expect female heterozygotes to be intermediate in any parameter which reflects gene action fairly closely. Data on female heterozygotes have shown the expected intermediate enzyme level or intermediate glutathione stability results. However, not all heterozygote females give intermediate test results. Some may be normal and some may even be in the low abnormal range. A population survey will yield the best estimate of gene frequency for this defect by sampling males, since enumeration of affected males will give the gene frequency. Population studies done in southern

Europe, and among Israelis and Negroes, are fully compatible with sex-linked inheritance. Studies on linkage with color blindness indicate close linkage with the gene for color blindness (Siniscalco, et al., 1960; Adam, 1961).

By determining the frequency of male reactors (p) the theoretical population frequency of female heterozygotes under random mating

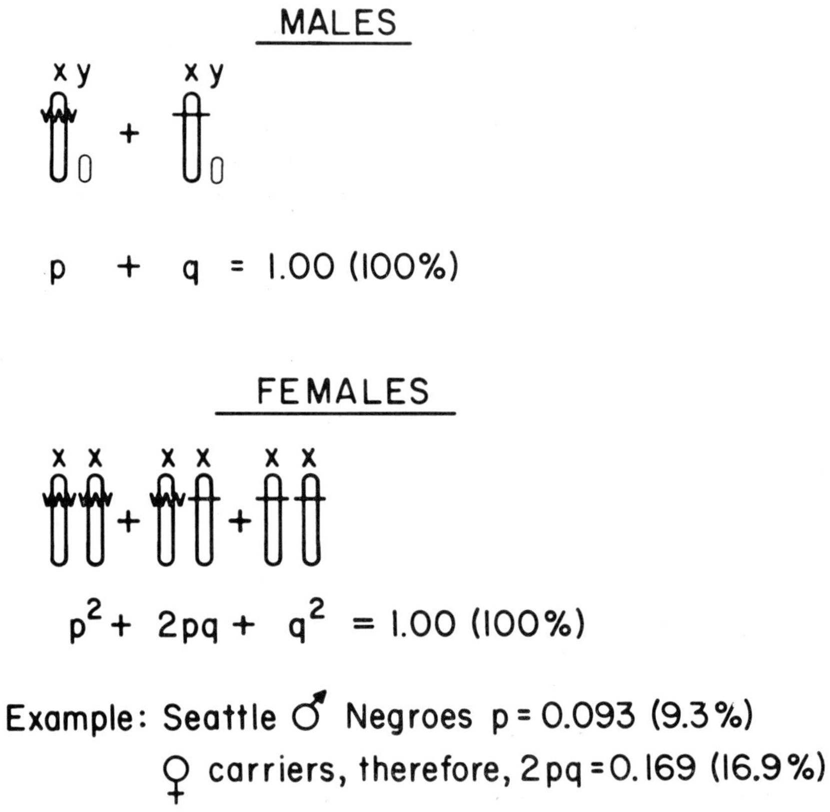

MALES

$$p + q = 1.00 \ (100\%)$$

FEMALES

$$p^2 + 2pq + q^2 = 1.00 \ (100\%)$$

Example: Seattle ♂ Negroes p = 0.093 (9.3%)
♀ carriers, therefore, 2pq = 0.169 (16.9%)

Fig. 2—Genetic mechanism of a sex-linked trait. The wavy line refers to the mutant gene. Note two genotypes in the male and three genotypes in the female.

(2pq) can be calculated. (See fig. 2) The actually determined frequency of female heterozygotes in populations always has been lower than the calculated incidence. However, Marks and Gross (1959a) as well as Adinolfi, et al., (1960) detect practically all female carriers by enzyme assay.

As in most heterozygote detection programs, the frequency of detectable heterozygotes increases with more refined techniques. There has been some confusion on this point since only 50-60 per cent of female heterozygotes can be detected wih the glutathione stability test. Since only half the females are thus detected, the actual percentage of "affected" males and females in a population may be quite similar. Population data for this trait are only genetically meaningful if males and females are considered separately.

In a sex-linked trait, there should be no father-to-son transmission. However, in a population where a sex-linked gene is frequent, a significant number of matings of heterozygote females with affected males will occur. Considering all matings of heterozygote women, the fraction involving affected males will equal the gene frequency (p = % affected males) of the trait among males. Where this gene is common, one would therefore find spurious father-to-son transmission occasionally. Pedigrees, where heterozygote mothers with normal test results had mated with affected fathers, are particularly confusing and appear to contradict a sex-linked mode of inheritance unless these factors are considered.

If the sex distribution of favism in children is known in a population, a rough idea of the gene frequency can be obtained. The rather rare occurrence of favism in female children suggests that only girls with marked depression of enzyme level will be affected. Most such girls will be homozygotes (p^2) rather than heterozygotes ($2pq$). The ratio of

TABLE 1—*Ratio of Affected Female Homozygote (p²) and Affected Male Hemizygotes (p) Indicates Gene Frequency (p) or Male Trait Frequency*

$\dfrac{\text{No. affected female children } (p^2)}{\text{No. affected male children } (p)}$	Gene frequency p=trait incidence in males (%)
$\dfrac{1}{100}$	1
$\dfrac{1}{20}$	5
$\dfrac{1}{10}$	10
$\dfrac{1}{6.8}$	15
$\dfrac{1}{5}$	20
$\dfrac{1}{3}$	30
$\dfrac{1}{2.5}$	40

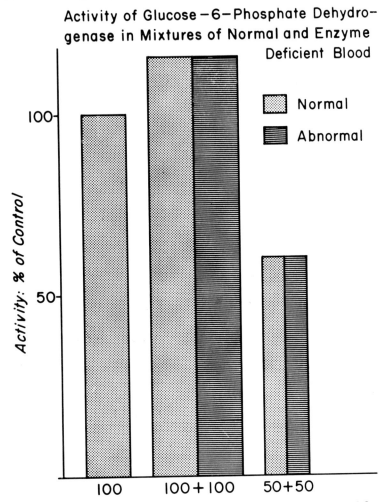

Activity of Glucose –6–Phosphate Dehydro-genase in Mixtures of Normal and Enzyme Deficient Blood

Fig. 3—Mixing of normal and abnormal hemolysates. Note lack of inhibition of normal enzyme activity.

female children with favism to male children with favism will therefore be p^2/p which equals p. The gene frequency (p) is therefore apparent immediately when the number of female and male children with clinically apparent favism is known. Table 1 shows some model data. Data obtained in this manner check fairly well with actually determined gene frequencies.

The role of inbreeding deserves short comment. Inbreeding will not lead to increased gene frequency, but will cause an increase of matings of affected males with heterozygote females, thus producing more female homozygotes. In a population with much inbreeding, the increased number of female homozygotes might be detectable since there would be an excess of females with a low enzyme level over what would be expected under random mating.

Nature of Genetic Defect

Enzyme deficiency is an operational term and may include a variety of genetic biochemical lesions. Figure 3 indicates that no inhibitor of glucose-6-phosphate dehydrogenase can be detected in abnormal cells. Several investigative teams have done such experiments by mixing normal and abnormal hemolysates without finding inhibition of normal activity (see Kirkman 1959).

The possibility of a qualitatively altered enzyme molecule was considered and suggested by abnormal heat lability of impure enzyme preparations (Motulsky, et al., 1959; Marks 1960). Studies with purified enzyme preparations from enzyme deficient Negroes, however, failed to reveal any difference between normal and abnormal enzymes when enzyme kinetics was studied (see Kirkman 1959).[1] Recent data from Israel suggest that there is neither qualitative nor quantitative abnormality of the enzyme in deficient Jewish subjects but that deficient enzyme activity may be caused by the absence of a stromal enzyme activator from abnormal cells (Rimon, et al, 1960). Similar results have been obtained with red cells of enzyme deficient Italians (Grignani 1960). However, no evidence for a stromal activator has been found in enzyme deficient Negroes (Marks, et al, 1961).

Test System

To do population studies it became necessary to develop a test system suited for field work. A full glucose-6-phosphate dehydrogenase enzyme assay requires a Beckman DU spectrophotometer and is not a field test. The glutathione stability test also requires more complicated equipment and does not measure enzyme activity. We were interested in finding a test system by which we could get as close to the gene product as possible and at the same time test as many individuals as possible. We were able to work out a test system which was based on decolorization of the dye brilliant cresyl blue (Motulsky and Campbell, in press) (table 2).

---

[1] Investigations with purified enzyme preparations from a patient with a type of glucose-6-phosphate dehydrogenase deficiency associated with nonspherocytic hemolytic anemia revealed qualitative differences from both normal and enzyme deficient Negroes (Kirkman 1960). These data suggest that this condition is caused by a different biochemical lesion than the more common enzyme deficiency not accompanied by chronic hemolytic anemia.

The actual test system is described in table 3. The spread of decolorization times for an American Negro population in Seattle is shown in figure 4. Decolorization times of more than two hours indicated enzyme

TABLE 2—*Chemical Reactions Underlying Dye Test System*

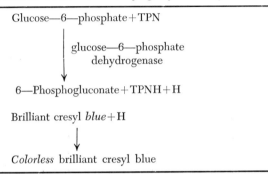

Glucose—6—phosphate + TPN

glucose—6—phosphate
dehydrogenase

6—Phosphogluconate + TPNH + H

Brilliant cresyl *blue* + H

Colorless brilliant cresyl blue

deficiency. The tests of most enzyme deficient Negro subjects decolorized in between two and four hours. Borderline values were few and must be considered potentially deficient. A series of 100 Sardinian males showed a very sharp bimodal pattern with normal decolorization time of 25 to 75 minutes. Sardinian abnormals decolorize at 12 hours and longer. (Adinolfi, et al, 1960). These differences between enzyme deficient Caucasians and Negroes have been consistently observed in these tests. A full study of this problem with quantitative enzyme assays indicated

TABLE 3—*Glucose-6-Phosphate Dehydrogenase Dye Test*

G-6-P DEHYDROGENASE DYE TEST

0.02 ml. whole blood
1.0 ml. H₂O

⌈ 0.1 ml. Sodium Glucose-6-Phosphate   ⌉*
      (825 mg./100 ml.)
  0.1 ml. TPN (50 mg./100 ml.)
  0.25 ml. Brilliant cresyl blue (32 mg./100 ml.**)
  0.2 ml. TRIS buffer (pH 8.5)
⌊   (8.96 Gm./97 ml. + 3 ml. conc. HCl ⌋

Top with oil. Incubate at 37° C.
Observe decolorization time
Normals: 40-60 minutes
Abnormal males: 90 minutes-24 hours

* *The bracket indicates that these reagents may be premixed.*
** *It is essential that National Aniline dye be used; Coleman and Bell dye does not decolorize in the test system.*

that the mean enzyme level in enzyme deficient Caucasians was significantly lower than that in enzyme deficient Negroes (Marks and Gross 1959b). These data and the above cited enzyme kinetics studies make it likely that the basic defect in the common variety of glucose-6-phosphate dehydrogenase deficiency (not associated with chronic hemolytic anemia) is different in Negroes and Caucasians.

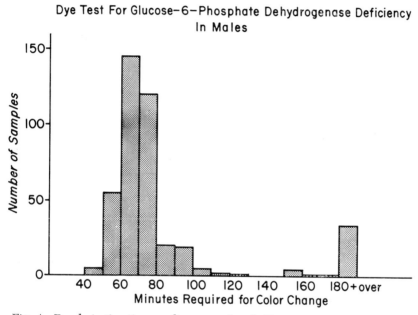

Fig. 4—Decolorization time results among Seattle Negroes.

As many as 250 tests per day have been done in the field. Tests can be performed on finger puncture blood collected into a .02 ml. hemoglobin pipette. The blood is hemolyzed immediately in test tubes containing water and may be kept in ice in insulated containers for several hours before the tests are actually performed. Storage of hemolyzed cells at 4° to 6° C. for seven to eight hours did not interfere with the test results. At tropical room temperature, tests on the hemolyzed specimens can be delayed up to about four hours after collection. Specimens obtained by venipuncture are best collected into ACD solution and can be kept for several weeks in the refrigerator before being tested. Our test was standardized with incubation of the test mixtures at 37° C. If no water bath or incubator is available to maintain such a temperature, the test system can be run without incubation. Decolorization, however, requires a much longer time. A makeshift water bath can be made by mixing boiling and cold water to 37° in a vessel into which the test tube racks with test mixtures are placed.

A low hematocrit level might conceivably be of importance in anemic subjects with fewer red cells and consequently diminished quantities of enzyme activity. There is no linear relationship between quantitatively determined enzyme activity and decolorization time in this test system and consequently patients with half-normal hematocrits will still give normal decolorization times. If the initial hematocrit is below twenty-four, however, the blood specimen should be adjusted to a higher hematocrit. Our screening system is not sensitive enough to detect differences between normal and half-normal amounts of enzyme. Since, however, the usual enzyme deficient male has about 15 per cent or less of normal enzyme activity the test is excellent for detecting enzyme deficient male subjects.

Since many heterozygote females have only mild deficiency, our screening system is not ideal for heterozygote detection. By careful attention to timing of decolorization (i.e., reading every minute) and simultaneous control testing of normals, a significant percentage of female heterozygotes, however, can be detected. Using this technique, we were able to identify in a large female population in a Sardinian village twelve out of fifteen mothers of boys with a history of favism.

A possible source of error is the presence of young red cells in the erythrocyte population. There is exponential decline of glucose-6-phosphate dehydrogenase activity with advancing age of the cell (Marks,

TABLE 4—*Glucose-6-P Dehydrogenase Deficiency in Asiatics and Indigenous Americans*

GROUP		SOURCE
Asiatics		
Asiatic Indians	3-8%	Vella 1959(a); Motulsky & Campbell, in press
Filipinos	12.7%	Motulsky & Campbell, in press
Chinese	2%	Vella 1959(a); Beutler, et al, 1959
Japanese	0%	Motulsky & Campbell, in press
Micronesians	0-1%	Blumberg, Campbell & Motulsky, 1960.
Iranians	8.5%	Walker & Bowman 1959
Americans		
Eskimos (Alaskan)	0%	Motulsky & Campbell, in press
American Indians	0%	Motulsky & Campbell, in press
Peruvian Indians	0%	Best, 1959
Oyana Indians	18%	Keller, et al, 1960.
Caribs	2%	Keller, et al, 1960.

Frequencies refer to male subjects.

et al., 1958; Lohr, et al., 1958). The average age of a normal red cell population is 60 days; with active hemolysis, such as during fava bean or drug hemolysis, the older cells are destroyed and red cells with a younger mean age and higher enzyme amounts are left in the blood. These cells, although still exhibiting decreased enzyme activity on quantitative assay, considering the younger mean cell age, may give a falsely normal screening test result in an enzyme deficient patient. Our test system, therefore, tends to underestimate the incidence of the trait in populations with active hemolysis such as during fava bean season.

Geographic Distribution and Relation to Malaria (Motulsky, 1960)

About 10 per cent of American Negroes were enzyme deficient (figure 4). Results, including those of other workers on Asiatic and native American populations are shown in table 4. The percentages refer to sampling of male populations. Among Asiatic Indians from different areas of India, first sampled among a student population in Seattle, we found an incidence of about 6-7 per cent of deficiency. More extensive studies done by Dr. Vella on Indian residents in Singapore revealed a somewhat lower figure (Vella 1959a). Incidence among Filipino cannery workers in Alaska was 12.7 per cent. We knew that favism existed in southern areas of China (Vella 1959b). Studies among Chinese in Singapore showed a 2 per cent incidence (Vella 1959a). So far, among about 100 Japanese, we have failed to find an enzyme deficient individual.

TABLE 5—*Glucose-6-P Dehydrogenase Deficiency in Africans*

GROUP		FREQUENCY SOURCE
Africans		
American Negroes	9-11%	Motulsky & Campbell, in press
Leopoldville Negroes	18-23%	Vandepitte & Motulsky, unpub.
		Sonnet, et al, 1959
Stanleyville Negroes	14-15%	Motulsky, Dherte & Ninane, unpub.
Bayaka (S. Congo)	15-28%	Motulsky & Vandepitte, unpub.
	(over 20%)	
Bwaka (N.W. Congo)	6%	Motulsky, unpub.
Watutsi	1-2%	Motulsky, unpub.
Bahutu	7%	Motulsky, unpub.
Bashi	14%	Motulsky, unpub.
Pygmies	4%	Motulsky, Dherte & Ninane, unpub.
S. African Bantus	2%	Charlton & Bothwell, 1959
S. African Bushmen	1-2%	Bothwell, pers. comm.
Nigerians	10%	Gilles, Watson-Williams & Taylor, 1960

Frequencies refer to male subjects.

The incidence of favism in Iran, especially on the southern shore of the Caspian Sea, is relatively high. Based on the sex incidence of favism (9 female, 48 male) (Wallstrom, pers. comm.) as explained above, we calculated a 13 per cent gene frequency. Recently, glutathione stability tests showed a 10 per cent frequency in that area (Walker and Bowman 1959). It was claimed that the trait frequency was fairly high among Eskimos as tested by the glutathione stability test (Kellermeyer, et al., 1958). Personal study of about 200 Eskimos failed to reveal any reactors including repeat specimens on those that had been claimed to be affected. The earlier data probably were caused by spoiling of specimens during storage, leading to abnormal glutathione stability. Peruvian Indians were tested by Best (1959). These are populations who 500 years ago descended from a highland area. They do not have the trait. In Surinam, the Oyana Indians living in a highly malarial area have an incidence of 18 per cent (Keller, et al., unpub.).

Table 5 shows the African data. In Leopoldville, which is a conglomerate of many tribes, up to 23 per cent were affected. Stanleyville, also a metropolitan area with representatives of many tribes, showed a 15 per cent incidence. Among the Bayaka, we found varying frequencies. The average was about 20 per cent, ranging from, as low as 15 to 28 per cent frequency. The Bwaka had a lower frequency. The Watutsi had a very low incidence. The Bahutu had a 7 per cent frequency.

The incidence of the enzyme deficiency correlated well with that of the sickling trait, except in Pygmies (figure 5). The two traits did not necessarily affect the same individual. The low enzyme deficiency rate among Pygmies may be a spurious result in view of the known incidence of chronic liver disease and protein malnutrition in this population which may lead to active hemolysis, causing an increase in enzyme level (see above).

The incidence of individuals with both defects in Africa was not higher than expected by chance. A slight, but not yet statistically significant, increase of individuals with both thalassemia and enzyme deficiency was seen in the Sardinian studies (Bernini, et al., 1960; Siniscalco, et al., 1961, see below).

The good correlation with the sickling trait also held for South African Bantu populations (Charlton and Bothwell 1959). Both the enzyme deficiency and the sickling trait frequency are quite low in South Africa. In view of the known role of the sickling trait in protecting against death from malaria, the occurrence of a different genetic trait of the red cell at similar frequencies suggested that enzyme deficient subjects also may enjoy a selective advantage against malaria.

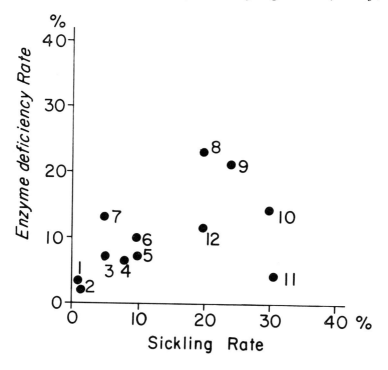

1. S. African Bantu
2. Watutsi
3. Usumbura
4. Bahutu
5. Bwaka
6. American negro
7. Bashi
8. Bayaka
9. Leopoldville
10. Stanleyville
11. Pygmies
12. Nigerians

Fig. 5—Sickling frequency (heterozygotes) and enzyme deficiency (male frequency-gene frequency) in Africa. Note the good correlation of the two traits.

The distribution of the trait in Sardinia was especially noteworthy (Siniscaleo, et al., 1961). We had known from earlier work that the incidence of thalassemia was low in the mountains of Sardinia (2-3 per cent) and high on the east coast (18 per cent) (Ceppellini 1959). It was also known that the malaria frequency was very high on the coast but non-existent in the mountains. We thought it would be of value to test these

GLUCOSE – 6 – PHOSPHATE DEHYDROGENASE
DEFICIENCY IN SARDINIA

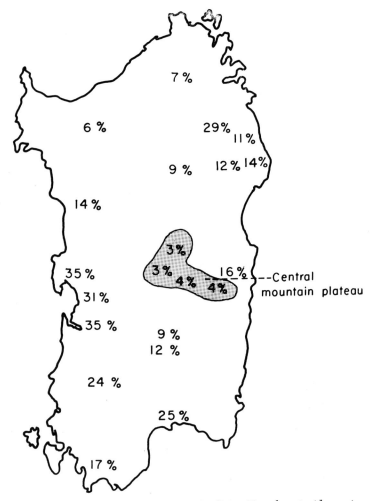

Fig. 6—Enzyme deficiency frequency in Sardinia. Note low incidence in central mountain plateau (*elevation 600 to 1000 meters*).

and other villages. Blood group studies in east coast, west coast and mountain villages showed identical distribution of the ABO, MN, and Rh blood groups (Bernini, et al, 1960), suggesting the basic genetic similarity of these populations. The frequency of enzyme deficiency varied markedly. In the mountains we found a frequency of 3 to 4 per cent enzyme deficiency. In the coastal villages of the East (Baronia) with 18 per cent thalassemia, the initial enzyme deficiency trait frequency was 12 to 14 per cent.[2]

The marked difference in closely neighboring villages with different malarial frequencies in the past (see figure 6) and appparently otherwise identical population is interesting. A coastal village had a frequency of 16 per cent and not far from it a mountain village had a 4 per cent frequency. Other areas in Sardinia such as the highly malarial west coast showed frequencies as high as 35 per cent (see figure 6). The difference in incidence between the previously highly malarial East and equally malarial West coasts of Sardinia is not quite clear yet.

Figure 7 plots the frequency of the thalassemia trait against frequency of the enzyme deficiency in 14 communities of Sardinia. There is good correlation between the two traits, again suggesting selection by a common environmental agent: malaria. There was excellent chance for malarial selection to occur on this island since Sardinia was known to be one of the highest malarial areas in Europe until 1946 when malaria was eradicated. The Sardinian data also suggest that above a certain threshold frequency (approximately 18 per cent) of enzyme deficiency, the relatively less harmful enzyme deficiency is more rapidly selected than the more harmful thalassemia gene since a different regression curve can be fitted to the higher enzyme deficient frequencies (figure 7) (Bernini, et al., 1960).

The incidence of thalassemia is very high in the Po Valley in Italy around Ferrara. We know that favism occurs among Ferrarans in Sardinia.

Enzyme deficiency appears to occur with high frequency in Greece. Many cases of favism have been reported from the Peloponnesus and the Khalkidiki peninsula (Zennos-Mariolea and Chiotaskis 1959). Again, these provinces had high malarial endemicity in the past. Sickling also occurs in these regions. Greece is thus the only area in the world where all three blood traits exist in the same population.

Dr. Allison has confirmed and extended these data by demonstrating

---

[2] Initial testing had revealed a frequency of only nine per cent. This was in spring 1959. Spring is the season of flowering fava and of fresh fava bean ingestion. Dr. Siniscalco also determined the haptoglobin level of these individuals and found a higher percentage of ahaptoglobinemia. He knew from previous studies that ahaptoglobinemia did not exist in this area. Since ahaptoglobinemia can also be caused by hemolysis, this finding suggested that we were dealing with ahaptoglobinemia produced by hemolysis from fava beans. The later findings of higher frequencies indicated that this assumption was correct. The fava poison had destroyed the susceptible old red cells, leaving a red cell population with many young cells which registered as normal on the screening test, giving a falsely low incidence in this population.

that tribes in East Africa with low malarial incidence in the past had a frequency of 1.7 to 2.9 per cent enzyme deficiency, while tribes with very high malarial incidence in the past had an incidence of 15 to 28 per cent. These data again correlate well with similar frequencies of the sickling trait in these areas (Allison 1960).

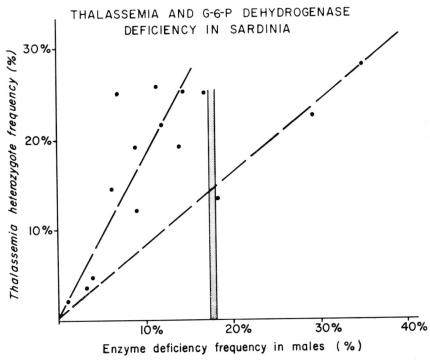

Fig. 7—Thalassemia (heterozygotes) and enzyme deficiency in Sardinia. Note the good correlation of the two traits. Above approximately 18% enzyme deficiency, a different regression line can be fitted the data (see text).

TABLE 6—*Glucose-6-P Dehydrogenase Deficiency in Jews*
[Szeinberg, et al., 1958(b)]

Jews	
Kurdish Jews	60%
Persia Iraqi Jews	25%
Turkish Jews	5%
Yemenite Jews	5%
N. African Jews	2%
Ashkenazi Jews	0.2%

Table 6 shows the data obtained by Dr. Sheba's group on the frequency of the trait among different Jewish tribes in Israel. Kurdish Jews have the highest incidence. Enzyme deficiency is also high among the Persian Jews, becomes lower among other Sephardic Jewish groups and is extremely rare among European Jewish (Ashkenazi) populations (Szeinberg, et al., 1958b). The Kurdish Jews are well known for their high incidence of thalassemia. Recent data from Israel indicate a frequency of the thalassemic trait of 22 per cent and an incidence or enzyme deficiency of over 50 per cent in this group. The traits occur independently of each

TABLE 7—*Countries and Islands with Favism or 8-Aminoquinoline Induced Hemolytic Anemia or Both*

Portugal	Rhodes	Turkey	India
Spain	Crete	Egypt	China
Southern Italy	Cyprus	Lebanon	Formosa
Minorca	Corfu	Iran	Burma
Sardinia	Bulgaria	Iraq	Java
Sicily	Greece	Israel*	Mauritius

* *(Non-Ashkenazi Jews only)*

other (Cohen, et al., 1959b). Kurdish Jews have a high rate of inbreeding. If the basic gene pool from which the different Jewish groups come is similar, we have 3,000 years (from 586 B.C. to the present) for the action of natural selection to produce these marked differences in gene frequency. Assuming the mutation occurred 3,000 years ago or earlier, natural selection in the form of malaria could have increased or decreased this frequency to its present values. It is unlikely, however, that selection alone explains these differences. Undoubtedly, population mixture as well as genetic drift plays an important role. More data are needed on the frequency of the trait on non-Jewish populations in the Near East.

Other areas in which favism and aminoquinoline-induced anemia have been reported are listed in table 7. The world distribution of glucose-6-phosphate dehydrogenase deficiency and of falciparum malaria are indicated in figures 8 and 9.

The type of malaria playing a role in selection of this polymorphism needs to have a high mortality. The most efficient selective agent needs to kill children; falciparum malaria qualifies for this "distinction." Vivax malaria probably can be ruled out since it parasitizes young cells. Young red cells, even in enzyme deficient individuals, have a significantly higher enzyme level than old cells (Marks, et al., 1958; Lohr, et al., 1958). Vivax malaria also has a lower mortality than falciparum malaria.

In what manner, if any, is the abnormal cell a less efficient host for the malarial parasite? We do know that the malarial organism needs gluta-thione for *in vitro* growth (Trager 1941; McGhee and Trager 1950). It is also known that the malarial organism *in vitro* needs cysteine. Fifty per cent of the cysteine requirements of the malarial organism are supplied by glutathione (Fulton and Grant 1956). Glutathione, however, is already decreased and is easily depletable in enzyme deficient cells. There is also some suggestion that the oxidative pathway may be used by malarial parasites (Geiman 1951). For these various reasons, malarial parasites

DISTRIBUTION OF GLUCOSE-6-PHOSPHATE DEHYDROGENASE DEFICIENCY

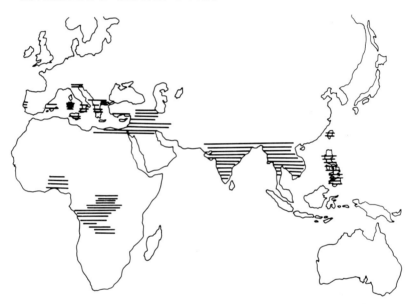

Fig. 8—World distribution of glucose-6-phosphate dehydrogenase deficiency.

may grow suboptimally in enzyme deficient cells. Since malarial mortal-ity appears to be related to the number of parasites present in the red cell, a child with fewer parasites is less likely to die and is therefore at an advantage. Drs. Vandepitte and Motulsky in the spring of 1959 attempted a direct demonstration of this hypothesis by relating parasite density of falciparum malaria to the enzyme deficiency in 600 Bayaka male children between 6 months and 10 years of age. The Kwango dis-trict in the southern area of the Republic of the Congo where the Bayaka live is still a highly malarious area. Because of external circumstances, it turned out that 85 per cent of the children were 5 to 10 years of age. Unfortunately, acquired immunity to malaria in the older children appeared to blur the demonstration of the critical genetic protection against malarial proliferation in the younger child. In older children very high parasite counts may occur which do not harm these individuals. Figure 10 shows a portion of the data relating parasite counts in normal and enzyme deficient subjects. The material counts were not significantly different in the three classes of individuals. Although the mean parasite count was somewhat lower in enzyme deficient subjects, the difference was not statistically significant.

DISTRIBUTION OF FALCIPARUM MALARIA

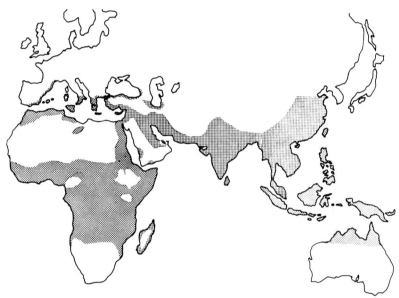

Fig. 9—World distribution of falciparum malaria.

In 1960, Dr. Allison was fortunate to study children 4 months to 4 years of age in east Africa (Tanganyika). His data show that the enzyme deficient younger individuals have a significantly lower parasite count (Allison and Clyde, 1961).[3]

What is the mechanism by which this polymorphism maintains itself?

[3] Dr. Gilles, University College, Ibadan, Nigeria (Gilles 1960), has accumulated 23 male hospital cases of proven clinically severe Falciparum malaria. None of these patients was enzyme deficient. Based on the enzyme deficiency frequency of 20% in Ibadan, the expected incidence in this group would have been between four and five individuals (4.6). These data again strongly suggest protection by enzyme deficiency against severe malaria but need to be extended.

With sickling, the situation is fairly straightforward because sickle cell anemia is a lethal disease early in life. We know the loss of genes due to sickle cell anemia and can calculate the advantage of the sickle cell trait in protecting against malarial mortality. Enzyme deficiency presents a somewhat different situation. We are dealing with a sex-linked trait and with individuals who may at the same time enjoy malarial protection but

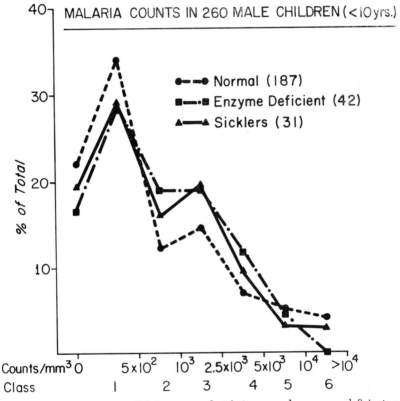

Fig. 10—Parasite counts (falciparum malaria) in normal, enzyme deficient and sickling trait Bayaka children.

also suffer a disadvantage from the trait. The mortality of favism in Mediterranean countries was 2-17 per cent in hospitals (Sansone, et al, 1958) but most patients with favism do not go to hospitals. The mortality of all patients with favism is probably quite low. We do not know whether the fava bean exists in Africa; however, it is not unlikely that other foods contain the active principle producing hemolysis. It occurs in Mediterranean countries and in the Near East. It is known, however, that individuals with enzyme deficiency may develop hemolytic anemia during viral and bacterial infection (Marks 1960). This complication is probably a more important disadvantage than the hemolytic anemia from foods.[4] We therefore have a gene which in affected males may protect against malarial death but at the same time cause death from hemolytic anemia of the newborn or from hemolytic episodes from infection or from foods.

The sex incidence of favism in children shows a marked excess of males (Sartori 1957). Presumably most female children with favism are homozygotes. In middle age, however, the deficiency of females disappears and statistics on favism at middle age show that the incidence of favism is approximately similar in males and females. Young heterozygote girls before reproduction, therefore, appear relatively protected against the disadvantage of the gene. After reproduction, this disadvantage is no longer important in terms of natural selection. The entire balance may therefore be carried by the female heterozygote who may have a slight selective advantage to malaria but be protected against death from hemolytic anemia.

It is difficult to present exact calculations on gene balance at this time. In contrast to sickle cell anemia, no exact figure can be given for the extent of the loss of fitness. Quantitative treatment is therefore difficult and will have to await better data. Dr. Sheila Maynard-Smith and Dr. Penrose have kindly made some calculations, but because of the many uncertainties, it would be premature to offer these considerations here. It is interesting, however, that a very slight advantage of the female might set up a stable polymorphism in this system.

In conclusion, we would like to stress the role of food and drug idiosyncrasy in uncovering polymorphisms in man. Over the past few years, three interesting polymorphisms in man have been detected in this manner. In addition to glucose-6-phosphate dehydrogenase deficiency, the genetic basis of serum cholinesterase polymorphism was discovered by noting unusual responses to administration of the drug succinyldicholin (Kalow 1959). The genetic control of the variable responses of individuals to isoniazid was discovered when drug metabolism was studied

---

[4] Recent studies in Singapore, Greece and Sardinia (Fessas 1961; Smith and Vella 1960; Panizon 1960; Weatherall 1960) have indicated another serious harmful effect of this gene. A considerable number of cases of severe hemolytic disease of the newborn—not associated with blood group incompatibility—were traced to glucose-6-phosphate dehydrogenase deficiency. In view of the demonstrated high death rate in these cases, especially when untreated, this manifestation of the defect is probably much more harmful than hemolytic anemia from foods or viral infections (Motulsky, 1961).

(Harris, et al., 1959a). By looking carefully for such drug reactions and food reactions, many more interesting polymorphisms will undoubtedly be found in the future.

Drug reactions provide a model for defining genetically conditioned susceptibility to disease (Motulsky 1957). Certain individuals harbor a harmless enzyme deficiency. In the presence of an environmental agent, such as the drug, severe disease occurs only in these predisposed individuals. The drug in usual doses and the enzyme deficiency alone produce no disease. Only interaction of the enzyme deficiency and drug administration in the same individual produces severe illness. It is likely that much genetically controlled biochemical variability exists in man which determines susceptibility to disease from a variety of external and internal agents.

DISCUSSION

DR. KROOTH: I asked to be excused from discussing Dr. Motulsky's paper, principally because this is an area in which I personally have never worked. Although, like everyone, I have been extremely intrigued by this field of study, I hesitate from inexperience to act as a discussant.

What I thought I would do instead is make a couple of quite general comments. One of them which I wanted to ask both Dr. Motulsky and Dr. Neel concerns the relative role of malaria in mortality in England and in the South of this country. I gather principally from occasional readings in text books and journals of medical history that, in London up to the 18th century, malaria infection was an important source of mortality, and, of course, in this country, up through the Civil War, there were huge areas of the South where malaria apparently contributed appreciably to mortality.

What I wonder—perhaps this is similar to the question which Dr. Dublin asked—is why population homeostatic mechanisms similar to the sickle cell one have not evolved in some of these areas. Perhaps it was the wrong parasite, or perhaps infection was insufficiently intense.

I should like now to raise one point which was touched on briefly in some of the earlier papers. I suspect we stand in an excellent position to increase our knowledge of some of the polymorphic systems by the study of the interaction between them and rare diseases.

I am aware that, *prima facie*, this would seem an extremely dull and unpromising approach. In systems such as the blood groups, for example, the work that has been done on the association of blood groups and disease has been concerned chiefly with the association of common antigens, such as the ABO groups, with comparatively common disease, such as peptic ulcer, pernicious anemia, and diabetes. I wonder whether it would not also be helpful to examine rare diseases to see if affected people have rare antigens.

If it is permissible to argue that balanced polymorphism keeps the common antigens common, then it should be permissible to argue that unidirectional selection may keep the rare antigens rare. If this is so, and if selection acts by morbidity, then perhaps persons with rare antigens ought to be predisposed to get rare diseases.

For example, one can use rare diseases which are thought to have immunologic significance such as the demyelinating ones, or the rare collagen diseases and purpuras. The associations of rare diseases and rare antigens or biochemical traits, if they exist, are apt to be striking and could reveal clues as to what supports the more common polymorphism.

I should be surprised if this point hasn't occurred to others, and I know one feels a certain contempt for persons who get up and suggest research projects and then sit down.

The only other point I wish to make concerns the role of a common polymorphism in the expression of one rare disease. This is a disease in which I have been interested for a couple of years. It is called diaphysial aclasis, and it is characterized by the development of numerous osteochondromata, predominantly from the ends of the long bones, but also at a great many other sites.

Stocks and Barrington (1925) demonstrated that the disease was determined by an autosomal dominant gene. Although they did not explicitly say so, they did show quite clearly that this was the most likely genetic mechanism.

Harris (1948) adduced strong evidence that the disease could be suppressed in females by a second autosomal dominant gene at a different locus. In other words, the disease was determined by two genes, the first was an autosomal dominant which caused the disease, and the second was another autosomal dominant which suppressed the disease in the female.

Our own experience with this disease which is quite common among the Chamorro people of Guam suggested that the second gene affected the severity rather than the penetrance of the first one.

This is one particular family we saw on Guam (figure 1) and I will show you the pelvic x-rays on both sisters. Both of these women were clinically involved, and both of them, as you can see, transmitted the gene, but they differed considerably in the severity of their involvement.

Figure 2 is an x-ray of a woman whom I suppose Harris would say did not have the autosomal modifying gene, and she has this huge pelvic osteochondroma.

Figure 3 is an x-ray of her sister. I don't think it shows too well in this x-ray but she had slight clinical involvement elsewhere. She is a woman whom I suppose Harris would say did have the autosomal dominant gene that tends to suppress the disease.

Well, this must seem like an inexcusable digression, but the point is that Harris' computations, which I personally believe, indicate that the frequency of the modifying gene is of the order of 30 per cent in European populations. So here presumably is a polymorphism, and it is quite possible that it is one of the known ones; one of the blood

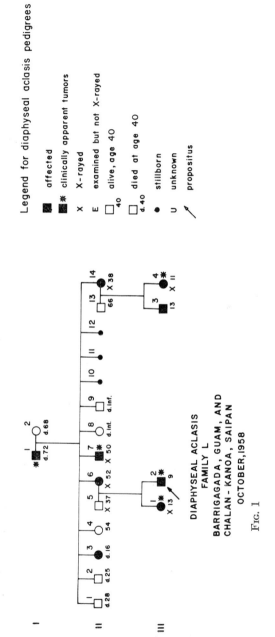

Legend for diaphyseal aclasis pedigrees

affected

clinically apparent tumors

X   X-rayed

E   examined but not X-rayed

40   alive, age 40

d.40 died at age 40

stillborn

U   unknown

proposᵢtus

DIAPHYSEAL ACLASIS
FAMILY L
BARRIGAGADA, GUAM, AND
CHALAN-KANOA, SAIPAN
OCTOBER, 1958

Fɪɢ. 1

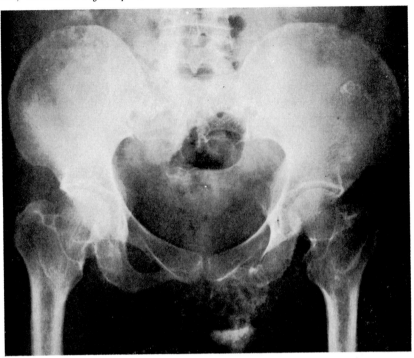

Fig. 2

groups or one of the biochemical abnormalities which Dr. Motulsky and Dr. Gartler are discussing.

We have not as yet collected evidence on that.

I wonder whether such phenomena might not be comparatively common. Of course, you are all familiar with the published cases of phenylketonuria and other diseases which appear greatly attenuated in occasional people who have had no therapy.

I should think that to study the role of known polymorphisms on diseases such as these, where the basic abnormality is biochemical and where the enzymatic mechanism is known, would put one into a strong position to inquire further into the way in which the common genes modify the rare ones. And one should end up by learning more about the action of the common gene, since one will see it acting on a known biochemical system.

Dr. Blumberg: Dr. Boyer, could you please comment on Dr. Motulsky's paper.

Dr. Boyer: I have only a very few comments. I am in the position of a second-year medical student being asked to comment on Cannon's diagram of the shock syndrome.

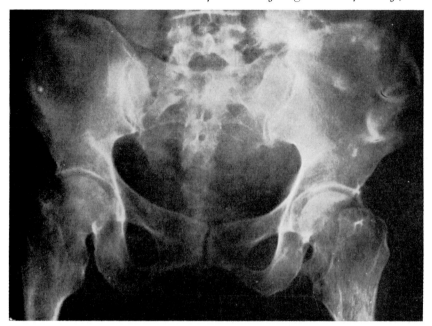

Fig. 3

I have heard accounts of this system before but I know of no system that has so rapidly become so complicated and at once seems to admit, on the one hand, to a great number of simple solutions, and a great number of imponderables on the other. This is a very unstable system, dependent on such things as Mussolini and the ecology of flowering plants. I want to ask if any work has been put forward on this. Do the mountains of Sardinia have fava beans? Do they flower at later times? Are they different in any way?

I would wonder what advantages, if any, a heterozygous mother might possess, and I might wonder about the fate of a fetus she was carrying which was hemizygous, particularly when she was exposed to flowering plants in the spring and at the time of pregnancy.

This, of course, brings into the very bright focus the problems raised by Dr. Neel this morning on the relative importance of differential survival and differential fertility. This, I think, would become particularly true in the United States where we no longer have very much malaria, and where aside from infants eating mothballs and some people getting primaquine for a variety of other reasons, we may be comparatively free of risk.

The Pygmies interested me very much, particularly the high level of sickling in that area, and I wondered if the sickling alone might be enough to handle the malaria. What do you feel about additive effects of these two genes (G-6-PD deficiency and sickle) in a high malarial area, and their relative roles. I also wondered if the Pygmies might have in their genetic constitution certain factors that made them overly susceptible to glucose-6-phosphate dehydrogenase deficiency.

I'd like to throw this problem out to this group because these people are hard to find, namely, a Negro with Klinefelter's syndrome.

We have one such. When they are found, a study of the family may help us distinguish between primary meiotic non-disjunction and secondary meiotic non-disjunction. Given the right sort of family we may get some help from this.

DR. LILIENFELD: Is there any age variation in the frequency of this trait?

DR. MOTULSKY: We don't have enough data to say that about any given population. Whenever we did these screening studies, we had between 100 and 1,000 subjects. Very frequently they were school children.

DR. LILIENFELD: These were all based on school children?

DR. MOTULSKY: In Sardinia, we tested school children almost exclusively. In Africa, there were some older subjects, but the majority were also children.

DR. H. GORDON: I thought that at this late stage of the afternoon, it might interest the group to hear something of the nonmedical application of glucose-6-phosphate dehydrogenase deficiency studies.

We often hear a lot of discussion about the Falasha Jews. These are a group of dark skinned Jews who live among the Ethiopians in Abyssinia. They claim that they descended from the Queen of Sheba and King Solomon about 950 B.C. That is their tradition. Some Biblical scholars, however, feel that they are of somewhat later origin, having descended from Oriental Jews who arrived in Ethiopia around the beginning of the Christian era; while a third group of spoilsports have said that these aren't Jews at all but are Ethiopians who had been converted before the Middle Ages to a form of Judaism which they have since maintained.

You will be interested to hear that Szeinberg and Sheba and their associates in Israel have found that the enzyme deficiency trait does not occur in the Falasha Jews. In this respect they resemble the rest of the non-Jewish Ethiopian community and they differ from other Oriental Jewish groups. This is in keeping with the theory of their non-Hebrew origin. While not of great public health significance, these observations should be of interest to archaeologists and Biblical scholars.

DR. BLUMBERG: We are very fortunate to have Dr. Wilson with us who, in addition to being the Executive Secretary of the Genetics Study Section, is also a botanist.

DR. WILSON: Now that I have heard these reports I'd be interested in learning what the exact distributions of these plants are.

DR. MOTULSKY: I tried to find out about distribution of the fava bean in Africa and I couldn't find it. I was told that it doesn't exist.

DR. BOYD: It is not always called the fava bean.

DR. NEEL: Is there just one or are there several species of fava bean?

DR. BOYD: It is the only one of that genus used for human food, isn't it, as far as I know. But it's a good question.

DR. MOTULSKY: The ordinary kind of bean we eat here (Phaseolus) does not produce hemolysis in susceptible individuals.

DR. BOYD: They are not the same genus.

DR. BLUMBERG: An observation which may have some bearing on the present discussion was made by Earle (1941). He reported an acute hemolytic anemia in Jamaicans following the ingestion of "bush tea," which is brewed from *Lignum vitae*. It's of interest that this article is adjacent to that of Lederer describing Baghdad Spring Fever, one of the original reports of favism in Eastern Jews.

Can anyone suggest any other natural foods which might be related to the G-6-PD deficiency?

DR. BOYD: No. There are many plants with much stronger hemagglutinins than the fava bean has, but none of them as far as I know cause any disease like this. The funny thing about fava beans is that they are active when cooked, so the active agent is probably not a protein.[1]

DR. SUTTON: I noticed that it is now possible to buy toasted fava beans in this country for consumption with cocktails.

DR. BOYD: There is nothing new about that. I have been serving them to guests for at least five years.

DR. BLUMBERG: Do you consider this a proper way of getting cases, Dr. Boyd?

DR. BOYD: Haven't got one yet.

DR. WITKOP: There are some beans in Africa that produce a photo-dynamic effect, the trail bean. This is a hot weather plant. With trail bean ingestion and sunlight the patients are prone to eruptions and blisters. One of the antiparasite drugs tested in London worked without side effects but in sunny Africa caused severe photodynamic effects.

DR. SELLA: One striking fact about favism is that in Italy it spreads mainly in regions where fava is raised and not in regions where fava is uncommon. Lombardy, for instance, raises very little fava and has no favism.

---

[1] (*Footnote added by Dr. Motulsky, April 1961*) Cooked fava beans usually do not produce hemolytic anemia. (See also Bowman and Walker 1961)

DR. SUTTON: Are you talking about the difference between raising and eating it?

DR. SELLA: Yes.

DR. SUTTON: They eat it in Lombardy?

DR. SELLA: Very little and certainly less than in southern Italy.

DR. BOYD: What about Italy? They eat it commonly there and favism isn't common.

DR. MOTULSKY: We don't have studies on trait frequency in metropolitan Italy yet. You read in Herodotus that the Egyptian priests forbade ingestion of fava beans. One wonders whether they prohibited it for fear of possible hemolysis. The Pythagoreans also were forbidden to eat beans; their center was in southern Italy.

DR. GARTLER: Do you find any relationship between the cultivation of the bean and the frequency of the trait?

DR. MOTULSKY: Dr. Siniscalco is trying to get these data from the Agricultural Department in Italy.

DR. BEARN: Has any fractionation of the fava bean been carried out?

DR. MOTULSKY: Italian investigators have performed work in this field with no clear results. I don't know of any recent studies trying to find the chemical factor in the bean which is responsible for hemolysis.[1] It is known that susceptible persons may develop hemolysis from passing by a flowering field of fava beans. It has been pointed out that, contrary to popular belief, the pollen is not responsible. Presumably, a volatile substance comes off the flowering plant, since people working in fava storage bins, where there is no pollen in the air, develop hemolysis by inhaling the volatile products of freshly stored fava beans.

Answering Dr. Krooth's question, the type of malaria seen in England and the southern United States is vivax malaria which is infrequently lethal and therefore not an important selective agent.

In relation to Dr. Boyer's question, nothing is known about the effect on pregnancy and fertility rates and sibship numbers. Such data need to be collected.

I have wondered whether there is an additive effect of these genes (sickling, glucose-6-phosphate dehydrogenase deficiency, and thalassemia) for malaria protection. I would like to think that natural resist-

---

[1] Bowman and Walker (1961) have recently reported that incubation with erythrocytes of fresh young whole beans of *Vicia faba* or saline extracts of fresh beans, pollen, or pistils all show a selective reduction of glutathione in erythrocytes of sensitive (enzyme deficient) compared with nonsensitive subjects. They also showed that this effect was not due to other common reducing agents such as ascorbic acid and cysteine, nor was the effect found with other plants tested such as whole peas and runner beans.

ance to malaria might work like natural resistance to many of the other diseases discussed yesterday. Where this has been genetically studied, it turns out to be a polygenic system. Maybe sickling, thalassemia, and the enzyme deficiency are components of a polygenic system. Probably, there are many more genes involved.

For instance, the West African Negro is very resistant to vivax malaria. He is natively resistant but I don't know why. The sickling and enzyme deficiency genes do not appear to be involved.

Protection conferred by these red cell abnormalities may be relatively small, but together they may add up in a polygenic system that might become very important. One might suppose that if two of the traits are present together in a person, they might be more protective than one alone. Data on these points should be accumulated.

Other studies required are: What is the hematologic effect on red cell survival in individuals who inherit both the enzyme deficiency and sickling trait? It appears that they are phenotypically normal if not exposed to drugs or beans. What about red cell survival in people who have thalassemia and the enzyme trait? Since younger cells have more enzyme even in deficient subjects, thalassemia has been demonstrated to raise the enzyme level of deficient subjects (Adinolfi, et al, 1960, and Siniscalco, et al, 1961). The effect of this interaction on red cell survival needs to be studied.

DR. REED: Why don't these effects express themselves at birth instead of waiting for several years, if they are genic?

DR. MOTULSKY: They are expressed at birth. If you have an enzyme deficiency you are born with it. This enzyme, in contrast to many other enzymes, is present in cord red cells. If a child is deficient he starts out being deficient.

DR. REED: I mean there is a change in the percentage of persons immune between birth and 10 years, is there not?

DR. MOTULSKY: Yes.

DR. REED: But there is not a change in the genic components of these people who have become immune in the 10 years.

DR. MOTULSKY: But this is a completely different mechanism. Acquired immunity develops and acts quite independently from natural acquired resistance such as is determined by sickling or enzyme deficiency. An infant in a malarial environment is born with antibodies acquired from the mother, that is, passive immunity against malaria. These antibodies will have disappeared by six months. The baby is now highly susceptible to malaria.

At this point, and until the child has built up its own acquired immunity to malaria, it makes a difference whether the child is a sickler or enzyme deficient in terms of whether it will or will not die from malaria. By the age of four years, sufficient actively acquired immunity has developed that malarial deaths probably are uncommon after such an age. The period from six months to four years is the critical period of malarial mortality. Active immunity has not yet developed, and at this time slight genetic differences may mean the difference between survival and death from malaria. Consequently, critical studies to demonstrate these effects need to be done at this time.

DR. NEWMAN: I am curious as to the 18 per cent of the deficiency you got in one group of South American Indians.

DR. MOTULSKY: I didn't get that. These are Oyana Indians, a very small tribe. Dr. Marks and his group obtained these data. There are about 90 individuals, and one is not sure how much relatedness there may be. The figure may be falsely high.

DR. NEWMAN: But if so, isn't this the first reaction, presumably genic, that one can see in New World aborigines to malaria?

DR. MOTULSKY: Yes. We are very interested in mapping the incidence of this gene in aboriginal North and South American populations starting from Alaskan Eskimos, Alaskan Indians, North American and South American Indians. The data we have indicate absence of the gene in Alaskan Eskimos and Indians.

DR. BOYD: This proves malaria is a new disease in the New World.

DR. BOYER: I wonder whether you have sufficient data within Seattle to give us a tridimensional plot, a plot involving fava distribution, glucose-6-phosphate-dehydrogenase deficiency and ahaptoglobinemia.

DR. GIBLETT: It doesn't fit very well. The Pygmies had a high incidence of ahaptoglobinemia, but a low incidence of enzyme deficiency.

DR. BOYER: But you don't know about the beans there or any other flowering plant.

DR. MOTULSKY: We don't know about the bean or possible other hemolytic foods among the Pygmies. The low frequency of the enzyme deficiency among the Pygmies might be a spurious result. It may be that they are exposed to a hemolytic agent all the time. Their general health was worse than anyone else. Our screening test would give a falsely low population incidence if these Pygmies were actively hemolyzing. Under these circumstances, the severely enzyme-deficient red cells would be gone. The remaining cells would have enough enzyme to give a normal screening test. It would be nice to study the Pygmies with the spectrophotometric test.

DR. BOYER: Do they have ahaptoglobinemia in higher frequency?

DR. GIBLETT: It was one of the tribes with the highest frequency. The urban areas were relatively free of ahaptoglobinemia. But in the rural areas it varied from something like 15 to 30 per cent.

DR. MOTULSKY: There was a good correlation between social status and living conditions and the incidence of ahaptoglobinemia. Among the Pygmies the incidence of ahaptoglobinemia was quite high, while among African school children living in a fairly decent nonmalarial area it was very low.

There is no relationship between enzyme deficiency and ahaptoglobinemia in nonmalarial Seattle Negroes.

9

COMMENTS ON THE POPULATION DYNAMICS OF β-AMINOISOBUTYRIC ACIDURIA

*STANLEY M. GARTLER**

INTRODUCTION

B ETA-AMINOISOBUTYRIC ACID (BAIB) is a non-protein amino acid derived from the catabolism of thymine, and which has been found in
significant amounts only in human urine (Gartler, et al., 1956; Fink, et al.,
1956). Approximately 90 per cent of Caucasoid individuals excrete less
than 40 mg. of BAIB per day (low excretors) whereas some 10 per cent
may excrete up to 300 mg. per day (high excretors) (Harris 1953). Individual differences are relatively constant and in general have no obvious
pathological associations. Though environmental factors are known to
affect BAIB excretion, most of the variation between individuals is under
genetic control, with high excretors being homozygous for a single recessive gene and low excretors either homozygous or heterozygous for the
dominant allele (Harris 1953; Calchi-Novati, et al., 1953; Gartler 1956;
Gartler, et al., 1957). These genotypic differences apparently lead to
phenotypes differing in their utilization of BAIB and consequently in their
urinary excretion rates of this substance (Gartler 1959[a]; Gartler
1959[b]). Population studies have revealed marked differences in the frequency of high excretors in various racial groups, the range, at a time when
only a handful of groups have been investigated, already extending from
10 to 90 per cent (Gartler, et al., 1956; Gartler, et al., 1957; Sutton and
Clark 1955; Allison, et al., 1959; Blumberg and Gartler 1959). It can be
seen that β-aminoisobutyric aciduria represents one of the many polymorphisms almost ubiquitous in man, and it is on the question of the nature
of the forces acting on this polymorphism that I will talk today.

For any given polymorphism, one would like to know the magnitude
and direction of the selective and mutational forces involved, and the
particular migrational patterns and population structures. Given such
data, an equation can be written describing the polymorphism; that is,
its stability, or if instability, its direction and rate of change.

It is doubtful whether such complete information has ever been col-

---

* U. S. Public Health Service Senior Research Fellow.

lected for any polymorphism. In those systems where there is severe selection against one genotype, quantitative considerations may still be profitably attempted in spite of incomplete data. Stability of the polymorphism can be safely assumed, and if the compensatory requirement for stability is large enough, it is possible that some direct quantitative evaluation of the system can be made.

For most polymorphisms where there are no obvious selective differences between the genotypes, field quantitation of the problem may present a Herculean task. The order of magnitude of the forces required in such systems is so low that numerous explanations are possible and statistical demonstration may require prohibitive numbers. The stability of such systems is often implied from the observation of similar polymorphisms in ancestral forms. However, in the case of β-aminoisobutyric aciduria, this argument cannot be used, since this variant has only been found in man. A survey of over 55 primates (Gartler, et al, 1956) and of a number of small laboratory mammals failed to reveal a single instance of high or even moderate excretion of BAIB. Parenthetically, it should be pointed out that the existence of similar polymorphisms in different forms is far from good evidence for the stability of a polymorphism, since it is almost certain that there would be molecular heterogeneity between the systems.

Because of these difficulties, investigators have concentrated on indirect approaches to such systems. Three types of information have generally been collected: distributional data, disease associations, and general physiologic and biochemical correlations. It is from these three standpoints that I will consider the presently available data on β-aminoisobutyric aciduria.

DISTRIBUTIONAL DATA

Distributional data can be of special significance in a number of instances. A restricted geographic and/or racial distribution suggest relationships of the polymorphism to local environmental factors or perhaps origin and radiation of a new variant. Extreme populational variability (a flat or U shaped distribution of populations with respect to gene frequency) indicates drift as the major force affecting the system. However, most polymorphisms exhibit wide geographic distributions with approximately a normal distribution of populations with respect to gene frequency. Such distributions are subject to a number of interpretations and therefore are of limited analytic value. It is of course necessary to collect such data, even if only to exclude possible definitive distributions. Furthermore, such data may be of considerable interest in determining affinities of different groups and tracing migrational histories.

The distributional data available for BAIB excretion are at present quite limited (table 1). However, they clearly exclude a restricted dis-

TABLE 1—*Frequency of High BAIB Excretors in Various Populations*

Population	Source	Number	Frequency
American Whites	Gartler 1956	280	7
English Whites	Harris 1953	345	9
Italian Whites	Calchi-Novati, et al, 1953	792	7
Apache Indians	Gartler, et al, 1957	115	59
Pima Indians	Gartler and Kraus, Unpub.	118	50
Papago Indians	Gartler and Kraus, Unpub.	42	50
Athabascan Indians	Allison, et al, 1959	25	56
Eskimos	Allison, et al, 1959	120	23
Marshall Islanders (Rongelap Island)	Blumberg and Gartler, 1959	188	86
New York Negroes	Gartler and Firschein, Unpub.	40	29
Black Caribs	Gartler, et al, 1957	245	39

tribution both racially and geographically. There appears to be amazing uniformity among populations within the different racial groups but again the data are too limited to consider this significant. The general picture at present is that of low frequencies of high excretors in Caucasoids, intermediate in Negroes, and relative high frequencies of high excretors in Mongoloid groups. It would be of interest to compare eastern and western European populations to see if a cline in the distribution of BAIB excretion rates was present similar to that found for the Rh gene. The low frequencies of western European groups and the high frequencies found in Mongoloids predicts such a cline.

DISEASE ASSOCIATIONS

The search for possible associations between various diseases and polymorphisms has been a widely used approach to the problem of the dynamics of the ubiquitous polymorphisms. Such associations, when demonstrated, do not in themselves prove selective differences, though this appears to be often implied. However, they may offer valuable clues to our understanding of the biology of the particular polymorphism, and in this sense are very valuable.

A number of reports have appeared indicating possible relationships between β-aminoisobutyric aciduria and various diseases. The first association of this type was that between malignancy and BAIB excretion. Fink (1951), one of the discoverers of BAIB, first isolated BAIB from the urines of subjects with malignant disease. At least two more papers have appeared reporting increased urinary BAIB excretion in malignant disease (Gartler, et al., 1956; Ishihari, et al., 1951). However, it appears most likely that increased BAIB excretion in these cases results from nongenetic causes. Any significant increase in DNA metabolism, as may be found in malignant conditions, would lead to an increase in BAIB excretion. This follows, since BAIB is derived from the reductive catabolism of thymine, which in turn is a major constituent of DNA. Further complications are introduced in these diseases by the use of therapeutic agents (e.g., nitrogen mustard, radiation) which interfere with nucleic acid metabolism, and in fact are known to increase BAIB excretion (Awapara and Shullenberger 1957; Rubini, et al., 1959). Though the increase in urinary BAIB excretion in malignant conditions appears to be primarily the effect of the degenerative disease, it must be admitted that the possibility of a more direct association has not been ruled out.

A second possible disease association with BAIB excretion was that of mongolism. Wright and Fink (1957) reported an increased incidence of high BAIB excretors in mongolism. An unpublished study from our laboratory (Gartler and Shepard, unpub.) on some 60 mongoloids failed to confirm Wright and Fink's observation. We observed but 5 high excretors in our group of mongoloids, which is not different from normals. Recently, Perry, et al., (1959) reported on a large study of BAIB excretion in mongolism and also were unable to confirm Wright and Fink's earlier report.

A more intriguing possibility was that between diabetes mellitus and BAIB excretion. The derivation of BAIB from thymine suggested the possibility that the diabetogenic pyrimidine, alloxan, might also be involved in BAIB metabolism, and that this might result in an association between diabetes and BAIB excretion. Fink and Fink (1958) reported such an association. They found fewer high excretors among diabetics than would be expected in the general population. Since the expected frequency of high excretors in the control group was low (Caucasoid sample), their test was not very sensitive. Dr. Bertram Kraus and I (Gartler and Kraus, unpub.) investigated the possibility of this relationship in the Pima Indians, who have both a high frequency of β-amino-isobutyric aciduria (~45%) and a high frequency of diabetes. The frequency of high excretors among some 80 diabetics (~46%) was not less than among the normals. Since then, work in our laboratory (Gartler 1959[a]; Gartler 1959[b]; Gartler, unpub.) has indicated that thymine is the only significant source of BAIB in man, and that alloxan is definitely not involved in BAIB metabolism. This casts further doubt on the possibility of a diabetes-BAIB correlation.

There have been other scattered reports of possible associations between BAIB excretion and disease, the most interesting being that of Pare and Sandler (1954) on march hemoglobinuria. In a series of 12 cases, they found 9 subjects whom they classified as high BAIB excretors. Other associated traits such as increased cystine excretion in these cases suggests that the increased BAIB excretion is a secondary manifestation of the condition. However, these observations should be confirmed.

It appears that the data gathered thus far in this area are not very encouraging. However, it should be kept in mind that the surface has barely been scratched and more promising leads may develop in the future.

GENERAL PHYSIOLOGIC AND BIOCHEMICAL DATA

We know now that neither renal differences nor differences in pyrimidine metabolism are involved in the biochemical genetics of this polymorphism. Rather, it appears that the basic difference involves the metabolism of BAIB, high excretors excreting most of their BAIB, while low excretors metabolize most of theirs. What step or steps may be involved in the metabolism of BAIB are unknown, and it may be that such information could be critical with regard to possible selective factors underlying this polymorphism. One possibility which should be investigated in this respect is a report by Lindon (1954) on the inhibitory effect of BAIB on the growth of yeast. She observed that pantothenic acid reversed this inhibition and suggested that the inhibitory action of BAIB might be due to the formation of α-methyl pantothenic acid. It might be very rewarding to examine this possibility in man.

CONCLUSIONS

It is obvious that the data available on β-aminoisobutyric aciduria are too scanty to permit any significant conclusions as to its population dynamics. Therefore, I should like to close with a few general comments, somewhat speculative in nature, but pertinent to the conference and, more specifically, to β-aminoisobutyric aciduria. We tend to assume that most polymorphisms are selectively balanced. There of course is no question as to the importance of this mechanism in the maintenance of hereditary variability. However, stability is not the salient feature of evolution, but quite to the contrary, change is its major characteristic. It follows that transient polymorphisms should be as important as the balanced ones and possibly as frequent, if not more so. I would suggest that β-aminoisobutyric aciduria may be a transient polymorphism. BAIB formation is essentially a waste pathway, and β-aminoisobutyric aciduria may simply represent a shortening of this pathway. The shortened pathway may have some slight selective advantage and therefore be increasing in frequency. On the other hand, there need be no significant selective differences involved, but only recurrent mutation pressure to the shortened pathway. The rate of change of such a system would be so slow as to be undetectable by our present methods, and one might argue that for practical purposes the polymorphism is stable. However, it is just such a fine difference which should make us wary of shackling ourselves too firmly to the concept of balanced polymorphism.

DISCUSSION

DR. BLUMBERG: Dr. Gartler, were your studies on the lower primates extensive enough to rule out a polymorphism in these species?

DR. GARTLER: No, Dr. Blumberg. However, I would stress the fact that people have been using paper chromatography extensively on a variety of biologic materials, and except for trace amounts, BAIB has been found in high concentrations only in human urine.

DR. BLUMBERG: Dr. Neel, would you like to make some comments on Dr. Gartler's paper, with particular reference to his last provocative remark about the prevalence of transient polymorphisms?

DR. NEEL: There is really no reason to take exception to Dr. Gartler's remarks. Certainly, evolution comes about in several ways. One is through balanced polymorphic systems, and another is through fixation of "new" genes, that is, substitution of one gene for another.

One of the great problems of population genetics today is to decide the relative frequency with which these two types of systems exist in populations.

For instance, in the consideration of matters of radiation genetics, one of the major arguments has arisen from differences of opinion concerning the extent to which the human species is buffered by these balanced polymorphic systems. So I couldn't argue with Dr. Gartler's remarks at all. We have to be prepared to recognize both kinds of genetic systems.

On a somewhat different matter I do have a question, Dr. Gartler. As we all know, the trend in the last ten or twenty years is to recognize that the so-called recessive biochemical traits do have heterozygote manifestations. With your hypothesis that high excretors are homozygous—what about heterozygotes? Shouldn't we be looking for a trimodality?

DR. GARTLER: We have compared the BAIB excretion rates of known heterozygotes and controls, but have found no difference.

DR. NEEL: I thought your feeding experiments were beautiful; wouldn't this be a way to go at it?

DR. GARTLER: It would be worth a try. However, I would favor concentrating on the problem of what happens to BAIB in low excretors. I believe that if we knew more about this step, the detection of heterozygotes might be achieved.

DR. NEEL: Even without knowing that step, you can isolate some families where you are reasonably sure the non-excretor is a homozygote, and

other families where you are reasonably sure the excretor is a homozygote, and do feeding experiments.

DR. GARTLER: Yes.

DR. SUTTON: Following up this particular line of reasoning, I think there are some facts to be considered concerning the delicate question of whether or not BAIB is excreted.

In the induced excretions, it seems that almost any small increase in tissue destruction, whether by radiation or not, causes BAIB to appear in the urine. Yet, we know that tissue destruction is a perfectly normal process, in fact, a rather large process (Leblond and Walker 1956). So that we have here, if one considers it quantitatively, a very small percentage of increase in this normal process which throws a normal person into the excretor range.

This is a rather odd situation, and I think it is particularly odd that the heterozygous individuals, of whom one would assume the metabolism of BAIB is decreased, are able to handle just 100 per cent of normal, but not 110 per cent. There is no leeway.

You also mentioned there was no age effect. I think you did use five years as your lower limit.

DR. GARTLER: At very early ages I believe there may be an age effect.

DR. SUTTON: But I believe Calchi-Novati, et al., (1954) in their Italian population did report that those they consider to be heterozygotes below the age of five years were high excretors. There is a certain time during the early years when an individual who is heterozygous becomes a low excretor by their standards. This obviously introduces some problems in population studies if a person can change his phenotype with age.

DR. NEEL: I'm not quite sure I'm with you on this delicate balance argument. It seems to me that either radiation or leukemia is a fairly traumatic experience in terms of stepped-up tissue destruction. How big a slug of radiation does it take to convert nonexcretors to excretors?

DR. SUTTON: Am I not correct, that it is only people who show other signs of radiation sickness that excrete it?

DR. BLUMBERG: I happen to have the paper describing such a study with me.

Rubini, et al., (1959) studied 8 people who received mixed neutron and gamma radiation as a result of an industrial accident at Oak Ridge, Tennessee. The total exposure ranged from 21 to 276 rads. The BAIB excretion was markedly increased (and the increase appeared to be proportional to dose), but within 8 days had decreased considerably.

DR. GARTLER: Later Rubini, et al., showed they all went back to normal, and I think they were all normally low excretors.

DR. SUTTON: In any event, in tissue destruction there is a large daily turnover, when you consider the turnover in blood-forming elements and things of this sort. Then there is the slightly increased tissue destruction resulting from, say, radiation.

DR. NEEL: That is where we part company, you see. I don't know whether it is only a slightly increased tissue destruction. Two hundred or three hundred roentgen of radiation is a fairly traumatic experience for most people.

DR. BLUMBERG: There is a report available on the urinary BAIB excretion of the Micronesian inhabitants of Rongelap who received relatively high doses of radiation in 1954 (Blumberg and Gartler 1960).

DR. NEEL: The last estimate of this exposure was 175 roentgen.

DR. BLUMBERG: There was no significant difference in the BAIB excretion of the exposed and unexposed groups (in fact, the prevalence of high excretors was high in both), nor was the BAIB excretion related to the body load of Cesium [137] or Zinc[65].

DR. MOTULSKY: I would like to amplify Dr. Gartler's final remarks. One should consider that one might get a mutation to a trait which at the time of the mutation might have a selective advantage, and lasts for a number of generations and then finally disappears. A mutation protecting against an extinct infectious disease might be an example.

By natural selection many generations ago such a trait may reach a certain frequency. Once the selective advantage has disappeared, the trait may be quite neutral and thus continue at its attained frequency from then on.

DR. BOYER: What do nitrogen mustards do to the excretion of BAIB?

DR. GARTLER: They will also increase BAIB excretion. Awapara and Shullenberger (1957) reported on this and demonstrated that nitrogen mustard therapy had much the same effect as radiation in leading to an increase in urinary BAIB.

DR. REED: I would like to agree with Dr. Gartler that transient polymorphisms are no doubt much more important in the evolution of our species or any other, because they are the way in which the new genes become fixed. Whether they are more common than balanced polymorphisms is, I think, still an open matter. I would never insist that the balanced polymorphisms are more important in any given sense. They are merely one of the two possible types.

As far as his remark on blood groups, we cannot prove they are balanced, but I think if you consider that our former ancestors swinging in the trees have some of these same antigens now and are polymorphic themselves—we have to consider that possibility.

DR. BOYD: I also don't doubt that transients are very important in evolution. I don't see how you could have evolution if you didn't have transients. I am not too convinced you have one here, because you haven't shown loss of any one of the genotypes.

In the blood groups we haven't shown that either, and in the case of PTC—which I have always thought is a balanced polymorphism because you find polymorphism way down in the evolutionary scale—I don't know of any evidence that any one of the genotypes is lost preferentially. I think maybe this is harder to prove.

It is not always too easy to prove that you have a balanced polymorphism. The difference in fitness doesn't have to be very great to result in equilibrium, according to Fisher's mathematical theory. If the fitness of the heterozygote is just a little greater than that of the homozygote, you will have an equilibrium.

DR. SUTTON: One of the points which Dr. Gartler made is that there are clearly nonhereditary factors which influence this trait.

DR. GARTLER: Such as exposure to radiation.

DR. SUTTON: In looking at some of your data with your new method of measurement, I find analysis of variance indicates some residual individuality within the high excretor group. Do you have any evidence that this is a nonhereditary variation?

DR. GARTLER: In our Carib family study, we analyzed the variability within and between high excretors in different families and found that this variation was compatible with random or nonhereditary causes.

DR. SUTTON: So far as the diet effects go, we did one very small experiment involving only one high excretor and one low excretor, putting these individuals on what seemed to be the proper sort of diet to cut down excretion. And after a week on this diet, there was absolutely no difference in the levels excreted.

DR. GARTLER: What did you consider the proper sort of diet?

DR. SUTTON: A non-meat protein diet.

DR. GARTLER: That is quite interesting.

DR. SUTTON: So I feel that the trait, whatever the cause is, is reasonably free of short-term environmental effects.

DR. DUBLIN: I had two questions I wanted to address to Dr. Gartler, but before doing so I had a comment that seemed to be apropos, or perhaps it is one the members of the conference will challenge.

Within the last ten years or so, with the introduction by Enders and others of tissue culture techniques, there followed a rapid flurry of isolations of new viruses. So much so, that we went into a period in which virologists started playing a game called "viruses in search of disease." More recently, a wide variety of new methods of detecting biochemical traits have been introduced and perhaps we are approaching another scientific game of "biochemical traits in search of pathology or abnormal physiology." It seems to me that the process that Dr. Gartler has described is just that: What is the significance of an abnormal biochemical trait in terms of human physiology?

Well, this is my early morning philosophic comment. But it leads to two questions: Is there substantial evidence for the genetic basis of BAIB excretion? Have you done studies of familial groups in which your index person is a high or low excretor? Although I think you indicated that it was Harris who proposed the genetic explanation, I missed some of your discussion of that hypothesis.

My second question concerns further studies of this trait. Since this trait is related to some type of cellular metabolic process, is it possible to study it in an experimental culture system? In other words, could you identify tissues in which the formation of this biochemical compound takes place, so that it might be possible to simplify some of your studies of the metabolic processes by use of a tissue culture experimental model?

Dr. GARTLER: There have been five family studies of the variation in BAIB excretion (Harris 1953; Calchi-Novati, et al., 1953; Gartler 1956; Gartler, et al., 1957; and De Grouchy and Sutton 1957). The results of all these studies have demonstrated that most of the variation between the individuals in BAIB excretion is controlled by genetic differences. The first four studies are compatible with a single gene difference underlying the observed variation in BAIB excretion, while De Grouchy and Sutton feel the genetics is more complicated.

Your second question about tissue culture and BAIB is something I am quite interested in. We have tried to work with this system in tissue culture but so far have been completely unsuccessful in attempting to demonstrate BAIB formation in mammalian cell cultures. Unfortunately this is going to be a serious problem for the future of somatic genetics of mammalian cells. That is, though genetic differences may be clearly expressed in the intact organisms, these same genetic differences may be completely masked in cell cultures derived from these organisms.

Dr. NEEL: My comment was just to take Dr. Dublin up on his first comment. One philosophic remark leads to another.

Dr. Dublin, this remark has been made a number of times in recent years, that we are in the situation of having new genetic systems where we are looking really for their physiologic counterparts. And I think your remark forms a natural bridge to the considerations of the latter part of this morning in the following sense, that when one sees somebody prostrate with a fulminating disease, one is pretty sure he has been struck by some etiologic agent. If one follows the well recognized techniques of isolating possible agents, one is liable to find a virus or bacteria. You know if you do the right thing something is going to come out the other end.

Our problem is that many of these polymorphisms are such that we do not know where to look for the physiologic counterpart, and we're somewhat suspicious, since there are so many that they can't all have major effects. Therefore, we must start looking for small physiologic correlations, and when we do that, working with populations, we are in an order of magnitude of research effort which rather shakes a lot of us.

Dr. Myrianthopoulos: I would like to make some comments of a very general nature. I have made these comments before in print, but I feel that they would not be out of place if they are reiterated here.

During these two and a half days of conference, we have heard from epidemiologists and we have heard from geneticists. We all know that the epidemiologist studies the natural history of disease by determining its frequency, sex and geographic distribution, population selectivity and so on. And the geneticist who is interested in population genetics, studies the natural history of genetic disease, as Drs. Neel and Schull have pointed out in their excellent book (Neel and Schull 1954), by considering the dynamic balance between mutation and selection. In doing so, he uses epidemiologic tools.

I think it has become clear to all of us during this conference that the areas of activity of the epidemiologist and the population geneticist overlap to a great extent. Although in the past, these two disciplines have cooperated loosely, I think the next step should be to integrate them a little more formally, by establishing within the National Institutes of Health and in Departments of Genetics and Public Health in other institutions, functioning epidemiologic-genetic teams.

There are many areas in which the epidemiologic-genetic team would do a more efficient job and in a shorter period of time, than if the two disciplines were working independently or loosely together. I would like to give two examples from our own experience, where the cooperation of the geneticist and the epidemiologist may be instrumental in the solution of puzzling and important problems.

Dr. Mackay and myself feel that we have demonstrated a genetic factor operating in multiple sclerosis (Mackay and Myrianthopoulos 1958; Myrianthopoulos and Mackay, 1960). This genetic factor is obviously not clearcut. Now, multiple sclerosis has a peculiar geographic distribution. It is more frequent in colder climates than in warmer ones (Kurland and Westlund 1954). It is possible, perhaps, by an epidemiologic-genetic effort to investigate whether climatal environmental agents exert some kind of inhibitory influence over the genetic factor in multiple sclerosis, resulting in reduced penetrance in some areas.

Another striking example is the history of amyotrophic lateral sclerosis. This disease has a uniform distribution in the United States and other countries, except on the Island of Guam, where in some places about 10 per cent of the deaths are due to amyotrophic lateral sclerosis (Kurland 1957).

There is evidence that genetic factors are involved in the etiology of amyotrophic lateral sclerosis. In the United States only a small percentage of cases has positive family history. On Guam, however, there seems to be a familial concentration of cases indicative of dominant inheritance (Kurland and Mulder 1955). Why is this so? It has been suggested that the Spaniards may have introduced the gene for the disease on Guam when they colonized the Island. This seems unlikely because Spaniards have a high frequency of the Rh negative gene which we don't find on Guam (Myrianthopoulos and Pieper 1959).

On the other hand it is possible that the gene was so introduced, or that it arose by mutation and then it was fixed to its present high frequency by some selective mechanism involving geographic isolation and population size. This situation on Guam is within the realm of investigation of the epidemiologic-genetic team.

These are areas in which the epidemiologist and the geneticist can function profitably together. I suggest that these two disciplines be given the opportunity to integrate in a functional way, not only here but in other institutions where there is an interest in population genetics.

DR. MOTULSKY: The opening of a section on population genetics can help in a variety of ways. So often when one studies a disease which differs in frequency in different populations the first question that comes to mind is: Is this environmental or genetic?

One way to facilitate research on a given disease is to study different populations living in rather similar environments. Careful study of the differences in incidence and natural history of diseases in genetically distinct populations that exist here in the United States would be a logical step. We have a large American Negro population for instance. You have heard about the studies on the American Indian population done by Dr. McDermott's group on which other people have commented. Again, further genetic refinement might be brought into these investigations. There is a large American Jewish population which could be studied profitably from these viewpoints.

We have here three well defined population groups in the United States that could be extensively studied. In many cases geneticists have performed such investigations only from their angle and epidemiologists only from theirs. A combination of the two approaches through this Institute would help us to find out more about such diseases.

Another population geneticist's paradise is Hawaii. Dr. Newton Morton has been doing studies there recently. Here again we have genetically varying populations living in essentially the same environment.

I mentioned the Jewish populations in Israel. They are of quite different ethnic origins, and from what I observed last year, some material aid would be of great help in finding out differences in these populations which would be helpful not only from a genetic and anthropologic but also from a medical viewpoint.

One other area that comes to mind is contact with the recently formed National Research Council committee investigating tropical disease conditions in various areas of the world. It would be worthwhile to familiarize this committee with the population genetic implications of some of their surveys. Valuable hints for future studies of the type discussed here might be forthcoming from such liaison.

There has been mention in this conference of malaria and its possible interaction with hereditary blood conditions. In my contact with malariologists, I have found that many have not paid much attention to the interaction of genetic traits and malaria or they have been quite skeptical about any attempts to study this interaction. Here again, it is necessary to get the geneticists and malariologists together for more detailed studies than have been possible by individual effort. Similarly, at the World Health Organization there is a lot of effort spent on malaria control. From what I can gather from their publications, they are not too much concerned with the type of approach we have been discussing here.

I would like to mention a few specific studies which have been suggested to me by my colleagues in Seattle, who are interested in other areas of medical population genetics.

Dr. Decker, at our university, recently discovered that the incidence of gout is 20 times as high among Filipinos as in a Caucasian population in Seattle. He has amplified these studies and determined uric acid levels in a large Filipino population in comparison with European-American and Japanese populations. It is clear that the normal uric acid level in Filipinos is significantly higher than in Europeans.

He is presently trying to find out whether he is dealing with a single-gene or with a polygenic system. Family studies in the Philippines would help his studies considerably, and need to be encouraged.

Dr. Rubin in Seattle is very interested in celiac disease and sprue, basically caused by a genetic defect of the bowel. He has suggested a study on sprue to be done in India. He has very good techniques that permit him to do rapid bowel biopsies on many population members. This has a possible bearing on arteriosclerosis because of the absorptive defects.

He also pointed out the interesting geographic limitation of Plummer-Vincent syndrome. This particular tissue manifestation of iron deficiency is seen in Scandinavian countries but is not seen in other areas of the world. Is there a genetic predisposition that leads Scandinavians to develop this?

Lastly, I think this section probably should concern itself with sponsoring conferences on a given population or a given disease. For instance, a variety of experts on a population could be brought together—archeologists, historians, social anthropologists, physical anthropologists, in addition to geneticists and epidemiologists. In this way a lot of detailed background knowledge can be brought to bear on a population and its genetically conditioned diseases. In many cases the individual worker attempts to get this information, which is difficult to obtain. Often, there are a lot of experts around who could tell us what we want to know. An attempt was made by the Ciba Foundation to study Etruscan biology in this manner (Wolstenholme and O'Connor, Editors, 1959). There are a number of populations such as the American and African Negro populations and Jewish populations which could be discussed more thoroughly and efficiently, and valuable contributions could come out of such conferences.

Dr. BLUMBERG: Another example of striking differences in disease prevalence is that of W. bancrofti filariasis. In the village of Moengo, in Surinam, it was found that there was nearly five times as much microfilaremia in the Creole (Negro) populations as in the Indonesians (Blumberg, et al, 1951). Both of these groups live under similar environmental conditions, although there are differences in nutrition and cultural habits.

There are several intriguing communities where populations of very different origins live under similar environmental conditions. In Surinam, for instance, there are African Negroes (the so-called Djukas) who have had very little intermixture with other races. In addition, there are Indonesians. Hindus, Chinese, and others. There is also a white community which has been resident in Surinam for two hundred years or more. American Indians of various tribal affiliations are the aboriginal inhabitants.

Dr. DUBLIN: At the risk of being facetious, I can see that our next winter's schedule of conferences is already getting quite full.

Dr. J. E. Gordon: First off I would like to endorse the suggestion made about malaria. I wish particularly to suggest at least two people in this country who should be brought into any discussion of malaria as related to human genetics, namely Lewis Hackett and Paul Russell. Those two people, as long-time students of malaria, would contribute much of importance in evaluation of much of the material presented here today.

More generally, I wish to stress the desirability of employing all of the major approaches to knowledge in the attempt to assess the significance of human genetics in present day medical problems. To my mind there are three, whatever the particular field in medicine. Facts are to be had through clinical investigation, or laboratory experiment, or field observation. Effort in this field of human genetics might well be examined to determine how well resources and emphasis are distributed between these three procedures. More pertinently, I recommend attention to the point I made on the first day of this conference, that effort often shifts desirably in the course of an investigation, and according to the progress of the research, with the result that the clinic is called upon to go to the field and the field to come back to the laboratory to refine its observations.

As a third broad consideration, I would be pleased if some attention were given in the general program to the promotion of health, in addition to the prevention of disease. For three days now, our attention has been directed almost completely to methods of preventing disease as a means toward a better state of health. Of course, the viewpoint which dominates the World Health Organization as it does our own United States Public Health Service, is a primary concern with disease rather than with health. I would like to believe in a changing emphasis in health endeavor, an approach toward health itself rather than indirectly. Some health interests as contrasted to disease interests, presumably to be investigated to advantage from the standpoint of genetic as well as cultural influences, would include population dynamics, the changing structure of populations, emotional disorder as distinguished from mental illness, and the problem of urbanization. Investigation in these areas has been predominantly from the social and cultural standpoint. I have the impression from observations in India and other places that a genetic influence could be investigated to advantage.

Dr. Reed: I would just like to extend Dr. Motulsky's consideration to a perhaps more specific proposal, which I think is probably obvious, but which could be of interest to both genetics and epidemiology: I would like to take particular advantage of the unique value of blood as a bearer of genetic information of various types.

If one has chosen a population of interest, be it whites, Negroes,

Jews, or whatever, I think that one very useful study which could be made would be an extensive cooperative investigation, taking bloods from, say, two different age groups, perhaps newborns or children as close to that as possible, and perhaps another cross-section in middle age, 40 to 50 years old. Test them in as many ways as we can for known and possible genetic traits, also analyzing for the presence of antibodies to various diseases as Dr. Paul has discussed. And then, say five years later, we might follow up that group, inquire into their disease experience, their mortality, and try to correlate this with the known genetic factors, thereby getting information on differential selection between various genotypes, if any.

And by this process we would acquire, at the very least, much more extensive descriptive information of the occurrence of these polymorphisms, and with luck we would get some information on the possible role of natural selection in maintaining these polymorphisms.

I think that negative information here, if based on a large sample, would be as valuable, almost as positive. I think, in the light of some studies that have been made so far, we should consider a sample of at least ten thousand for a beginning age group. A larger number would be better.

DR. NEEL: It seems to me our discussions here could take either one of two lines. We could discuss specific things that need doing, or some of the broader basic issues involved in getting the work done.

Each of us probably has some one of several specific projects in mind that he would very much like to get at some time. I know we do, and I am sure Dr. Motulsky does, and the rest of us.

I wonder, however, if it isn't about time that we took a very candid look at some of the general, overall problems involved. And Dr. Reed's remarks actually form an excellent preface to what I wanted to say.

As you brought out, we now have a number of genetic systems searching for functions, so to speak. On theoretic grounds, we have reason to think that in some cases the selective differences between genotypes are probably quite small, of the order of magnitude of one or two per cent, rather than the 25 per cent we are forced to postulate in relation to the sickling genes. And I submit that to come to grips with systems like this is going to take some doing. It will always be fun to nip into a previously unstudied area and determine the frequency of this, that, and the other trait—but to proceed to the next step of trying to find out what is making these systems tick in their local habitat, whether it be the United States of America or Africa or Hawaii, this now calls for an effort of an entirely different order of magnitude.

For instance, a group in our School of Public Health has staked out the town of Tecumseh, near Ann Arbor, for a continuing morbidity survey, trying to get a long-range picture of the illness pattern in a typical American community. They have generously permitted us to participate in their study. Our immediate objective is to type the inhabitants of the town with respect to as many blood groups as possible and to try to correlate the various blood groups with, say, the continuing morbidity picture.

Now in their study of Tecumseh, the School of Public Health investigators are drawing on many of the resources of the University of Michigan Medical School. The study is practical only because Tecumseh is just 25 miles from Ann Arbor and individuals with a variety of skills can participate from time to time in field examinations, with any specimens collected coming back to an already established laboratory. But you begin to talk about mounting that kind of study in far-away places, and it becomes an extremely formidable undertaking.

In this connection, I would draw attention to something we all know, but which nobody has pointed out specifically in this meeting, namely, that the selective circumstances that are responsible for some of the polymorphisms and some of the gene frequencies in which we are interested are changing very rapidly in the world today. The fact has come up again and again in the deliberations of committees at national and international levels that if we want to come to grips with some of these population problems we have to act in the near future, because 15 years from now it will be very difficult to find any community that is really as native as it was 100 years ago.

So I would say, Dr. Dublin, if the Public Health Service is really serious about moving into this area of geographic pathology, and particularly from the genetic slant, the Public Health Service should be given to realize by this gathering and others—if this is the sense of it—that they may be getting into a very expensive undertaking.

Just one other specific point. As Dr. Motulsky pointed out, our tropical disease specialists have not been genetically oriented. The program of WHO since its inception has been oriented toward the usual tropical diseases. There has been good and sufficient reason for this, namely, that there is so much "tropical disease" which can be cleaned up the world over that this is a large and obvious challenge. Nevertheless, times are changing, and WHO is changing with the times. Some of us participated a year ago in writing up a program in human genetics for WHO; this organization is becoming sensitized to the role it might play in this unfolding picture.

DR. DUBLIN: I would like to comment, before the thought gets too buried, on your reference to Tecumseh. Tecumseh, I think, does represent a new type of resource necessary for medical research of the future. There is an increasing number of very able investigators who firmly believe that we must think of research resources in much broader terms than of buildings and laboratory equipment.

We have been working with Dr. Francis and his associates over a period of several years, and I think that the Legislature of Michigan was wiser than some of our Study Sections and Councils were, in that Tecumseh passed through the transition from an idea in the minds of a few people located at Michigan into an operating entity by virtue of some free money appropriated by the Legislature and made available to the University for experimental design and research.

We are now supporting Tecumseh. We are supporting the Framingham Heart Disease Study, where a large segment of the population is being followed on an epidemiologic basis for a period of 20 or more years. We have given a sizeable grant to the California State Health Department, with Dr. Lester Breslow as the principal investigator, to establish a population laboratory in an area encompassing approximately a million population persons residing in the Bay area.

We anticipate that this type of activity will be met with increasing frequency, and because of the high costs involved in large scale field studies, NIH and other granting agencies may have to review and act upon requests for very sizeable and long-term support. We are not overly concerned about the magnitude nor the complexities and difficulties of large scale field study, if the scientists of the country really believe this is the need as well as a desirable avenue along which NIH should proceed. We need groups such as this clearly to express their views on the timeliness, the urgency and the opportunities that exist for resetting our sights from what has been traditionally the NIH approach, namely, the support of the individual investigator on a limited project for a limited time in the laboratory, or clinic.

What are the next steps? If you, as a group, feel that more time and more effort should be spent in planning and developing a type of research resource—a human population laboratory, if there is no better term for it—needed for studies in human genetics, we would like to provide a suitable opportunity for those of you who are willing to sit down and help us to visualize what these needs are and how best to move ahead in this area.

I am not at all disturbed when Dr. Reed says, "We need a population study of no less than 10,000" because it is much better to plan a proper study involving 10,000 or more in the study population and do it well than to support 100 projects in which the sample size is so small that you cannot possibly expect to get any of the answers which are needed. And I think this is a view shared by many of my colleagues here.

Dr. F. H. Allen: I wanted to add something to what Dr. Reed and Dr. Neel have said. When an expedition goes into the field, it would normally be possible, for a relatively small additional expenditure of money involving personnel who wouldn't necessarily have to have much education, to make collections of specimens which would be of enormous value to groups other than those who have planned the primary expedition. And I wonder if it might not be a proper function of this study group perhaps to snoop around and find out who is going where and even encourage or recruit, if necessary, the additional help for these expeditions to make possible these additional collections.

Dr. Newman, for example, some years ago showed clearly the value of this so-called coordinated study, where specimens were collected that were not in his primary field of interest, but which were valuable in the long run.

And in the collection of specimens, it seems to me that it is important not only to get large groups, as Dr. Reed mentioned, but also to get material from families and to get the pedigrees.

This material brought back does not necessarily have to be tested right away. Red cell samples and serum samples both can be frozen by modern techniques.

Dr. H. Gordon: Arising out of what Dr. Motulsky said, I should like to start by saying how much I agree that there seems to be enough genetic and racial polymorphism in the United States to keep the local scientists fully occupied. On the other hand, it is also noteworthy that we are living at present in what must be a unique era in history, in which certain countries, particularly the United States, are going out of their way to supply funds and other help to develop scientific research in countries who are less fortunate.

Apparently, this is being done entirely as a philanthropic gesture to help develop so-called underdeveloped countries. While we can only admire this attitude, may I suggest that this aid may not be entirely one-way and that certain benefits may come from these under-developed countries back to the United States and the other more privileged nations.

In this connection, we in Cape Town like to quote the work on coronary heart disease: much information has been collected, which we hope will be of benefit not only to the "underdeveloped" races studied, but also to those whom we might call the "overdeveloped."

Dr. Dublin: I wonder, Dr. Gordon, whether you are not pointing out an important reciprocal relationship in medical research on an international basis. I am reminded of a conference which I attended on the subject of cardiovascular disease in Latin America where I noticed that our Latin American hosts were less interested in the problem of atherosclerosis, since it was not now one of their major health problems. They could see less satisfaction coming out of studying atherosclerosis among a Latin American population while their big problems were still smallpox and diarrheal diseases. Their interest changed abruptly when one astute observer pointed out that they could look at the problem from a particular vantage point: "Maybe you could teach us something about the protective factors in your environment, and why you South Americans do not get atherosclerosis." It was a very important contribution to the conference, because this gave them a positive focus, namely, that they had something the highly developed or overdeveloped populations lacked.

Dr. H. Gordon: It is kind of you to say it may be a reciprocal relationship; this is what we eventually hope for. Nevertheless we are aware that, at present, the flow across the Atlantic from the United States is much greater than anything which might be flowing Westward from Africa.

As you have emphasized, the great problem in the less privileged countries is that of environmental disease. The local authorities are fully occupied with immense problems of malnutrition and infection and these naturally predominate in their minds over questions of genetic factors. Scientists there will encounter considerable official opposition to any suggestion to provide funds and facilities and to divert trained personnel for the study of genetics. The local authorities will refuse to embark on basic scientific research, which is not immediately productive, while they still have major environmental problems to contend with.

Therefore, I listened with considerable interest to your remarks about the possible availability of financial and other assistance for the study of genetic factors. Unless such external assistance is forthcoming, the adequate development of genetic research projects in Africa, Asia, and other areas cannot be expected.

In Southern Africa, for instance, there are sufficient institutions which could assist in the collection of serum samples for transmission to the U.S.A. for analysis, and the geneticists in this country should take advantage of them. These institutions, however, could serve a much more useful purpose by acting as hosts for visiting scientists from the United States. I do not believe that you should merely visit these institutions for a couple of weeks to collect a few score of blood samples and return home with them. Such visiting scientists would be better advised to stay for several months, during which time they could help to set up new laboratories in the existing institutions, train personnel in genetic procedures and initiate genetic research programs. These projects could then act as peripheral bases in the field for the parent institutions in U.S.A.

If I may take up another moment of your time, I should like to make one last point: that is the question of local controls. In Southern Africa, the whites and Negroes are kept apart not only socially but also in the hospitals. Few institutions are available where large groups of white and Negro patients can be studied at the same time. Accordingly, one often hears talk about the low incidence of a disease or trait in, for example, the African populations, or of its high incidence in the whites. Often this comparative observation is guesswork as the physician may be seeing only one race; or the "white controls" may be taken from someone else's published observations made in South America or Northern Scandinavia.

To put in a small "commercial plug" for my own University, I would point out that we are fortunate in having as our main teaching hospital one of the few large institutions in Africa which caters for both white and non-white patients. We are impressed every day by the striking differences in disease incidence and clinical pattern between the races. Some of these differences are predominantly due to environmental (mainly socioeconomic) factors, but others may well be due to genetic influences. In this natural human laboratory, which we have on our doorstep, we have taken advantage of the situation mainly in studying the role of environmental factors. I hope that, with the help of geneticists from the United States, advantage may also be taken to study genetic differences.

DR. SUTTON: Much of what I was going to say has been said just now by Dr. Gordon. This has to do with samples and their collection. I agree with Dr. Allen one can get valuable information from samples collected for other purposes. In fact, this is what most of my population studies have been based on. For this reason, I am aware of the shortcomings of these kinds of samples. It seems to me that to pursue many problems more effectively means setting up some sort of perhaps very modest type of laboratory facilities in the field, so that questions which come up six months after you come back home and start analyzing your samples can be answered.

I have some wonderful problems that have arisen in my samples, but the samples were collected a year or two ago and there is no one anywhere close to the source to follow them up.

BIBLIOGRAPHY

Adam, A., Nature, *189*:686, 1961.

Adinolfi, M., Bernini, L., Carcassi, U., Latte, B., Motulsky, A. G., and Siniscalco M., Rendiconti Accademia Lincei, Roma, Series 8, Vol. 28, No. 5, 1960.

Aird, I., Benthall, H. H., Mehigan, J. A., and Roberts, J. A. Fraser, Brit. M. J. 2:315, 1954.

Allàrd, R., Ann. Soc. Belge Méd. Trop., *35*:649, 1955.

Allee, W. C., Emerson, A. E., Park, O., Park, T., and Schmidt, K. P., *Principles of Animal Ecology,* W. B. Saunders, Philadelphia, 1949.

Allison, A. C., Brit. M. J., *1*:290, 1954 (a).

Allison, A. C., Ann. Human Genet., *19*:39, 1954 (b).

Allison, A. C., Trans. Roy. Soc. Trop. Med. Hyg., *48*:312, 1954 (c).

Allison, A. C., Clin. Sci., *15*:497, 1956.

Allison, A. C., Acta Genet., *6*:430, 1957.

Allison, A. C., and ap Rees, W., Brit. M. J., *2*:1137, 1957.

Allison, A. C., Blumberg, B. S., and ap Rees, W., *Nature, 181*:824, 1958.

Allison, A. C., Blumberg, B. S., and Gartler, S. M., Nature, *183*:118, 1959.

Allison, A. C., and Blumberg, B. S., Lancet, *1*:634, 1961.

Allison, A. C., and Clyde, D. F., Brit. M. J., *1*:1346, 1961.

André, L.-J., and André-Gadras, E., Méd. Trop., *17*:596, 1957.

Archibald, H. M., and Bruce-Chwatt, L. J., Brit. M. J., *1*:970, 1955.

Asdell, S. A., Science, *99*:124, 1944.

Awapara, J., and Shullenberger, C. C., Clinica Chemica Acta, 2:199, 1957.

Aycock, W. L., and McKinley, E. B., Internat. J. Leprosy, *6*:169, 1938.

Barnes, H. D., S. Afr. M. J. *29*:781, 1955.

Barnicot, N. A., Garlick, J. P., Singer, R., and Weiner, J. S., Nature, *184*:2042, 1959.

Bates, M., *The Nature of Natural History,* Chas. Scribner, New York, 1950.

Bates, M., *The Ecology of Health,* in *Medicine and Anthropology,* p. 56-77, International Univ. Press, New York, 1959.

Bearn, A. G., and Franklin, E. C., Science, *128*:596, 1958.

Bearn, A. G., and Franklin, E. C., J. Exper. Med., *109*:55, 1959.

Beckman, L. and Cedermark, G., Acta Genet., *10*:23, 1960.

Beet, E. A., E. Afr. M. J., *23*:75, 1946.

Beet, E. A., E. Afr. M. J., *24*:212, 1947.

Bennett, J. H., and Walker, C. B. V., Ann. Hum. Genet., *20*:299, 1956.

Benzer, S., Ingram, V. M., and Lehmann, H., Nature, *182*:852, 1958.

Benzer, S., Proc. Nat. Acad. Sci., *45*:1607, 1959.

Berkson, J., Biometrics Bull., *2*:47, 1946.

Berman, C., *Primary Carcinoma of the Liver,* H. K. Lewis, London, 1951.

Bernini, L., Carcassi, U., Latte, B., Motulsky, A. G., Romei, L., and Siniscalco, M., Rendiconti Accademi Lincei, Roma, Series 8, Vol. 29, Nos. 1-2, 1960.

Bersohn, I., Wayburne, S., Hirsch, H., and Sussman, C. D., S. African J. Clin. Sci., 5:35, 1954.

Bersohn, I., and Oelofse, P. J., S. Afr. M. J., *31*:1172, 1957.

Best, W. R., J. Lab. and Clin. Med. *54*:791, 1959.

Beutler, E., Blood, *14*:103, 1959.

Beutler, E., Dern, R. J., and Alving, A. S., J. Lab. and Clin. Med. *44*:439, 1954 (a).

Beutler, E., Dern, R. J., and Alving, A. S., J. Lab. and Clin. Med. *44:*177, 1954 (b).

Beulter, E., Dern, R. J., Flanagan, C. L. and Alving, A. S., J. Lab. and Clin. Med. *45:*286, 1955 (a).

Beutler, E., Dern, R. J., and Flanagan, C. L., Brit. M. J., *1:*1189, 1955 (b).

Beutler, E., J. Lab. and Clin. Med., *49:*84, 1957.

Beutler, E., Yeh, M. K. Y., and Necheles, T., Nature, *183:*684, 1959.

Bezon, A., Méd. Trop., *15:*419, 1955.

Bhatia, H. M., Thin, J., Debray, H., and Cabanes, J., Bull. Soc. Anthrop. (Paris), 6:199, 1955.

Blumberg, B. S., McGiff, J., and Guicherit, I., Doc. Neerlandica et Indonesica de Morbis Tropicis, *3:*368, 1951.

Blumberg, B. S., Allison, A. C., and Garry, B., Ann. Hum. Genet., 23:349, 1959.

Blumberg, B. S. and Bernanke, A. D., in preparation, 1961.

Blumberg, B. S., and Gartler, S. M., Nature, *184:*1990, 1959.

Blumberg, B. S., Proc. Soc., Exp. Biol. Med., *104:*25, 1960.

Blumberg, B. S., and Gentile, Z., Nature, *189:*897, 1961.

Blumberg, B. S., and Warren, L., Biochem. Biophys. Acta, *50:*90, 1961.

Blumberg, B. S., Campbell, J., and Motulsky, A. G., cited in "Medical Survey of Rongelap People Five and Six Years after Exposure to Fallout," by R. A. Conard, et al. Brookhaven National Laboratory, September 1960.

Bode, H., Mosteller, F., Tukey, J., and Winsor, C., Science, *109:*553, 1949.

Bowman, J. E., and Walker, D. G., Nature, *189:*555, 1961.

Boyd, C., *Genetics and the Races of Man*, Little, Brown and Co., Boston, 1950.

Boyd, W. C., *Fundamentals of Immunology*, Interscience, New York, 1956.

Brain, P., S. Afr. M. J., *26:*925, 1952.

Brock, J. F., and Gordon, H., Postgrad. M. J., *35:*223, 1959.

Büchi, E. C., Anthropologist, *1:*25, 1955.

Burnet, M., *Natural History of Infectious Disease*, Cambridge, 1953.

Cabannes, R., Algerie Méd., *61:*751, 1957.

Calchi-Novati, C., Ceppellini, R., Biancho, I., Silverstroni, E., and Harris, H., Ann. Eugen., *18:*335, 1953-54.

Carson, P. E., Flanagan, C. L., Ickes, C. E., and Alving, A. S., Science, *124:*484, 1956.

Carter, C., and Heslop, B., Brit. J. Prev. Soc. Med., *11:*214, 1957.

Ceppellini, R., *Blood Groups and Haematological Data as a Source of Ethnic Information*, in *Medical Biology and Etruscan Origins*, Little, Brown and Co., Boston, 1959.

Charlton, R. W., and Bothwell, T. H., S. Afr. J. M. Sc., *24:*88, 1959.

Chatterjea, J. B., *Haemoglobinopathy in India,* in *Abnormal Haemoglobins*, Blackwell, Oxford, 1959.

Childs, B., Zinkham, W., Browne, E. A., Kimbro, E. L., and Torbert, J. V., Bull. J. Hopkins Hosp., *102:*21, 1958.

Clarke, C. A., J. M. Education, *34:*400, 1959.

Clausen, J., J. Immunology, *84:*128, 1960.

Clemmesen, J., Lockwood, K., and Nielsen, A., Danish M. Bull., *5:*123, 1958.

Cohen, F., Zuelzer, W., and Evans, M., Paper presented at A.A.B.B. meeting, Chicago, Illinois, 1959 (a).

Cohen, T., Goldsmidt, E., Adam, Y., Matoth, Y., Theodor, E., and Szabo, M. A., Harefuah, *57:*233, 1959 (b).

Colbourne, M. J., and Edington, G., Brit. M. J., *1:*784, 1956.

Commission on Viral Infections, A.F.E.B., unpublished study on *Antibodies Against*

Typhus in French Morocco, submitted to the Office of the Surgeon General, U. S. Army, April 1954.

Comstock, G. W., Am. J. Hyg., *65:*271, 1957.

Connell, G. E., and Smithies, O., Biochem. J., *72:*115, 1959.

Connell, G. E., Smith, D. B., and Smithies, O., to be published.

Corcoran, P. A., Allen, F. H., Jr., Allison, A. C., and Blumberg, B. S., Am. J. Phys. Anthrop., *17:*187, 1959.

Cornfield, J., J. Nat. Cancer Inst., *11:*1269, 1951.

Crow, J. F., Hum. Biol., *30:*1, 1958.

Cutler, S., J. Am. Statistical Assoc., *50:*267, 1955.

Davenport, C. B., and Munsey, E. B., Arch. Int. Med., *18:*4, 1916.

Davenport, F. W., Hennesy, A. V., and Francis, T., Jr., J. Exp. Med., *98:*641, 1953.

Dean, G., Personal communication, 1960.

Dean, H. T., Arnold, F. A., Jr., and Elvove, E., Pub. Health Reports, *57:*1155, 1942.

de Grouchy, J., and Sutton, H. E., Am. J. Hum. Genet., *9:*76, 1957.

Delbrouck, J., Ann. Soc. Belge Méd. Trop., *38:*103, 1958.

Deliyannis, G. A., and Tavlarakis, N., Brit. M. J., *2:*301, 1955.

Deliyannis, G. A., and Tavlarakis, N., Brit. M. J., *1:*1488, 1956.

Denoix, P. and Schwartz, D., Bull. I. Cancer, *43:*387, 1956.

Dern, R. J., Weinstein, I. M., LeRoy, G. V., Talmage, D. W., and Alving, A. S., J. Lab. and Clin. Med., *43:*303, 1954.

Diehl, K., Handbuch der Tuberkulose, *1:*519, Thieme, Stuttgart, 1958.

Dobzhansky, T., *Genetics and the Origin of the Species,* Columbia Univ. Press, New York, 1941.

Dubos, R. and Dubos J., *The White Plague: Tuberculosis, Man and Society,* Little, Brown, and Co., Boston, 1952.

Dubos, R. J., *Mirage of Health: Utopias, Progress and Biological Change,* Harpers, New York, 1959.

Dunlop, K. J., and Mozumder, U. K., Ind. Med. Gaz., *87:*387, 1952.

Earle, K. V., Trans. Roy. Soc. Med. and Hyg., *34:*395, 1941.

Edington, G. M., Brit. M. J., *1:*871, 1954.

Edington, G. M., and Lehmann, H., Bull. W.H.O., *15:*837, 1956 (a).

Edington, G. M., and Lehmann, H., Man, *56:*34, 1956 (b).

Edington, G. M., and Laing, W. N., Brit. M. J., *2:*143, 1957.

Epstein, F. H., J. Chronic Dis., *5:*300, 1957.

Fenner, F., The Harvey Lectures 1957-1958, Academic Press, Inc., New York, 1959.

Ferguson, R. G., *Studies in Tuberculosis,* University of Toronto Press, 1955.

Fessas, Ph., Lancet, *1:*297, 1961.

Fink, K., Proc. Soc. Exp. Biol. Med., *76:*692, 1951.

Fink, K., Cline, R. G., Henderson, R. B., and Fink, K., J. Biol. Chem., *221:*425, 1956.

Fink, K., and Fink, R., Federation Proc., *17:*219, 1958.

Fisher, R. A., *The Genetic Theory of Natural Selection,* Oxford Univ. Press, Oxford, 1930.

Ford, E. B., In: *The New Systematics,* Oxford Univ. Press, Oxford, 1940.

Ford, D. D., Patterson, J. C. S., and Treuting, W.L., J. Nat. Cancer Inst., *22:*1093, 1959.

Ford, E. B., *Genetics for Medical Students,* London: Methuen, 1942.

Foy, H., Kondi, A., and Brass, W., E. African M. J., *28:*1, 1951.

Foy, H., Brass, W., Moore, R. A., Timms, G. L., Kondi, A., and Oluoch, T., Brit. M. J., *2:*1116, 1955.

Foy, H., Brass, W., and Kondi, A., Brit. M. J., *1*:289, 1956.

Frost, W. H., J. Prev. Med., *2*:325, 1928.

Fulton, J. D., and Grant, J. P., Biochem. J., *63*:274, 1956.

Galatius-Jensen, F., Acta Genet., *7*:549, 1957.

Galatius-Jensen, F., Acta Genet., *8*:248, 1958.

Garlick, J. D., and Barnicot, N. A., Ann. Hum. Genet., *21*:420, 1957.

Gartler, S. M., Amer. J. Hum. Genet., *8*:120, 1956.

Gartler, S. M., Firschein, I. L., and Gidaspow, T., Acta Genet. et Statis. Med.
    6:435, 1956.

Gartler, S. M., Firschein, I. L., and Kraus, B. S., Am. J. Hum. Genet., *9*:200, 1957.

Gartler, S. M., Arch. Biochem. and Biophys., *80*:400, 1959 (a).

Gartler, S. M., Am. J. Hum. Genet., *11*:257, 1959 (b).

Geiman, P. M., Parasite Infections in Man, Columbia University Press, New York.

Gershowitz, H., Behrman, S. J., and Neel, J. V., Science, *128*:719, 1958.

Giblett, E. R., Nature, *183*:192, 1959.

Giblett, E. R., Hickman, C. G., and Smithies, O., Nature, *183*:1589, 1959.

Giblett, E. R., and Steinberg, A. G., Am. J. Hum. Genet., *12*:160, 1960.

Giblett, E. R., and Zoutendyk, A., to be published.

Gibson, F. D., W. Afr. M. J., *7*:170, 1958.

Gilles, H. M., Personal communication, 1960.

Gilles, H. M., Watson-Williams, J., and Taylor, B. G., Nature, *185*:257, 1960.

Gillman, J., and Gillman, T., *Perspectives in Human Malnutrition*, Grune and
    Stratton, New York, 1951.

Glass, B., Amer. J. Hum. Genet., *2*:269, 1950.

Glynn, A. A., Glynn, L. E., and Holborow, L. E., Brit. M. J., *2*:266, 1959

Gordon, J. E., and Augustine, D. L., Am. J. M. Sc., *216*:343, 1948.

Gordon, J. E., *Ecological Investigation of Disease*, in *Research in Public Health*,
    Milbank Mem. Fund, New York, 1952.

Gordon, J. E., Milbank Mem. Fund Q., *31*:5, 1953.

Gordon, J. E., J. Roy. San. Inst., *74*:445, 1954.

Gordon, J. E., Am. J. M. Sc., *235*:337, 1958.

Gowen, J. W., Ann. Rev. Microbiol., *2*:215, 1948.

Gowen, J. W., *Genetics and Disease Resistance*, in *Genetics in the 20th Century*,
    Macmillan, New York, 1951.

Greenwood, M., Hill, A. B., Topley, W. W. C., and Wilson, J., *Experimental Epidemi-
    ology*, Med. Res. Council Spec. Rep. Series No. 209, H. M. Stationery Office,
    London, 1936.

Grignani, F., Cornicchi, D., and Maxia, C., Klin. Woch., *38*:1171, 1960.

Gross, R. T., Hurwitz, R. E., and Marks, P. A., J. Clin. Invest., *37*:1176, 1958.

Guinand, S., Tonnelat, J., Boussier, G., and Jayle, M. F., Bull. Soc. Chim. Biol., *38*:329,
    1956.

Gullbring, B., Acta Med. Scand., *159*:169, 1957.

Hackett, L. W., Chap. 28, Page 723 in Vol. I of *Malariology*, W. B. Saunders Co.,
    Philadelphia and London, 1949.

Haga, H., Jap. J. Genet., *4*:1, 1959.

Haldane, J. B. S., Trans. Camb. Phil. Soc., *23*:19, 1924.

Haldane, J. B. S., Proc. Camb. Phil. Soc., *28*:244, 1932.

Haldane, J. B. S., Acta Genet. et Statist. Med., *6*:321, 1957.

Hammon, W. McD., Lundi, H. W., Gray, J. A., Evans, F. C., Bang, F. and Izumi,
    E. M., J. Immunol., *44*:75, 1942.

Hansen, S., Hospitalstidende, *71*:767, 1928.
Hardin, G., Science, *131*:1292, 1960.
Harris, H., Ann. Eugen., *14*:165, 1948.
Harris, H., Ann. Eugen., *18*:43, 1953.
Harris, H., Robson, E. B., and Siniscalco, M., Nature, *182*:1325, 1958 (a).
Harris, H., Robson, E. B., and Siniscalco, M., Nature, *182*:452, 1958 (b).
Harris, W. H., Knight, R. A., and Selin, M. J., Clin. Res., 7:124, 1959 (a).
Harris, H., Robson, E. B., and Siniscalco, M., *Genetics of Plasma Protein Variants,* in *Ciba Foundation Symposium on Biochemistry of Human Genetics,* Churchill, London, 1959 (b).
Hart, E. W., Ann. Eugen., *12*:89, 1944.
Herrell, W. E., Heilman, F. R., and Wellman, W. E., Ann. N. Y. Acad. Sci., *53*:448, 1950.
Hetherington, H. W., McPhedran, F. M., Landis, H. R. M., and Opie, E. L., Am. Rev. Tuberc., *20*:421, 1929.
Hewitt, D., Brit. J. Prev. and Soc. Med., *9*:81, 1955.
Hiernaux, J., Am. J. Phys. Anthrop., *13*:455, 1955.
Higginson, J., Gerritson, T., and Walker, A. R. P., Amer. J. Path., *29*:779, 1953.
Higginson, J., Grobbelaar, B. G., and Walker, A. R. P., Amer. J. Path., *33*:29, 1957.
Hirschfeld, J., Nature, *185*:164, 1960.
Hockwald, R. S., Arnold, J., Clayman, C. B., and Alving, A. S., J.A.M.A., *149*:1568, 1952.
Hogben, L. T., *Genetic Principles in Medicine and Social Sciences,* Williams and Norgate, Ltd., London, 1931.
Holsti, L. R., and Ermala, P., Cancer, *8*:679, 1955.
Hopkins, R., Symposium Series, Am. Assoc. Advance. Sci., *1*:112, 1938.
Hunt, J. A., and Ingram, V. M., *The Genetical Control of Protein Structure: The Abnormal Human Haemoglobins,* in *Ciba Foundation Symposium on Biochemistry of Human Genetics,* London, Churchill, Ltd., 1959.
Ingram, V. M., Nature, *178:* 792, 1956.
Ingram, V. M., Biochim. Biophys. Acta, *36*:402, 1959.
Ishihara, I., Komori, Y., and Iida, H., Nagoya J. M. Sci., *14*:149, 1951.
Ishikuni, N., Nemoto, H., Neel, J. V., Drew, A. L., Yanase, T., and Matsumoto, Y. S., Am. J. Hum. Genet., *12*:67, 1960.
Jonxis, J. H. P., *The Frequency of Haemoglobin S and Haemoglobin C Carriers in Curaçao and Surinam,* in *Abnormal Haemoglobins,* Blackwell, Oxford, 1959.
Kalow, W., *Cholinesterase Types,* in *Ciba Foundation Symposium on Biochemistry of Human Genetics,* Little, Brown and Co., Boston, 1959.
Keller, J., Pi-Sunyer, Z., Plaut, T., and Marks, P. A., In preparation.
Kellermeyer, R. W., Tarlov, A., Schrier, S. L., and Alving, A. S., J. Lab. and Clin. Med., *52*:827, 1958.
Kimura, M., Proc. Nat. Acad. Sci., *42*:336, 1956.
Kirkman, H. M., Riley, H. D., Jr., and Crowell, B. B., Proc. Nat. Acad. Sci., *46*:938, 1960.
Kirkman, H. N., Nature, *184*:1291, 1959.
Kraus, A. S., Pub. Health Rep., *69*:1211, 1954.
Kwaan, H. C., McFadzean, A. J. S., and Cook, J., Lancet, *I*:132, 1956.
Kurland, L. T., and Westlund, K. B., Ann. N. Y. Acad. Sci., *58*:682, 1954.
Kurland, L. T., and Mulder, D. W., Neurology, *5*:182; 5:249, 1955.
Kurland, L. T., Proc. Staff Meet. Mayo Clinic, *32*:449, 1957.

Laidlaw, T. R., Lancet, *1*:1118, 1935.

Lambotte-Legrand, J., and Lambotte-Legrand, C., Mém. Inst. Roy. Colon. Belge, *19*:1, 1951.

Lambotte-Legrand, J., and Lambotte-Legrand, C., Sang., *23*:560, 1952.

Lambotte-Legrand, J., and Lambotte-Legrand, C., Ann. Soc. Belge Méd. Trop., *35*:53, 1955.

Lambotte-Legrand, J., and Lambotte-Legrand, C., Ann. Soc. Belge Méd. Trop., *38*:45, 1958 (a).

Lambotte-Legrand, J., and Lambotte-Legrand, C., Ann. Soc. Belge Méd. Trop., *38*:55, 1958 (b).

Larizza, P., Rass. Med. Sarda., *60*:319, 1958.

Laurell, C. B., and Nyman, M., Blood *12*:493, 1957.

Leblond, C. P., and Walker, B. E., Physiol. Rev., *36*:255, 1956.

Lehmann, H., Nature, *167*:931, 1951.

Lehmann, H., and Cutbush, M., Brit. M. J., *1*:404, 1952 (a).

Lehmann, H., and Cutbush, M., Trans. Roy. Soc. Trop. Med. Hyg., *46*:380, 1952 (b).

Lehmann, H., J. Clin. Path., *6*:329, 1953.

Lehmann, H., and Raper, A. B., Brit. M. J., *2*:333, 1956.

Lerner, I. M., *Genetic Homeostasis*, Oliver and Boyd, London, 1954.

Lerner, I. M., *The Genetic Basis of Selection*, John Wiley and Sons, New York, 1958.

Levene, H., *The Association between Blood Groups and Disease*, paper presented at the A.I.B.S. meeting, August 31, 1959.

Levine, P., J. Heredity, *34*:71, 1943.

Lilienfeld, A. M., Am. J. Hum. Genet., *6*:100, 1954.

Lilienfeld, A. M., Levin, M. L., and Moore, G. E., Arch. Int. Med., *98*:129, 1956.

Lilienfeld, A. M., Pub. Health Rep., *74*:29, 1959.

Lindan, R., Biochem. J., *57*:XXXI, 1954.

Livingstone, F. B., Hum. Biol., *32*:17, 1960.

Löhr, G. W., Waller, H. D., Karges, O., Schlegel, B., and Muller, A. A., Klin. Wochenschr., *36*:1008, 1958.

Lurie, M. B., Zappasodi, P., Dannenberg, A. M., Jr., and Weiss, G. H., Am. J. Hum. Genet., *4*:302, 1951.

Mackay, R. P., and Myrianthopoulos, N. C., Arch. Neurol. Psychiat., *80*:667, 1958.

Mackey, J. P., and Vivarelli, F., Brit. M. J., *1*:276, 1954.

MacMahon, B., and Koller, E. K., Blood, *12*:1, 1957.

Mandel, S. P. H., Heredity, *13*:289, 1959.

Manning, M. D., and Carroll, B. E., J. Nat. Cancer Inst., *19*:1087, 1957.

Marks, P. A., Johnson, A. B., and Hirschberg, E., Proc. Nat. Acad. Sci., *44*:529, 1958.

Marks, P. A., and Gross, R. T., Bull. N. Y. Acad. Med., *35*:433, 1959 (a).

Marks, P. A., and Gross, R. T., J. Clin. Invest., *38*:2253, 1959 (b).

Marks, P. A., Szeinberg, A., and Banks, J., J. Biol. Chem., *236*:10, 1961.

Marks, P., in Genetics (*Proc. of First Macy Conf. on Genetics*), Madison Printing Co., Madison, N. J., p. 199, 1960.

Martin, C. M., and Jandl, J. H., J. Clin. Invest., *38*:1024, 1959.

Mather, K., and Harrison, B. J., Heredity, *3*:1, *3*:131, 1949.

Matsunaga, E., Sapporo M. J., *6*:165, 1954.

Matsunaga, E., Am. J. Hum. Genet., *7*:66, 1955.

Matsunaga, E., and Itoh, S., Ann. Hum. Genet., *22*:111, 1958.

McDermott, W., Deuschle, K., Adair, J., Fulmer, H., and Loughlin, B., Science, *131*:197, 1960.

McGhee, R., and Trager, W., J. Parasitol., *36*:123, 1950.

Mentz, H. E. A., and Bersohn, I., S. Afr. M. J., *33*:939, 1959.

Merskey, C., Gordon, H., and Lackner, H., Brit. Med. J., *i*:219, 1960.

Miller, M. J., Trans. Roy. Soc. Trop. Med. Hyg., *52*:152, 1958.

Monnier, J. J., and Schoenbach, E. B., Antibiotics and Chemotherapy, *1*:472, 1951.

Moore, R. A., Brass, W., and Foy, H., Brit. M. J., *2*:630, 1954.

Morton, N. E., and Chung, C. S., Am. J. Hum. Genet., *11*:237, 1959.

Motulsky, A. G., Glucose-6-phosphate dehydrogenase deficiency, haemoglobin disease of the newborn, and malaria, Lancet *1*:1168-1169, 1961.

Motulsky, A. G., J.A.M.A., *165*:835, 1957.

Motulsky, A. G., Kraut, J. M., Thieme, W. T., and Musto, D. F., Clin. Res., *7*:89, 1959.

Motulsky, A. G., Hum. Biol., *32*:28, 1960.

Motulsky, A. G., and Campbell, J. M., (in press) Blood, 1960.

Mourant, A. E., *The Distribution of the Human Blood Groups*, Oxford: Blackwell, 1954.

Mourant, A. E., In: *Genetics and the Twentieth Century Darwinism*, Cold Spring Harbor Symposium on Quantitative Biology, Vol. 24. Cold Spring Harbor: The Biological Laboratory, 1959.

Mulder, J., and Masurel, N., Lancet, *1*:810, 1958.

Murdock, G. P., *Africa: Its People and Their Culture History*, pp. xiii and 456, McGraw-Hill Book Co., Inc., New York, 1959.

Myrianthopoulos, N. C., and Pieper, S. J. L., Jr., Am. J. Phys. Anthrop. *17*:105, 1959.

Myrianthopoulos, N. C., and Mackay, R. P., Acta Gen. Stat. Med., *10*:33, 1960.

Neel, J. V., Cold Spring Harbor Symp. Quant. Biol., *15*:141, 1951.

Neel, J. V., Am. J. Hum. Genet., *5*:154, 1953.

Neel, J. V., and Schull, W. J., *Human Heredity*, Univ. of Chicago Press, Chicago, 1954.

Neel, J. V., Hiernaux, J., Linhard, ., Robinson, A. R., Zuelzer, W. W., and Livingstone, F. B., Am. J. Hum. Genet., *8*:138, 1956.

Neel, J. V., *The Study of Natural Selection in Primitive and Civilized Human Populations*, in *Natural Selection in Man*, Wayne State Univ. Press, Detroit, Mich., 1958.

Niederman, J. C.: Unpublished studies from the Section of Epidemiology and Preventive Medicine, Yale Univ. School of Med.

Nyman, M., and Laurell, M., Scand. J. Clin. and Lab. Invest., *39*:11, 1959.

Odum, E. P., *Fundamentals of Ecology*, 2nd Ed., W. B. Saunders, Philadelphia, 1959.

Oehser, P. H., Science, *129*:992, 1959.

Oppenheim, F., and Voight, R., Krankheitsforschung, *3*:306, 1926.

Owen, J. A., Mackay, I. R., and Got, C., Brit. M. J., *1*:1454, 1959.

Owen, R. D., Wood, H. R., Foord, A. G., Sturgeon, P., and Baldwin, L. G., Proc. Nat. Acad. Sci., *40*:420, 1934.

Panizon, F., Lancet, *II*:1093, 1960.

Pare, C. M. B., and Sandler, M., Lancet, *266*:702, 1954.

Paul, J., *Clinical Epidemiology*, Univ. of Chicago Press, Chicago, 1958.

Paul, J. R., and Trask, J. D., J. Exp. Med., *61*:447, 1935.

Paul, J. R., Havens, W. P., and Van Rooyen, C. E., Brit. M. J., *1*:841, 1944.

Paul, J. R., and Hammon, W. McD.: Report of the Virus Commission's activities in Japan, Feb.-April, 1946. Unpublished. Submitted to Office of the Surgeon General, U.S. Army, May, 1946.

Paul, J. R., and Riordan, J. T., Am. J. Hyg., *52*:202, 1950.

Paul, J. R., Melnick, J. L., Barnett, Z. H., and Goldblum, N., Am. J. Hyg., *55*:402, 1952.

Paul, J. R., Melnick, J. L., and Riordan, J. T., Am. J. Hyg., 56:232, 1952.

Penrose, L. S., Smith, S. M., and Sprott, D. A., Ann. Hum. Genet., 21:90, 1956.

Perry, T. L., Shaw, K. N. E., Walker, D., Nature, 184:1970, 1959.

Pollitzer, W. S., Am. J. Phys. Anthrop., 16:241, 1958.

Polonovski, M., and Jayle, M. F., C. R. Soc. Biol., 129:457, 1938.

Poulik, M. D., and Smithies, O., Biochem. J., 68:636, 1958.

Raper, A. B., J. Trop. Med., 53:49, 1950.

Raper, A. B., Brit. M. J., 2:1162, 1954.

Raper, A. B., Brit. M. J., 2:1186, 1955.

Raper, A. B., Brit. M. J., 1:965, 1956.

Reed, T. E., Am. J. Hum. Genet., 8:257, 1956.

Reed, T. E., and Kelly, E. L., Ann. Hum. Genet., 22:161, 1958.

Reed, T. E., Am. J. Hum. Genet., ii:137, 1959.

Reed, T. E., and Ahronheim, J. H., Nature, 184:611, 1959.

Reed, T. E., This conference, 1960.

Reed, T. E., A study of eight blood group systems and reproductive performance, abstract, Proceedings of the Second International Conference of Human Genetics. Rome, 1961. Paper 83, Amsterdam, Excerpta Medica, 1961.

Riegel, C., and Thomas D., New Eng. J. Med., 255:434, 1956.

Rimon, A., Askenasi, I., Ramot, B., and Sheba, C., Bioch. Biophys. Res. Comm. 2:138, 1960.

Roberts, D. F., and Boyo, A. E., Ann. Hum. Genet., 24:375, 1960.

Roberts, J. A. Fraser, Ann. Eugen., 14:109, 1948.

Roberts, J. A. Fraser, Brit. J. Prev. Soc. Med., 11:107, 1957.

Roberts, J. A. Fraser, Brit. M. Bull., 15:129, 1959.

Robson, E., Personal communication (a).

Robson, E., Personal communication (b).

Rosenfield, R. E., Blood, 10:17, 1955.

Rosling, E., Undersgelser over Difteridisposition og Difteriimmunitet, Copenhagen: Arnold Busck, 1928.

Roth, R. B., Am. Rev. Tuberc., 38:197, 1938.

Rubini, J. R., Cronkite, E. P., Bond, V. P., and Fliedner, T. M., Soc. Exp. Biol. Med., 100:130, 1959.

Rucknagel, D. L., and Neel, J. V., The Hemoglobinopathies, Steinberg, A. G., Ed., in Progress in Medical Genetics, Grune and Stratton, New York, 1961.

Russell, W. T., and Salmon, G., Pulmonary Tuberculosis in Wales between 1911 and 1931, 1934.

Sabin, A. B., Ginder, D. R., and Matumoto, M., Am. J. Hyg., 46:341, 1947.

Sabin, A. B., Ann. N. Y. Acad. Sci., 54:936, 1952.

Sansone, G., and Segni, G., Lancet, 273:295, 1957.

Sansone, G., Piga, A. M., and Segni, G., Minerva Medica, 1958.

Sartori, E., Acta Paed. Latina, 10:505, 1957.

Schade, A. L., and Caroline, L., Science, 104:340, 1946.

Sheppard, P. M., Brit. M. Bull., 15:134, 1959.

Shope, R. E., J. Exp. Med., 63:669, 1936.

Shukla, R. M., and Solanki, B. R., Lancet, 1:297, 1958.

Shukla, R. M., Solanki, B. R., and Parande, A. S., Blood, 13:552, 1958.

Shultz, F. T., and Briles, W. E., Genetics, 38:34, 1953.

Siniscalco, M., Bernini, L., Latte, B., and Motulsky, A. G., Favism and thalassemia in Sardinia and their relationship to malaria, Nature 190:1179-80, 1961.

Siniscalco, M., Motulsky, A. G., Latte, B., and Bernini, L., Rendiconti Accademia Lincei, Roma (in press).

Smith, G., and Vella, F., Lancet, *1*:1133, 1960.

Smithies, O., Biochem. J., *61*:629, 1955.

Smithies, O., and Walker, N. F., Nature, *178*:694, 1956.

Smithies, O., *Zone Electrophoresis in Starch Gels and its Application to Studies of Serum Proteins,* in *Advances in Protein Chemistry,* Vol. 14, p. 65, Academic Press, New York, 1959.

Smithies, O., and Hiller, O., Biochem. J., *72*:121, 1959.

Smuts, J. C., *Holism and Evolution,* The Macmillan Co., New York, 1926.

Sokhey, S. S., and Chitre, R. B. G. D., Bull. Off. Int. Hyg. Pub., *29*:2093, 1937.

Sonnet, J., Vandepitte, J., Haumont, A., Ann. Soc. Belge Méd. Trop., *39*:691, 1959.

Soper, F. L., Penna, H., Cardozo, E., Serafim, J., Jr., Frobisher, M., Jr., and Pinheiro, J., Am. J. Hyg., *18*:555, 1933.

Stern, Curt, *Principles of Human Genetics,* W. H. Freeman, San Francisco, 1949.

Stewart, A., Webb, J., and Hewitt, D., Brit. M. J., *1*:1495, 1958.

Stocks, P., and Barrington, A., *Treasury of Human Inheritance, 3,* Part 1, 1925.

Struthers, D., Brit. J. Soc. Med., *5*:223, 1951.

Sukumaran, P. K., Sanghvi, L. D., and Vyas, G. N., Current Sci., *25*:290, 1956.

Sutton, H. E., and Clark, P. J., Am. J. Phys. Anthrop., *13*:53, 1955.

Sutton, H. E., Neel, J. V., Livingston, F. B., Binson, G., Kunstadter, P., and Trombley, L. E., Ann. Hum. Genet., *23*:175, 1959.

Sutton, H. E., Matson, G. A. Robinson, A. R., and Koucky, R. W., Am. J. Hum. Genet., *12*:338, 1960.

Szeinberg, A., and Sheba, C., Harefuah, *54*:281, 1958.

Szeinberg, A., Sheba, C., and Adam, A., Nature, *181*:1256, 1958 (a).

Szeinberg, A., Sheba, C., and Adam, A., Blood, *13*:1043, 1958 (b).

Taylor, G. L., and Prior, A. M., Ann. Eugen., *9*:18, 1939.

Tepperman, J., Persp. in Biol. and Med., *1*:293, 1958.

Thomsen, O., C. R. Soc. Biol., *97*:198, 1927.

Trager, W., J. Exper. Med., *74*:441, 1941.

Turnbull, A., and Biglett, E. R., Clin. Res., *8*:133, 1960.

Vandepitte, J., Ann. Soc. Belge Méd. Trop., *34*:501, 1954.

Vandepitte, J., and Delaisse, J., Ann. Soc. Belge. Méd. Trop., *37*:703, 1957.

Vandepitte, J., *Some Remarks on the Pathology of Haemoglobin S,* in *Abnormal Haemoglobins,* pp. 123-133, Blackwell, Oxford, 1959.

Van der Sar, A., *The Occurrence of Carriers of Abnormal Haemoglobin S and C on Curaçao,* Dijkstra's Drukkerij, N.V., Groningen, pp. viii and 157, 1959.

Vella, F., M. J. of Malaya, *13*:1, 1959 (a).

Vella, F., M. J. of Australia, *46*:196, 1959 (b).

Vinograd, J. R., Hutchinson, W. D., and Schroeder, W. A., J. Am. Chem. Soc., *81*:3168, 1959.

Vogel, F., Pettenkofer, N. J., and Hembold, W., Acta Genet., *10*:267, 1960.

Waddington, C. H., *The Strategy of the Genes,* Allen and Unwin, London, 1957.

Walker, A. R. P., and Arvidsson, U. B., Trans. Roy. Soc. Trop. Med. and Hyg., *47*:536, 1953.

Walker, D. G., and Bowman, J. E., Nature, *184*:1325, 1959.

Walker, W. Brit. Med. Bull., *15*:123, 1959.

Walsh, R. J., and Kooptzoff, O., Acta Chir. Belg., *53*:213 (Suppl. 1), 1954.

Weatherall, D. J., Lancet, *II*:835, 1960.

Wiener, A. S., *Blood Groups and Transfusion,* 3rd Ed., Thomas, Springfield, 1943.

Witkop, C. J., Jr., Acta Genetica et Statistica Medica, 7:236, 1957.

Witkop, C. J., Jr., Unpublished data from the Brandywine study.

Wolstenholme, G. E. W., and O'Connor, C. M., Editors, *Ciba Foundation Symposium on Medical Biology and Etruscan Origins,* Little, Brown and Co., Boston, 1959.

Woolf, B., Ann. Hum. Genet., 19:251, 1955.

Wright, S., in *The New Systematics,* J. S. Huxley, Editor, Claredon Press, Oxford, 1950.

Wright, S. W., and Fink, K., Am. J. Men. Def., 61:530, 1957.

Wynder, E., Personal communication, 1960.

Zannos-Mariolea, L., and Chiotaskis, P., *Favism in Greece,* paper read before the European Congress of Hematology, London, 1959.

Ziff, M., *Serological Tests for Rheumatoid Arthritis,* in *Population Studies in Rheumatoid Arthritis,* Arthritis and Rheumatism Foundation, New York, 1958.

Zinkham, W. H., Lenhard, R. E., Jr., and Childs, B., Bull. J. Hopkins Hosp., 102:169, 1958.

Zuelzer, W. W., and Cohen, F., *ABO Hemolytic Disease and Heterospecific Pregnancy,* in *The Pediatric Clinics of North America,* Saunders, Philadelphia, 1957.

INDEX

ABO blood group, 9-10, 22, 80-94, 124-129
Adaptive behavior, effects of, 27
Africa, studies in, 43, 51, 104, 106-120, 123, 129, 130, 139, 147, 149, 151, 156, 170, 186
Alaska, studies in, 44-45, 53, 126, 148, 169, 190
Albinos, 34
Alloxan, and β-aminoisobutyric acid metabolism, 195
Amino acid changes, 105
β-aminoisobutyric aciduria, 192-213
β-Aminoisobutyric aciduria, 192-213
 disease associations, 194-196
 distributional data, 193-194
Anemias, 56
 blood groups in, 84
 hemolytic, 83, 124, 159
 hookworm, susceptibility to, 110
 sickle cell (see Sickle cell disease).
Antibiotics, resistance to, selection affecting, 2, 3, 13
Antibody formation, 51
 blood group factors, 35
 innate tendencies for, 6
Arctic, studies in, 41, 44-45, 127
Arthritis, rheumatoid, 56
Australia, studies in, 126, 145
Autoimmune diseases, 6, 155

Balanced polymorphism, 15-20
Bias in sampling, 70, 127
Bladder cancer, and smoking, 63, 64, 68, 70
Blood studies, 50-60
 blood groups
 and blood pepsin levels, 59
 differences, 82, 88-93
 and disease, 9-12, 22, 25, 30, 31-32, 33, 35, 56, 75, 84-87
 and hemolytic disease of newborn, 83-84
 mother-child combinations, 127-128
 selection in, 80-94
 stable equilibrium of, 81

Blood studies, blood groups (cont.)
 viability differences, 82, 83-88, 107, 185
 lipids, 56
 pepsin, 56, 59
 pressure, racial differences in, 26
 samples, 24, 50-60, 207-208, 213
 storage of, 57-58, 59-60, 74-75
 transfusions, reactions in, 154, 155
Breast cancer, 77
Bronchopneumonia, blood groups in, 30, 31-32
Bush tea, effects of, 187

Canada, studies in, 34, 139
Cancer
 of bladder, and smoking, 63, 64, 68, 70
 of breast, 77
 of cervix uteri, 70, 74
 of colon, blood groups in, 10
 of lung, and smoking, 68, 70, 71, 100
 of prostate, 74
 of stomach, 74
 blood groups in, 10, 22, 75, 84
 virus studies, 75, 79
Carbohydrates in blood group substances, 35
Cardiovascular disease, racial differences in, 25, 31
Caries, dental, and fluorides in water, 66-68
Carotene levels, 56
Celiac disease, 206
Cervix uteri, cancer of, 70, 74
China, studies in, 169
Climate, effects of, 42-43, 45, 204
Colon, cancer of, blood groups in, 10
Consistency of population distribution of disease, 63-65
Cornell University, 31
Coronary heart disease, 43
 blood lipids in, 56
 racial differences in, 26
Cross sectional studies, 68
Cystine excretion, and β-aminoisobutyric aciduria, 196

225